INTRODUCTION TO ENGINEERING DESIGN

BOOK 1
SOLAR DESALINATION

JAMES W. DALLY

Professor, Mechanical Engineering
University of Maryland @ College Park

COLLABORATING WITH

THOMAS M. REGAN

Professor and Associate Dean
University of Maryland @ College Park

James W. Dally Associates

Knoxville, Tennessee

The manuscript was prepared by the author in Word 7 using 12 point Times New Roman font. The book was printed from camera ready copy by Publishing and Printing Inc. of Knoxville, TN.

Published By

James W. Dally Associates

8500-28 Olde Colony Trail

Knoxville, TN 37923, U. S. A.

ISBN 0-9655911-0-7

To my wife Anne

and my children Lisa, Bill and Michelle

who tolerated my many absences and inattention while working on textbooks or research papers. Their tolerance, love, patience and good spirits have supported me for many many years.

ABOUT THE AUTHOR

James W. Dally obtained a bachelor of science and a master of science degree, both in Mechanical Engineering from the Carnegie Institute of Technology. He obtained a doctoral degree in mechanics from the Illinois Institute of Technology. He has taught at Cornell University, Illinois Institute of Technology, and served as Dean of Engineering at the University of Rhode Island. He is currently a professor in the Department of Mechanical Engineering at the University of Maryland @ College Park.

Professor Dally has also worked at the Mesta Machine Co., IIT Research Institute, and IBM, Federal Systems Division. He is a fellow of the American Society for Mechanical Engineers, Society for Experimental Mechanics, and the American Academy of Mechanics. He was appointed as an honorary member of the Society for Experimental Mechanics in 1983 and elected to the National Academy of Engineering in 1984. Professor Dally was selected by his peers in the College of Engineering to receive the Senior Faculty Outstanding Teaching Award. He was also a member of the team receiving the 1996 Outstanding Educator Award sponsored by The Boeing Co.

Professor Dally has co-authored four other books: *Experimental Stress Analysis, Photoelastic Coatings, Instrumentation for Engineering Measurements, and Packaging of Electronic Systems.* He has written about 200 scientific papers and holds five patents.

ABOUT THE COLLABORATOR

Thomas M. Regan is Associate Dean of the A. J. Clark School of Engineering at the University of Maryland @ College Park and a Professor in the Chemical Engineering Department. He received his bachelor of science and doctoral degree in chemical engineering from Tulane University. Since 1990, he has been the principal investigator, at the University of Maryland, of the NSF sponsored ECSEL Coalition. He currently serves as the coordinator for the course ENES 100 <u>Introduction to Engineering Design</u> which incorporates active learning, hands-on experiences with students working in teams to design, build and test a prototype of a product.

Professor Regan received the Chester F. Carlson Award, for Innovation in Engineering Education from the American Association for Engineering Education. He was a lead member of the team that received the 1996 Outstanding Engineering Educator Award sponsored by The Boeing Co. He has been cited twice by the Dean of Undergraduate Studies at the University of Maryland with a certificate of Teaching Excellence. Within the College of Engineering, he was selected by his peers for the Senior Faculty Outstanding Teaching Award. He has also received the Allied Foundation Faculty Award in recognition of his outstanding contributions to undergraduate chemical engineering education.

CODE

FOR INSTRUCTOR AND STUDENT EXPECTATIONS

Learning and teaching require trust and mutual understanding between the student and the instructor. Trust and understanding lead to an enhanced learning environment. If we all recall a listing of expectations, a relation can be developed between the instructor and his or her class that significantly promotes the learning process. While many of these expectations may be self evident, we believe the list will remind everyone of their obligations for learning, increased understanding, communication, and respect. The list, shown below, was developed by the students and instructors in the ENES 100 course over the past five years.

Students expect the instructor to:

- Respect all students.
- Be fair in grading and in leading the class.
- Be committed to teaching an   lvising.
- Provide encouragement rather than discouragement.
- Clearly define course requirements and grading algorithms.
- Balance course workload with credit hours.
- Schedule office hours and be available accordingly.
- Provided candid and timely feedback on assignments.
- Arrive before the scheduled time and prepare the classroom.

Instructors expect the student to:

- Show respect to everyone involved in the program.
- Be responsible for their progress and learning.
- Be dedicated to understanding and learning.
- Stay current with materials and issues in class.
- Be a good team member.
- Be inquisitive and compete within the framework of a team.
- Be interested in engineering and product design.
- Arrive on time for class.

PREFACE

This textbook has evolved over a period of six years and reflects the ideas, opinions, and experiences of about 40 faculty member who have participated in teaching ENES 100 Introduction to Engineering Design at the University of Maryland @ College Park. The book is based on experiences that have been successful in teaching engineering design to first year students. Through presentations at meetings sponsored by the American Society for Engineering Education and informal discussions with colleagues from other colleges of engineering, the course was focused beyond our personal experiences Also, we were fortunate to be part of the ECSEL coalition because it gave us excellent opportunities to experiment with a curriculum that had not changed much over the past twenty five years. The Engineering Education Coalitions funded by The National Science Foundation gave credibility to many of us as we tried to change extensively the content of the first course in engineering. It was essential to develop a course which provided students a much better educational experience in their first encounter with the engineering curriculum.

The book is organized into five parts to present the various topics needed by the students as they proceed through a significant portion of product realization process beginning with the product specification and continuing through prototype evaluation. In this Book 1, we introduce the product realization process by considering the design of a solar desalination unit to produce fresh water from salt water. The approach is holistic as it avoids compartmentalization of knowledge. Design of a product is employed as an opportunity to integrate a spectrum of knowledge about many topics. We have found that developing a product really motivates the students. They learn much more on their own initiative that we could ever teach them in a course without the hands-on benefit of participating in the design of their own product, building the prototype, and testing it.

Part I of the textbook covers solar energy and solar desalination. We briefly introduce the product development process and the students role in a development team in producing a solar still. The product is described in Chapter 2 together with some important background on the World's water problem. A few concepts for the design of solar stills are introduced to make the students aware that solar stills have been designed for over a century. Solar energy is covered in some detail in Chapter 3. We try to show that the sun delivers a lot of energy to the earth, but the widespread application of solar energy is limited by the availability of the solar flux and relatively low flux levels. We conclude Part I with a detailed analysis of the operation a solar still. We recognize that this analysis is beyond the scope of the ordinary first year student; however, we present a graphical method of analysis that the students can follow. We expect the teams to be able to make a prediction of the rate of production of their prototype stills even if they do not completely understand all of the concepts of heat transfer that are involved.

Part II presents three chapters on engineering graphics. We begin in Chapter 5 with a relatively complete treatment of three-view drawings. Pictorial drawings including isometric, oblique and perspective are covered in Chapter 6. A treatment of Tables and Graphs is given in Chapter 7. The emphasis in Part II is on manual preparation of the graphics. CAD preparation of drawings and spreadsheet generation of graphs is covered later.

Part III describes three different software programs useful to the first year engineering student. A computer aided drawing program, CAD KEY Complete, is described in considerable detail with several example drawings. A spreadsheet program, Microsoft Excel, is described in Chapter 9. The coverage is intended to provide the students with entry level skills. With spreadsheets we expect the student to be able to perform calculations and to plot curves and prepare several types of charts. In Chapter 10 we provide a brief description of a computer graphics presentation program, namely Microsoft PowerPoint. Our experience is that the student can learn to master this program in one to two hours if they make use of the chart wizard incorporated in the program. The coverage of the capabilities of PowerPoint is tied to preparing a design briefing on the solar still.

Part IV is devoted to the product development process. We first describe development teams which are new to most students who have been educated in the secondary school system to act as individuals and to avoid cooperation in learning. We cover a number of useful topics such as team member traits, positive and negative team behavior, and effective team meeting. Experience with several thousand students have shown that many of them initially have trouble adapting to the team concept. (Males appear to have more trouble than females.) However, over the semester they slowly learn how to work as effective team members and they appreciate the opportunity to do so. The social bonding that takes place on the team with the first semester Freshman students is interesting to observe. Chapter 12 deals with the product development process. We have tried to incorporate a very wide range of material in this chapter. For this reason the coverage often is brief and we refer the student to more thorough higher level books on the topic. However, we cover that part of the product development process which is important to the assigned project. We start with the product specification and cover material on design concept generation and then concept selection. Methods are introduced that the student can effectively employ to arrive at design concepts and then to select the best concept though the use of a systematic design trade-off analysis.

Part VI treats the very important topic of communications. A chapter on technical reports describes many aspects of technical writing. The most important lesson here is that a technical report is different than a paper for the History or English Department. An effective professional report is written for a predefined audience with specific objectives. We describe the technical writing process and give many suggestions to facilitate composing, revision, editing and proofreading. The final chapter in the book covers design briefings. We draw a distinction between speeches, presentations and group discussions. Then we focus on the technical presentation and indicate the importance of preparing excellent visual aids. We make extensive use of PowerPoint in illustrating the types of visual aids to be employed in a design briefing. Finally, we include a discussion of the delivery of the presentation and the need for extensive rehearsing.

As we approach the next century, it is imperative that we think very seriously about ABET's (Accreditation Board for Engineering and Technology) new criteria for program accreditation. The new Criteria 2000 is very different than the current criteria for accreditation. We currently accredit our engineering programs based on input, and several pages of instructions are provide by ABET to guide in the assessment of that input. However, Criteria 2000 is based only on educational outcomes. Not a word is given in Criteria 2000 about input. The guide provided by ABET for assessment of educational outcomes is very terse (less than one page). It appears that it will be up to each department in each college of engineering to specify the intended educational outcomes for their program, to define the metrics used to measure these outcomes, and to plan and place into effect methods of measurement of these metrics over extended periods of time.

We have considered Criteria 2000 in this writing this book. We believe a first course in engineering such as ENES 100 should have the expected educational outcomes listed below:

Communication Skills

1. Engineering Graphics

    - Understand the role of graphics in engineering design.
    - Understand orthographic projection in producing multi-view drawings.
    - Understand three-dimensional representation with pictorial drawings.
    - Understand dimensioning and section views.
    - Demonstrate capability of preparing drawings using both manual and CAD techniques.
    - Demonstrate understanding by incorporating appropriate high-quality drawings in the design documentation.

2. Design Briefings:

    - Within a team format present a design review for the class using appropriate visual aids.
    - Each team member participates in the briefing.

3. Design Reports:

    - The team's design is documented in a professional style report incorporating time schedules, costs, parts list, drawings and an analysis.

Team Experience

- Develop an awareness of the challenges occurring in teamwork.
- Demonstrate teamwork in the product realization process through a systematic design concept selection process involving participation of all the team members.
- Demonstrate planning from conceptualization to the evaluation of the prototype.
- Understand and demonstrate share responsibility among team members.
- Demonstrate teamwork in preparing design reports and presenting design briefings.

Software Applications

- Demonstrate entry level skills in using spreadsheets for calculations and data analysis.
- Show a capability to prepare graphs and charts with a spreadsheet.
- Show a capability to prepare professional quality visual aids.
- Understand entry level skills in employing a CAD program.
- Demonstrate these skills in preparing appropriate materials for design briefings and design reports.

Design Project:

- The design project is the over arching theme of the course.
- Utilize all the skills listed above to assist in the product development process.
- Demonstrate competence in defining design objectives.
- Generate design concepts that meet the design objectives.
- Understand the basis for design for manufacturing, assembly and maintenance.
- Manage the team and the project effectively.

A comment is in order regarding the publisher of the book. After more than thirty years of working with large and well regarded publishers of engineering textbooks, the author has decided to self publish this book. It was not an easy decision because the editors and the technical representatives from these publishers are nice people. The problem is in the system employed by the large publishers. This system takes too long to bring a book to market. When the book arrives, it is too long for a single semester course (700 pages is typical) and it costs too much. The consequence is that the students tend to be overwhelmed by the tome and usually sell their book immediately after the final exam. Neither of these reactions on the part of our students are desirable educational outcomes.

We have attempted to bring this textbook to market quickly. It contains only the material needed for this course and is not loaded with material suitable for 40 different courses at 40 different colleges of engineering across the U. S. and Canada. It is priced at about 1/3 of the cost of a typical textbook. Hopefully students will feel more comfortable in retaining the book and begin to develop their own professional library.

Acknowledgments are always necessary in preparing a textbook because so many people and organizations are involved. First, we want to thank The National Science Foundation for their support. Their funding was important, but more critical than money was credibility. Without the Engineering Education Coalition Program, the need for curriculum reform would not have received adequate attention from the college administrators and our colleagues. The NSF basically called for a reform of the curriculum and with generous funding gave it the required status.

Second, we need to recognize the contributions of many of our colleagues at the University of Maryland. In 1990 the author taught the pilot offering of the course with the assistance of Dr. Guangming Zhang. Guangming attended every class and prepared an excellent set of notes that were essential in the second series of pilot courses that were taught by Tom Regan and Isabel Lloyd. Guangming also taught the course, with slight modifications, to several classes of high school women as part of an early entrance summer program at the University of Maryland. His success in teaching these 16 year old women clearly showed his superior ability as a teacher and the robust nature of the course material that we had developed. We need to thank Ms. Jane Fines who maintained contact with many of our students in several offerings of the course. She gave us very valuable feedback about the reactions of the students as we modified the course over the years.

As always thanks are due to the administrators who encouraged and supported the development of this course. George Dieter and Bill Destler, the former and current Dean of Engineering, authorized the small class size essential for effectively teaching this course and committed to significant long term expenditures necessary to support the faculty involved. They also publicly supported the efforts of the small group of instructors during the early years as we were institutionalizing the course. In fact Bill Destler, a Department Chair in 1992, took time from his busy schedule and taught the course.

Thanks are also due to Marilyn Berman, formerly an Associate Dean of Engineering, for her ability to cut the yards of red tape associated with beginning a new course offering at the University of Maryland. Without her help we would never have been able to schedule the pilot class. The Department Chairs also supported the concept of teaching product design and development in the first year. The author is particularly indebted to Bill Fourney and Bill Walston in the Mechanical Engineering Department for their support and encouragement. Special thanks go to Davinder Anand, Chair of Mechanical Engineering, for providing a leave this year permitting me to complete this book in a timely manner.

James W. Dally
Knoxville, TN

CONTENTS

PART I SOLAR DESALINATION

CHAPTER 1 INTRODUCTION

CHAPTER 2 SOLAR DESALINATION STILL

CHAPTER 3 SOLAR ENERGY

CHAPTER 4 ANALYSIS OF A SOLAR STILL

PART II ENGINEERING GRAPHICS

CHAPTER 5 THREE-VIEW DRAWINGS

CHAPTER 6 PICTORIAL DRAWING

CHAPTER 7 TABLES AND GRAPHS

PART III SOFTWARE APPLICATIONS

CHAPTER 8 CAD KEY Complete: DOS Version

CHAPTER 9 MICROSOFT EXCEL

CHAPTER 10 MICROSOFT PowerPoint

PART IV PRODUCT DEVELOPMENT

CHAPTER 11 DEVELOPMENT TEAMS

CHAPTER 12 A PRODUCT DEVELOPMENT PROCESS

PART V COMMUNICATIONS

CHAPTER 13 TECHNICAL REPORTS

CHAPTER 14 DESIGN BRIEFINGS

PART I

SOLAR

DESALINATION

CHAPTER 1

INTRODUCTION

PURPOSE OF THE TEXTBOOK

The principle purpose of this textbook is to assist you in learning about the product realization process and to provide an initial experience in engineering design. The textbook is written to support your efforts as you work within a team structure to develop a product. We recognize that most of our readers will have little or no design experience, and for this reason, we have selected a relatively simple product for your team to develop --- a small solar desalination still. We will ask you to understand the principles of operation of the solar still, and then to design it completely including the preparation of high quality engineering drawings. After the design is complete and released through a peer review, we will ask you to prepare an assembly kit with all of the parts that are necessary to actually build the still. Finally, you will assemble the still and evaluate its performance by conducting a test to measure its output.

Before we describe the requirements of the solar still let's briefly discuss the product realization process.

THE PRODUCT DEVELOPMENT PROCESS

We use hundreds of products every day. We are surrounded by products. This morning I prepared breakfast by toasting bread, frying eggs, and making coffee. How many products did I use in this simple task. The toaster (Black & Decker), the frying pan (T-FAL), the tea kettle (Revere), and the electric range (General Electric) are all products that are designed, manufactured and sold to customers both here and abroad. Some products are relatively simple, like the frying pan, but some are much more complex, such as your automobile.

Corporations world-wide continuously develop their product lines with minor improvements introduced every year or two with more major improvements every four or five years. Product development is a major responsibility of engineers entering the work place as is illustrated in Table 1.

TABLE 1

Responsibilities of Mechanical Engineers in Their First Position [1]

ASSIGNMENT		PERCENT OF TIME
Design Engineering		40
Product Design	24	
Systems Design	9	
Equipment Design	7	
Plant Engineering/ Operations/ Maintenance		13
Quality Control/ Reliability/ Standards		12
Production Engineering		12
Sales Engineering		5
Management		4
Engineering	3	
Corporate	1	
Computer Applications/ Systems Analysis		4
Basic Research and Development		3
Other Activities		7

An examination of Table 1, shows that designing, manufacturing, and selling product represents more than 80 % of the responsibilities of mechanical engineers in their initial position in industry.

The viability of many corporations depends on the introduction of a steady stream of successful products to the marketplace. A successful product must satisfy the customer by providing robust and reliable service that completely meets the customer needs at a competitive price.

Products are developed by interdisciplinary teams with representation from engineering, marketing, manufacturing, production, purchasing, etc. A typical organization chart for a team developing a relatively simple electro-mechanical component is shown in Fig. 1. The team leader coordinates and directs the activities of the designers (mechanical, electronic, and industrial), and is supported by a marketing specialist to ensure that the evolving product meets the needs of the customer. Assistance in finance, sales and legal issues is provided on as-needed basis by corporate staff.

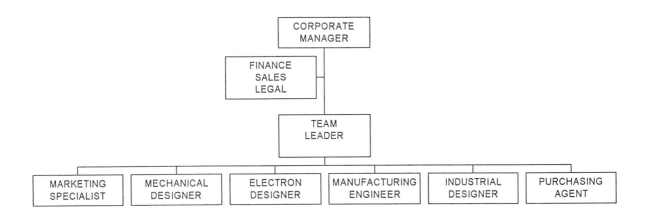

Fig. 1 Organization of a product development team a relatively simple product.

The team leader is also supported by a purchasing agent who interacts with the suppliers that provide materials and component parts used in the final assembly of the product. In the past decade, the relation between suppliers and end product producers has changed in a very significant manner. Suppliers become part of the development team. They often provide a significant level of engineering support that is external to the internal (core) development team. In some developments, this external (supplier funded) development team is larger than the internal development team. For example, the internal development team for the Boeing 777 airliner involved 6,800 employees, and the external team was estimated at 10,000 [2].

WINNING PRODUCTS

There are two primary aspects to developing successful products that win in the competitive market place. The first is the quality and price of the product. The second is the time and the cost of the development, and the cost to manufacture the product in production.

Let's discuss the product first. Is it attractive and easy to use? Is it durable and reliable? Is it effective? Does it meet the needs of the customer? If the answer to all of these questions is an unqualified YES, the customer may want to buy the product if the price is right. Next, you need to understand what is implied by product cost and its relation to the price paid for the product. They are distinctly different quantities. Product cost includes the cost of materials, components, manufacturing and assembly. The accountants also include other less obvious costs such as the prorated costs of capital equipment (the plant and its machinery), the tooling, the development cost, and even the inventory costs in determining the total cost of producing a unit of product. Price is the amount that a customer pays to buy the product. The difference between the price and the cost of a product is the profit, which is usually expressed on a per unit basis.

$$\text{Profit} = \text{Product Price} - \text{Product Cost} \qquad (1)$$

Equation (1) is the most important relation in engineering. If a corporation cannot make a profit it would soon be forced into bankruptcy, it's employees lose their positions, and the stockholders lose their investment. It is this profit that everyone employed by a corporation seeks to maximize while maintaining the vitality of a product line. The same statement can be made for a business that provides services instead of products. The price paid by the customer for a specified service must be more than the cost to provide that service, if the business is to make a profit and prosper.

Let's now discuss the role of development process in producing a line of winning products. Developing a product involves many people with talent in different disciplines and takes time and cost money. Let's first consider development time. Time, as it is used in this context, is time to market. This is a very important factor for a development team because of the many benefits of being first to market. Many competitive advantages accrue from a fast development capability. First the product's life is extended. For each month cut from the development schedule, a month is added to the life of the product in the marketplace with an additional month of sales revenue and profit. We show the benefits of being first to market on sales revenue in Fig. 2. The shaded region between the two curves to the left side of the graph is the enhanced revenue due to the longer sales.

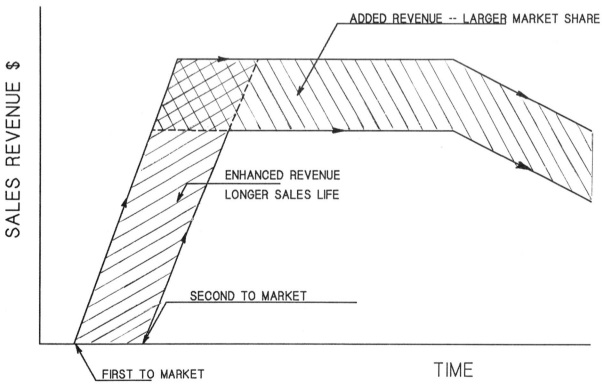

Fig. 2 Increased sales revenue due to extended market life and larger market share.

A second benefit of early product release is increased market share. The first product to market has 100 % of market share in the absence of competing product. For products with periodic development of "new models," it is generally recognized that the earlier a product is introduced (without sacrificing quality and reliability) the better chance that it has for acquiring and retaining a large share of the market. The effect of gaining a larger market share on sales revenue is illustrated in Fig. 2. The cross hatched region between the two curves at the top of the graph shows the enhanced sales revenue.

A third advantage of a short development cycle is higher profit margins. If a new product is introduced prior to availability of competitive products, the corporation is able to command a higher price for the product which enhances the profit. With time competitive products will be introduced forcing price reductions. However, in many instances, relatively large profit margins still can be maintained because the company that is first to market is reducing their manufacturing costs. They learn better methods for producing components and assembling the product. The advantage of being first to market with a product where a manufacturing learning curve exists is shown graphically in Fig. 3. The manufacturing learning curve reflects the reduced costs with time in production. These cost reductions are due to many innovations introduced by the workers after mass production begins. With production experience it is possible to drive down costs.

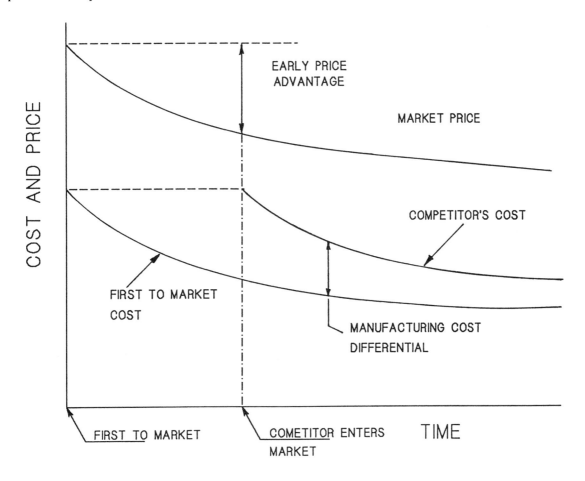

Fig. 3 The development team bringing the product to market first enjoys an initial price advantage and subsequent cost advantages from manufacturing efficiencies.

Let's next consider development costs because they represent a very important investment for the companies involved. Development costs include the wages of the members of the development team, money paid to subcontractors, costs of pre-production tooling, costs of supplies and materials, etc.. These development costs can be significant and most companies must limit the number of developments in which they invest. The size of the investment can be appreciated by noting that the development cost of a new automobile is estimated [2] at $1 billion, with an additional investment of $500 to $700 million for the new tooling required for production.

We have included this discussion on time and cost of product development to help you begin to appreciate some of the business aspects of developing winning products. Any company involved in the sale of products depends completely on their ability to continuously introduce winning products to the marketplace in a timely manner. To win, the development team must bring a quality reliable product to market that meets the needs of the customer. The development costs must be minimized in relation to a product development schedule that permits an early (preferably first to market) introduction of the product.

YOUR PRODUCT DEVELOPMENT

The best way to learn about product design is simply to work on a development team and develop a prototype. For this reason, we have selected a product for your first development effort --- a solar desalination unit. You are to work as a member in a team of five or six students to develop a prototype of a solar still. A prototype is the first working model of a product. In some instances, companies develop three or four prototype before finalizing on a particular design of a product. Time available during this semester will limit each team to a single prototype.

We understand that the development of a solar still is a significant task particularly when the assignment is made so early in your engineering program. However, our experience with several thousand students entering the engineering program indicates you will gain significantly from your efforts. Individually you are very creative and can work within a team to design and build successful prototypes if they are not overly complex. Since beginning this course at the University of Maryland at College Park, in 1990, the students participating have developed play ground equipment, windmills for the generation of electricity, furniture, human power water pumps, wind powered vehicles and a solar cooking unit. Extensive student surveys clearly indicate that the students spend a lot of time on the project, have fun doing so, learn a lot about engineering, and appreciate the lessons learned in working as a member of a development team.

PROTOTYPE DEVELOPMENT

In this course, we divide the prototype development process into three major phases which include:

1. Designing the prototype.
2. Preparing the assembly kit.
3. Prototype assembly and evaluation.

We will begin the process by providing you with a typical description of the solar still. The description will initially be in general terms. You will be provided with design requirements pertaining to the input – the amount of solar energy and the quality of the brackish water involved in the distillation process. The design requirements will also specify the output which is the rate (liters/day) of condensate that is to be produced by the still. We will also provide you with some information on solar energy and heat transfer that should help you understand the distillation process. Some hints will be given on concentrating solar energy to start your creative insights regarding the design. We suggest that you make full use of the library to search the literature and the patent files.

After you understand in general terms the requirements in the design of the still, we will introduce the product specification [3]. The product specification is usually prepared in tabular format, and it tersely states design requirements and design limits. Remember we will always design with constraints and/or limits. These limits are stated in the product specification very early in the development process. Also all of the performance criteria are included in the specification. Finally the specification provides design targets on weight, size, power, cost, etc.

We will place explicit design constraints which limit your flexibility in designing the prototype. First there is a limit of $25.00 (maximum) per team member for the cost of materials, supplies, and components purchased for the still. The idea is to keep the out-of-pocket expenses for the students at an affordable level, while giving the team adequate funds to build a good prototype. We will also limit the size of the still, so that our laboratory facilities and workshops can handle the large number of stills to be produced this semester.

DESIGN CONCEPTS

After you and each member of your development team understands the design specification and the design limitations, you are ready to begin to generate design concepts. (A much more complete description of the design requirements, constraints, etc. is given in Chapter 2 together with some initial design ideas for you to consider). Design concepts are simply ideas for performing each function involved in the operation of the still and in meeting the product specifications. To illustrate design concepts, let's examine the functions (processes) involved in a distillation as depicted in Fig. 4.

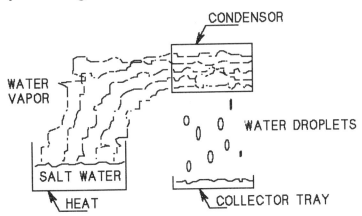

Fig. 4 Functions involved in the distillation process.

In a distillation still, we heat a quantity (batch) of salt (or impure) water to convert it from a liquid to a vapor. As we change the phase of the water from a liquid to a vapor, we purify the output. The salt remains in the residual water because it does not vaporize at the temperatures achieved in the still. Accordingly, the vapor produced is pure (salt free), while the concentration of salt in the remaining charge of impure water increases. Next, we collect the water vapor in a device call a condenser where the vapor is cooled. When the temperature of the vapor is reduced sufficiently (to the dew point temperature), the vapor condenses into small droplets of water on the surfaces of the condenser. Drops of condensate, that are pure (distilled) water, fall from the condenser into a collection tray. The condensate is pure in the sense that it is salt free; however, it may not be biologically pure. In fact, at the temperatures likely to be achieved in your still, bacteria growth may be enhanced.

Now that we understand the various functions involved in the distillation process, we are ready to generate design concepts (ideas) for performing each function. Consider first the need to add heat to the initial charge of salty water. We know that the heat is to come from the sun , but will the solar flux (F) be sufficient to produce an adequate amount of heat to change the water into vapor quickly enough to satisfy the specified rate of production of the distillate? How can we increase the heat delivered from the sun into our basin of salty water? Let's look at a very important relation that relates solar flux to the rate of heat transferred.

$$q = FA \qquad\qquad (2)$$

where.......q is the rate of heat transfer measured in Watts (W).
.....F is the solar flux Watts/unit area (W/m^2).
....A is the cross section area through which the flux is transmitted (m^2).

Two different approaches to the design of the solar still are suggested by Eq. (2). The relation shows that we can increase the rate of heat transferred (q) into the still by increasing either the area (A) or the solar flux (F). If we increase the area, the size of the still will increase. On the other hand, to increase the solar flux requires us to use some method (usually optical) to concentrated the solar flux (radiation) from the sun. Most of us have used a magnifying glass to focus (and concentrate) solar radiation producing a flux sufficiently high to ignite paper. This experience leads us to consider lenses as a design concept for concentrating solar flux. What other design idea can you suggest for concentrating solar radiation? What do you think about mirrors as a means of concentrating the sun's intensity?

We now have three rather vague ideas about the design of our solar collector:

1. We can make it large to increase the area A.
2. We can concentrate the flux by using a lens.
3. We can also increase the flux by using mirrors.

You need to pursue each of these ideas in much more detail and develop preliminary design proposals incorporating each of the design concepts. The more completely you develop the design proposals the better prepared you are to conduct what is termed a design-trade-off analysis, where you compare several design concepts and select the best one.

To perform a design-trade-off analysis, we consider each design proposal individually and list its strength and weaknesses. Factors usually considered in this analysis include size, weight, cost, ease of manufacturing, performance, appearance, etc. After the strengths and weaknesses of each design proposal has been listed, we can compare and evaluate each design proposal and select the most suitable for our prototype development.

We have discussed design concepts, design proposals and design trade-off analyses for a single function (heat input) that is involved in the distillation process. You have several other functions to consider such as transporting the vapor, designing the condenser and collecting the condensate. The procedure in design is to generate ideas for performing each function, expanding these ideas with more detail until they can be treated as design proposals, and finally to perform a design trade-off analysis where the merits and faults of each proposal are evaluated.

When the design proposals are selected for each of the four different functions involved in the distillation process, the four proposals must then be integrated into a seamless system that heats the initial charge of water, transports the water vapor to the condenser, insures that the temperature of the condenser surface is sufficiently low to convert the vapor to liquid, and finally collects the droplets of pure water which form on the condenser.

We often refer to a device that performs some function as a subsystem. The collection of all of the subsystems constitute a complete system, which is the prototype of the solar still. The integration of the various subsystems is often difficult. One subsystem influences the design of the others. The manner in which the subsystems interact is define as the interface between subsystems. In a mechanical application, the fit of a shaft in a bearing is an interface. Frequently interfaces between the subsystems are troublesome and difficult to manage. It is vitally important that the interfaces be controlled thereby permitting seamless integration of all of the subsystems without loss of effectiveness and efficiency.

The final step in designing the prototype is the preparation of the design package. The package, which is an extended engineering document, contains engineering sketches illustrating the concepts, engineering assembly drawings that describe how the various components fit together to form the complete system, and engineering drawings of all of the component parts in sufficient detail to permit the component to be manufactured by anyone capable of reading drawings. We recognize that many of you may need instruction in graphics, and we have included four chapters in this text to help you learn how to prepare three-view drawings, pictorial drawings and to make tables and graphs. One of the four chapters covers a computer aided drafting program, KEY CAD Complete, that will be of great assistance to you as you prepare the drawings for your design package.

The design package also contains a parts list that identifies every unique part employed in the assembly of the prototype. The quantity required of each component is also included on the line describing the component. For example, if you are going to use twelve No. 8 wood screws to fasten together the joints of your solar still, you would:

1. Assign a part number on the parts list identifying the need for these screws.
2. List the quantity required as 12 in the quantity column.
3. Describe the screws in sufficient detail so that another team member can go to the store and procure exactly the type of screw that you want.

The description is brief, but complete and precise. (i. e. No. 8 wood screw, flat headed slotted, brass, 1 in. long). In this description, No. 8 gives the diameter; wood refers the type of application for the screw; flat headed describes its head; slotted indicates that you will use a flat blade screw driver in the installation; brass is the material from which the screw is fabricated; 1 in. is the length of the screw

The parts list contains all of the items that are to be purchased for your prototype. It also contains the components that must be manufactured. If the component is to be manufactured it is identified on the parts list by its name and a drawing number. We show an example of a parts list in Fig. 5.

PARTS LIST FOR SOLAR STILL

NUMBER	NAME OF ITEM	DESCRIPTION OR DRAWING NUMBER	QUANTITY	PRICE
1	BASIN	ALUMINUM PAN, DWG NO. ENES 100- 01	1	$ 1.45
2	FELT PAD	1/8 THICK BLACK FELT, CUT TO FIT PAN	1 SQ. YD	$ 4.50
3	BASE INSULATION	FOAM INSULATION, CUT TO FIT PAN	1 SQ. YD	$ 1.25
4	COLLECTING TROUGH	ALUMINUM TROUGH, DWG NO. ENES 100-2	2	$ 1.75
5	PLASTIC FILM	TRANSPARENT MYLAR, 0.003 THICK	3 SQ. YDS	$ 1.50
6	ALUMINIZED FILM	ALUMINIZED MYLAR, 0.003 THICK	1 SQ. YD	$ 2.50
7	FRAMING	1/4 x 17 DOWEL ROD	17	$ 0.75
8	FRAMING	1/4 x 12 DOWEL ROD	8	$ 0.45
9	CONNECTOR TYPE 1	CONNECTOR 1 DWG NO. ENES 100-02	12	$ 0.25
10	CONNECTOR TYPE 2	CONNECTOR 2 DWG NO. ENES 100-03	4	$ 0.40
11	CONNECTOR TYPE 3	CONNECTOR 3 DWG NO. ENES 100-04	4	$ 0.65

Fig. 5 Parts list for the solar still.

An engineering report is also included as part of the design package. This report supports the design by describing the key features of your still. Your report should treat each function involved in the distillation process, and describe the design concepts that your team considered. A rationale for each design proposal that was adopted based on a systematic design trade-off studies is an essential element. Additionally, the design report contains theoretical analyses that you may have performed to predict in advance the performance of your prototype of the actual test to evaluate its performance. More information on the preparation of an engineering report is given in a chapter include in this textbook on writing technical reports.

The design phase of the product development process is concluded with a final design presentation. This is a formal review of the design of the still that your team presents to the class (peer review), to the instructor, and the teaching fellow. It is the team's responsibility to describe all of the unique features of the design and to predict the performance of the product. It is the responsibility of the class (peer group) and the instructors to question the feasibility of the design and the accuracy of the predicted performance. If you note a shortcoming or a flaw in the design, identify the problem to the team presenting their work. As a peer reviewer of another team's design, be tactful in your critique. Criticism is always difficult to offer to another. Offer your suggestions in good faith and in good taste.

The purpose of the design review is to locate deficiencies and errors. It is better to correct errors in the paper stage of the process, not later in the hardware phase, when it is much more difficult and costly to fix the problems.

PREPARING THE ASSEMBLY KIT

The second major phase of the product development process is to prepare what is called an assembly kit. An assembly kit is a collection of all of the parts, in the appropriate quantities, that are required to completely build the prototype. The parts list is the essential document that directs our procurement and manufacture of the components needed to build the prototype. The parts list identifies everything that we need and indicates the precise number of each item.

An efficient method for collecting the required parts is to divide the list into three groups:

1. Those parts to be purchased.
2. The materials and supplies to be purchased
3. The components to be manufactured.

One or two team members handle purchasing while the other team members work in the student workshop to fabricate the parts according to the detailed drawings prepared in the design phase. It is important to recognize that the drawing defines the part that is being manufactured. Always work from the drawing and not your memory or understanding of the part geometry.

It is suggested that one team member serve as the " inspector" to check the finished parts against the drawings for the parts that have been manufactured. If the parts have been purchased, the "inspector" should check the purchased items against the parts list to insure that the item meets the description, and that the correct quantity has been procured.

PROTOTYPE ASSEMBLY

When the assembly kit is complete and checked against the parts list, we can begin the final phase --- prototype evaluation. The first part of the evaluation is to assemble or build the prototype. We often call this step the "first article build" because it is the first time that we have attempted to put together all of the components involved in the prototype together. The "first article build" can go well if all of the parts are available, they all fit together properly, if the tolerances on each part and each feature are correct, and if the surface finish on all of the parts is acceptable. Prototype design is often judged against the four Fs--- form, fit, finish and function. The first article build permits us to assess how well the team performed with regard to the first three of the Fs --- form, fit, and finish.

If the parts do not fit, modifications of one or more parts are required. These modifications required design change that is a dreaded and costly process in the real world. In fact one of the most important criterion used by management to judge the quality of a development team is the number of design changes required both before and after the introduction of a product to the market place. Clearly, we want to design each part in a product correctly during our first effort and to minimize the number of design changes.

We anticipate that each team will make a few errors in the preparation of the detail design drawings and changes will be required. The natural tendency is to take the offending part to the model shop and to correct (modify) it, and get on with the first article build. This behavior is acceptable only if the team revises the drawing of the offending part to reflect the modification made to correct the design deficiency. In the real world, the drawing package is more important than the prototype. The second and all subsequent assemblies will be fabricated from the details shown in your drawings and not the from the prototype. The first prototype is often scrapped after it has been built and tested.

PROTOTYPE EVALUATION

After the assembly of the prototype is complete, it should be carefully inspected to insure it is safe. Fortunately, a solar still is a relatively safe product since there are no moving parts, and the pressures and temperatures developed within the solar still should be modest. However, make sure that you have eliminated all of the sharp edges and points on the prototype, and that you have avoided introducing pinch points. Be careful with hot water or vapor that is produced to avoid burns.

The final step in this development process is to test your prototype. This is a big day and indeed a big hour. A one hour time slot has been scheduled for evaluating each team's prototype in the solar facility available in the ENES 100 Laboratory. Your prototype will be judged based on the following criteria:

1. Performance ---- rate of condensate produced (liter/hour).
2. Cost ---- minimize.
3. Design innovation.
4. Quality of parts and assembly.
5. Appearance.

TEAMWORK

In this course, you are required to participate on a development team. There are three reasons for this requirement. First, the project is too ambitious for an individual to complete in the time available. You will need the collective efforts of the entire team to develop a quality solar still during the semester. We plan on pressing the development teams to complete the project on a prescribed schedule. Second, we want you to begin to learn teamwork skills. Experience has shown us that most students entering the engineering program have not developed these skills. From K-12, the educational process has focused on teaching you to work as an individual often in a setting where you competed against the other students in your class. We will demand that you begin functioning as a team member where cooperation, following, and listening are more important than individual effort. Leadership is important on a team, but following is also a critical element for successful team performance. The final reason is that you will probably find yourself on a development team early in your career if you take a position in industry. A recent study [4] by the American Society for Mechanical Engineers (ASME), the results of which are shown in Table 2, ranked teamwork as the most important skill to develop in an engineering program. Teamwork was the first skill in a list of 20 skills considered important by managers in industry. We are hopeful that this course will be instrumental in beginning to develop the team working skills so necessary for a successful career.

TABLE 2

Skills Considered Important for New Mechanical Engineers
with Bachelor Degrees
Priority Ranking

1. Teams and Teamwork
2. Communication
3. Design for Manufacture
4. CAD Systems
5. Professional Ethics
6. Creative Thinking
7. Design for Performance
8. Design for Reliability
9. Design for Safety
10. Concurrent Engineering
11. Sketching and Drawing
12. Design for Cost.
13. Application of Statistics
14. Reliability
15. Geometric Tolerancing
16. Value Engineering
17. Design Reviews
18. Manufacturing Processes
19. Systems Perspective
20. Design for Assembly

As you work within your team in the development of the solar still, you will be introduced to many of the 20 topics listed in Table 2. We trust that you will begin to develop an appreciation the need for these skills and begin to enhance your level of understanding of the design process that is inherent in many of these skills.

OTHER COURSE OBJECTIVES

While your experience in developing a prototype solar still is the primary objective of this course, there are several other related objectives. You will quickly recognize a critical need for graphics as you attempt to describe your design concepts to fellow team members. We have included four chapters on graphics to help you learn the basic skills required at this entry level. These chapters include materials on three view drawing, pictorial drawing, graphs and tables, and in developing entry level skills in KEY CAD Complete, which is a computer aided drawing program.

You will also be required to become familiar and use three additional software application programs. These include a word processing, a spreadsheet, and a graphics presentation program. Our experience indicates that nearly all of you are already proficient with word processing so we will not cover this topic here. However, many of you are not familiar with a spreadsheet. Accordingly, we have included a chapter describing Microsoft Excel to help you prepare your parts list, to perform calculations and to prepare graphs. Spreadsheets represent a very powerful tool, that you will find useful in many different ways for the remainder of your life. We trust that you will take this opportunity to learn how to use this important application program. We have also included a description of Microsoft PowerPoint to aid you in the preparation of world class slides for your design briefings.

As you proceed with the development of the solar still, we will require you to communicate both orally and in writing. Design reviews before the class give you the opportunity to learn presentation skills such as style, timing and the preparation of world class visual aids. The design report will give you an experience in preparing a complete high quality engineering drawings, and in writing a technical report containing text, figures, tables and graphs.

The final objective of the course is design analysis. We understand that your engineering analysis skills have yet to be developed. For this reason, we will present key equations that mathematically model the processes involved in the solar distillation unit. We do not expect you to completely understand all of the theoretical aspects of the relatively complicated processes involved (heat transfer, radiation, vaporization, condensation, surface tension, flow, etc.). Most of you will take several courses later in the curriculum dealing with these subjects in great detail However, at this stage of your career, we want you to begin to appreciate the inter relationship between analysis and design. To help you with the analysis we have included a chapter that covers these various topics in a very brief and introductory manner.

REFERENCES

1. Valenti, M. "Teaching Tomorrow's Engineers," Special Report, Mechanical Engineering, Vol. 118, No. 7, July 1996.
2. Ulrich, K. T., S. D. Eppinger, Product Design and Development, McGraw-Hill, New York, NY, 1995, p. 6.
3. Cross, N., Engineering Design Methods, 2nd Edition, Wiley, New York, NY, 1994, pp. 77-81.
4. Anon, "Integrating the Product Realization Process into the Undergraduate Curriculum," ASME report to the National Science Foundation, 1995.

EXERCISES

1. List ten products that you have used today and the companies that manufactured and marketed them.
2. Suppose that you do not want to work on product development, manufacturing or sales. What opportunities remain for you in Engineering?
3. Write an Engineering brief describing the characteristics of a winning product.
4. Write the most important equation in engineering or business.
5. Why is Ford Motor Company reluctant to develop a brand new model of an automobile?
6. What is a design concept? How many concepts will your team generate in developing the still this semester?
7. Why is Eq. 2 important in the design of the solar still? Would it be possible for you to design the solar still if Eq. 2 had not been presented in this textbook?
8. Why is it important to prepare a parts list during a development program?
9. What is an assembly kit and why do we prepare one in the development of the first prototype?
10. Why do we invest company funds in assembling a prototype?
11. What are the safety considerations with which you must be concerned in testing the prototype solar still?
12. Why do you believe industry representatives ranked teams and teamwork as the most important skill for new Engineers?

CHAPTER 2

SOLAR DESALINATION STILL

THE WORLD'S WATER PROBLEM

A solar desalination still is the product selected for the 1996-97 class of ENES 100 to design, build and evaluate. We have divided the class into teams each with five or six members. Each team will have the responsibility for developing a solar still that will convert salt water into fresh water.

Before describing the specification, for the still let's consider some basic facts about the distribution of fresh water across the world. The location of the arid and semi-arid lands, that are classified according to the amount of annual precipitation, is shown in Fig. 1. The regions in black are classified as arid where the amount of annual rainfall is less than 10 inches. The shaded regions are semi-arid where the rainfall is less than 25 inches per year. It is clear that the rainfall in the arid regions is insufficient to support agriculture (crops), and in the semi-arid regions, the type of crops that can be planted is limited and the agricultural yields are uncertain.

In many parts of the world, the freshwater available for drinking is limited and the population there is forced to drink poor "quality" water. The quality of water acceptable for human consumption has been defined by the U. S. Public Health Service according to dissolved solids (ions) as listed in Table 1. Most desalination facilities seek to reduce the salinity of the water produced to less than 500 parts per million (ppm), which is the maximum amount of dissolved solids allowed in what we define as potable water.

You should note that the individual concentrations in the two columns in Table 1 do not add to give the total values shown for the dissolved solids. This discrepancy is due to the listing of the optimum or maximum allowable concentration of the specified chemical. In the optimum concentration column, when one chemical is near its upper limit, other chemicals must be lower in concentration than their respective limits. In this way the total of the dissolved solids will not exceed the specified limit.

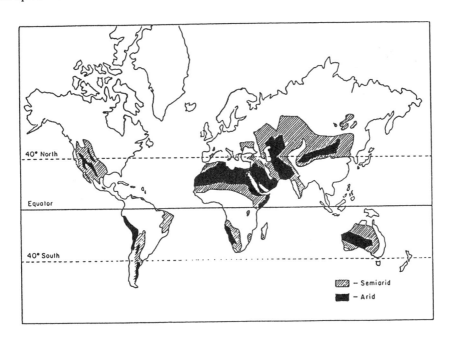

Fig. 1 Distribution of arid and semi-arid land in the world (from reference [1]).

TABLE 1

STANDARDS OF THE U. S. PUBLIC HEALTH SERVICE FOR POTABLE WATER BASED ON DISSOLVED SOLIDS OF CHEMICALS [2]

CHEMICAL	OPTIMUM CONCENTRATION (ppm)	MAXIMUM CONCENTRATION (ppm)
Lead	0	0.1
Copper	0	3.0
Zinc	0	15.0
Iron & Manganese	0	0.3
Sulfate	250	250
Chloride	250	
Magnesium	125	125
Fluoride	0.5	1.5
TOTAL	500	1500

It should be recognized that many public water supplies do not meet the chemical standards specified in Table 1, and many people are consuming water with saline content much higher than 1500 ppm. Dixey [3] reports that water with dissolved solids exceeding 4000 ppm is used in Northern Mexico, 3400 ppm in Senegal and 3130 ppm in Australia. Surveys of municipal water supplies in the U. S. made in 1964 and 1969 [4] showed that about 10% of the localities were distributing water with more than 500 ppm of dissolved solids. It appears that there is a need for the improvement of the water supplies in the U. S. and in many other parts of the world.

We are not addressing the problem of bacterial contamination of our water supplies which is becoming more widespread in the U. S. That is separate and a much more serious problem, although it is easier to kill the biological contaminates than to remove salt from our water supplies.

This brief review of the "quality" of water indicates that the ability to productively employ very large regions of the world's land is curtailed by the availability of fresh water. However, in many of these regions sea (salt) water or brackish water is available. The problem is to find an method that is economic feasible for converting this water with a high level of dissolved solids into potable with dissolved solid of less than 500 ppm.

There are several approaches to purifying water, but we will focus on a batch type distillation process that includes the following elements.

1. A quantity (batch) of salt water is placed in the still.
2. The water is heated and the liquid is converted into a gas (vapor).
3. The water vapor is condensed to produce pure water.
4. The water from the condenser is collected and stored.

The conversion from the liquid state to the gaseous state produces pure water vapor. The dissolved solids remain in the liquid and increase in concentration as the pure water vapor is drawn from the original charge.

SOLAR ENERGY

An essential element in the distillation process is the heat required to increase the temperature of the initial charge of water. It is the increased temperature which enhances the rate of conversion of the water from its liquid phase to its vapor phase. The heat supplied to our still is to be provide by solar energy.

The sun's energy originates from a nuclear fusion reaction occurring deep within the huge mass of gas that comprises the sun. The sun is classified as a common dwarf yellow star spectral type DG. Its surface temperature is about 10,000 °F, and the temperature at the interior is 20×10^6 °F. The energy from the sun is propagated into space as black body radiation from the outside the gaseous envelop. The photons in this radiation propagate at a velocity of 300,000 km/s and travel the 93 million miles to earth in about eight minutes. The intensity of the solar radiation in space, but near earth, is essentially constant. However, on the surface of the earth the solar intensity varies markedly as it is affected by latitude, season, and the clarity of the atmosphere. For any specified location in the Northern Hemisphere, the solar radiation is a maximum at summer solstice (June 21) and a minimum at winter solstice (December 22). Of course, the intensity of the radiation is zero from sunset to sunrise, and then it increases to a maximum at about noon and gradually decays to zero at sunset.

The maximum intensity of the solar radiation is about 400 BTU/(ft²-hr) on a horizontal surface at noon. Our solar distillation unit for collecting solar energy must be capable of absorbing this maximum intensity. It must also be designed to effectively utilize the lower radiation intensities that occur at other times and to accommodate the radiation arriving at other angles. Solar stills are usually designed with stationary surfaces that do not follow the sun. The most common design employs nearly horizontal surfaces where the magnitude of the solar radiation for the entire day is about 2600 BTU/(ft² - day), on a clear summer day at a latitude of 40°. In the winter this intensity is only 800 BTU/(ft² - day) on bright clear days and is much less on cloudy days. The total diurnal radiant flux in BTU/(ft²- day) is presented for several different latitudes in Fig. 2. Diurnal refers to a periodic variation of the intensity of the radiation from the sun onto the surface of the earth during the day and night,

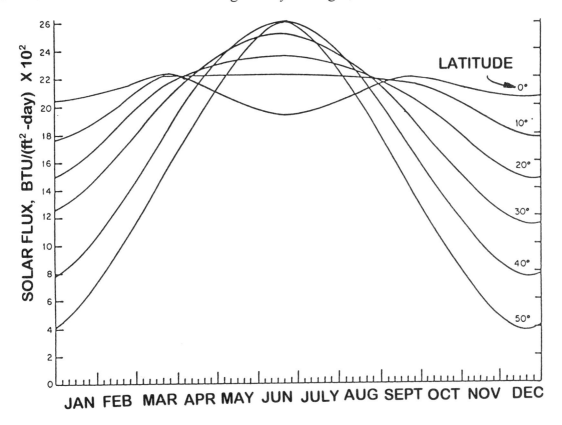

Fig. 2 Solar flux on a horizontal plane on the surface of the earth as a function of the month and latitude (Northern Hemisphere).

Before we go on to discuss the history of solar desalination, let's define some of the quantities that we have been using and call to your attention the fact that much of the data we need to develop our still is expressed in different and often strange units. We will address these units in several different sections of this textbook. Let's start by noting that heat is measured in either BTU or Calories. A BTU (British Thermal Unit) is the amount of heat required to increase the temperature of one pound of water by one degree Fahrenheit. A calorie is the amount of heat required to increase the temperature of one gram of water by one degree Celsius. We can convert between the BTU and the calorie by using a conversion factor 1 BTU = 252 calories.

HISTORY OF SOLAR DESALINATION

Never reinvent the wheel, or any thing else. When you begin to design a new product, it is essential that you understand the competitive products that are on the market, and all of the engineering features involved in the functioning of those products. Your team does not need to invent a solar still because it was invented more than a century ago. What you need to do is to design a solar still that meets the specifications that are given in the next section of this chapter. You begin the design process by reviewing the literature describing in detail the solar distillation process. We will help you begin by giving you the description of two early developments together with some key references.

An understanding of the thermodynamics upon which solar distillation is based was known long before the first significant installation of a still in Las Salinas in Chile [6] in 1872. This installation covered an area of 50,000 ft² and produced 5,000 gallon of fresh water per day. The output was used to water mules that were employed in the mule trains used to transport nitrate ores from the Chilean desert to the Pacific coast. The still was functional for more than 40 years. Its use was discontinued when a railroad was built to transport the ore, and the water was no longer required.

During the second world war (WWII), a collapsible still was designed for use on life-rafts [7]. These units incorporated a float with a hemispherical top and a weighted conical bottom. A horizontal felt sheet was saturated with sea water and deployed under the transparent plastic dome. The water vapor formed within the dome condensed partly on the inside of the plastic cover and partly on the inside surface of the cone. The distillate flow down the surfaces of the hemisphere and the cone and was collected in the submerged apex of the cone.

Additional information on early developments of solar desalination is given in references [8 - 12].

THE PRODUCT SPECIFICATION

We seek a small light weight solar still that is capable of producing at least one fluid ounce of fresh water in an hour. Since your prototype will be evaluated in early December 1996, when the availability of solar energy is uncertain, we will provide a radiation flux with a bank of infrared lamps arranged in a circular array as illustrated in Fig. 3. The seven lamp head has three separate on/off switches to let you choose the radiation level that you need. The head, mounted on a telescoping upright pole, can be raised, tilted, and turned at any angle to orient the radiation direction. The solar radiation produced by the lamps is not uniformly distributed. Instead, the flux is a maximum directly below the center of the lamp array and decreases as we move away from the center as shown in Fig. 4.

You will be provided with a saline solution containing approximately 2 lb/ft³ of NaCl (common table salt). You are to charge your solar desalination unit with a sufficient quantity (your team must specify the volume) of the saline solution. The still may be operated for 45 minutes. The fresh water output is to be collected and the volume produced with be measured in a graduate.

Fig. 3   Infrared lamp array used in the laboratory to simulate the solar radiation for prototype evaluation.

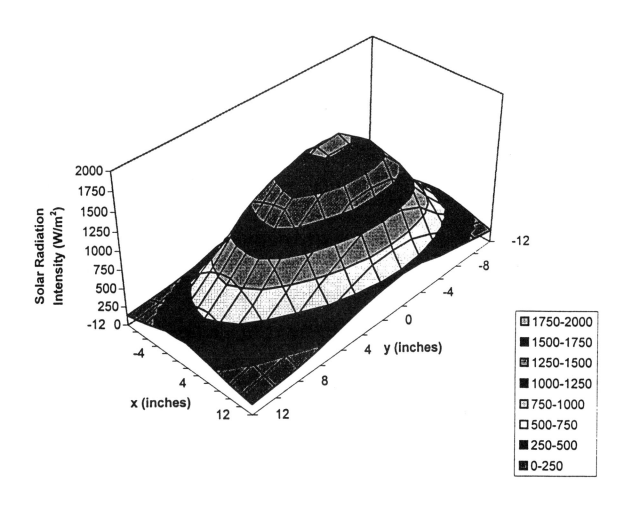

Fig. 4   Distribution of the solar flux on a footprint 24 inches below the infrared lamps.

Criteria used to judge the merits of your prototype development effort will include:

1. Performance --the volume of freshwater produced during the 45 minute test.
2. Cost of the materials used in building the prototype --minimize.
3. Ease of manufacturing the parts --simplicity.
4. Ease of assembly and disassembly -- minimize tooling and time.
5. Total weight --minimize.
6. Package size --see paragraph below.

The criterion package size needs more explanation as it is more involved than the other criteria for determining the merits of your development. The package size is a design constraint. The specific requirement is that all of your parts must fit into a cardboard box that normally contains ten packages of copy paper. These boxes measure 11 x 17 x 9 inch, and are available without cost at the copy centers on campus.

You will also be required to assemble your unit using only simple hand tooling such as a drill, screw driver, hammer and etc. You will be required to assemble your still in 45 minutes immediately before the class period scheduled for your test. Also, you will be required to disassemble the unit, placing all of the parts back into the copy paper box, in 15 minutes immediately following your test. Unless you receive instructions to the contrary from your instructor, you will have only one opportunity to test your still. When the test is complete, pack the still in its box, and dispose of it in an environmentally sensitive manner.

The product specification for the solar desalination unit is presented in Table 2. You may not understand some of the features listed in this specification such as basin, condenser, collector, etc. However, we will present a few preliminary design concepts in the next section to help you define some of these terms and to start you thinking about various design concepts that you may choose to employ in your design.

DESIGN CONCEPTS

Basin type solar desalination stills have been employed successfully in a number of commercial applications. The basin design depicted in Fig. 5 follows directly from the natural hydrological cycle, but on a very much smaller scale. Recall that the hydrological cycle begins with the sun warming the surface of the sea producing water vapor. The winds then carry this water vapor to land. The water vapor entrained in the air is elevated and cooled over the land until it condenses and falls as rain. The basin desalination units replicate this natural sequence of events.

Reference to Fig. 5 indicates that a shallow container (basin) of water is enclosed by a transparent cover. The cover is shaped so that it slopes towards the perimeter of the basin where a collection trough is placed. The basin is blackened to improve the absorption of the incident solar radiation. The cover is transparent permitting the radiation to enter. It also forms a vapor tight enclosure preventing the water vapor from escaping. The cover serves as a radiation shield and reduces the energy lost by reflections from the water surface. Finally, the cover provides a relatively cool surface and acts as the condenser required to convert the water vapor to a liquid. Glass plates or transparent plastic films are used to fabricate the cover as they transmit most of the solar radiation and only reflect and absorb a small amount of the incident energy. Because the heat absorbed by the cover is so small, it remains sufficiently cool to act as condenser. Clearly the three key features --evaporation, vapor transport, and condensation of the hydrological process are replicated in the basin type still.

TABLE 2
ENGINEERING SPECIFICATION
PROTOTYPE SOLAR DESALINATION UNIT

ITEM	PERFORMANCE OR GUIDELINES
Output	Fresh water 1 oz/hr minimum
Input	Salt water (2 lb $NaCl/ft^3$) Solar radiation as shown in Fig. 4. @ normal incidence

Basin
     Lateral area
     Depth
	
	 Open
	 Open

Condenser
     Area
     Inclination angle
	
	 Open
	 Open

Solar Collector
     Area
     Coatings
	
	 Open
	 Open

Solar Concentrators
     Mirrors
     Lenses
	
	 Open
	 Open

Distillation Collector	Open
Power	Solar energy only
Weight	Minimum
Packing size	11 x 17 x 9 in. box

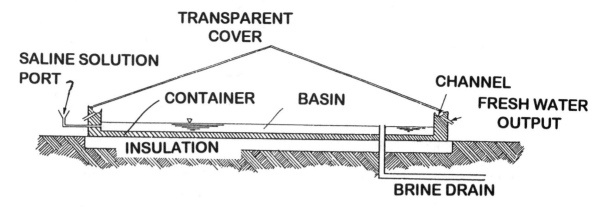

Fig. 5 Schematic illustration of a cross section of a basin still.

Solar stills differ from one another since different materials are employed in their construction and different shapes are used in designing the covers. Nevertheless, they all incorporate a water basin, a sloping transparent enclosure, and a line of collection troughs for the condensate. The water basin is often insulated to prevent heat loss to the ground. The slope of the cover must be sufficiently steep for the condensate to flow by gravity to the condensation channels. If the slope of the cover is too shallow, the condensate will form into drops that fall back into the basin and are lost. The condensate channels are arranged to permit flow into some collection point where the fresh water is stored, usually outside the enclosure of the still.

A commercial still includes methods for supplying the salt water, discharging the spent solution (brine), and storing the fresh water that is produced. In your prototype, we suggest that you employ a "batch" still where a quantity of water (two or three times the amount of fresh water expected to be produced) is placed in the basin at the beginning of the prototype evaluation.

The cross sectional view of a basin type desalination unit shown in Fig. 5 is typical of large scale installations where basin sizes range from 4000 to 93,000 ft^2 (see Table 3).

Other more creative designs that may be more suitable to the smaller solar desalination units capable of a few liters of fresh water on bright clear summer days are shown in Figs. 6 to 9.

We hope that the information presented in this chapter is sufficient for you to understand that the availability of "quality" water is a very real problem over every large desert and semi-arid regions in the world. Solar desalination is an approach that can, in certain instances, provide a limited amount of water to alleviate this problem. With this background information, a prototype has been described, that your team is to develop during the semester. The characteristics of the solar still to be developed has been described in general terms. The solar still has also been described in a relatively open engineering specification. Finally, we have shown you some designs by others, which you may consider as you begin your design.

TABLE 3

LARGE COMMERCIAL INSTALLATIONS OF SOLAR DESALINATION UNITS

COUNTRY	LOCATION	BASIN SIZE (ft^2)	OUTPUT (gpd)*
Australia	Muresky	4,000	220
	Cobber Pedy	34,000	1,680
	Caiguna	4,000	205
	Hamelin Pool	6,000	320
	Griffith	4,500	240
Cape Verde Islands	Santa Maria do Sal	8,000	560
Greece	Aegina	16,000	1,120
	Patmos	93,000	6,900
	Kimolos	27,000	2,000
	Nisiros	22,000	1,600
India	Bhavnagar	4,100	240
Spain	Las Marinas	9,400	680
Tunisia	Chakmou	4,700	140
	Mahdia	14,000	1,100
West Indies	Petit St. Vincent	18,400	1,300

*gpd...gallon per day

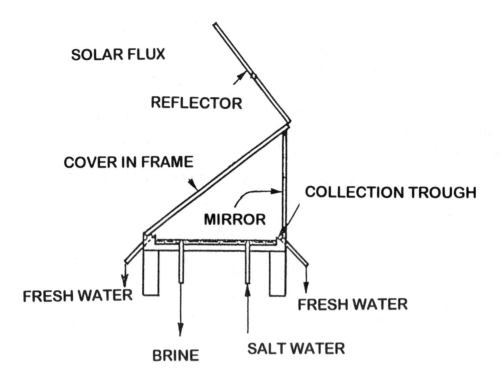

Fig. 6 Enclosed evaporating pan with reflecting surfaces (after reference[8]).

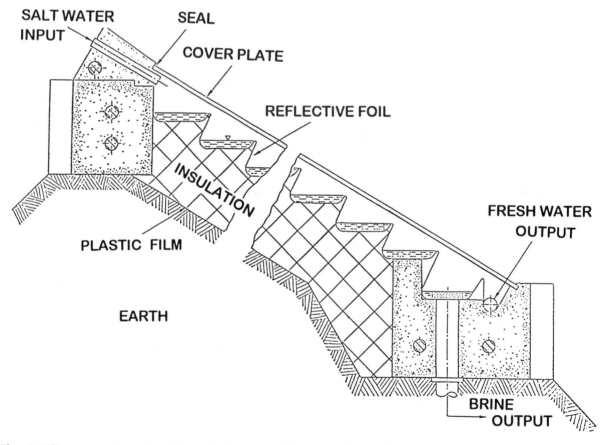

Fig. 7 Tilt-tray solar still with multiple stepped basins (after reference [9]).

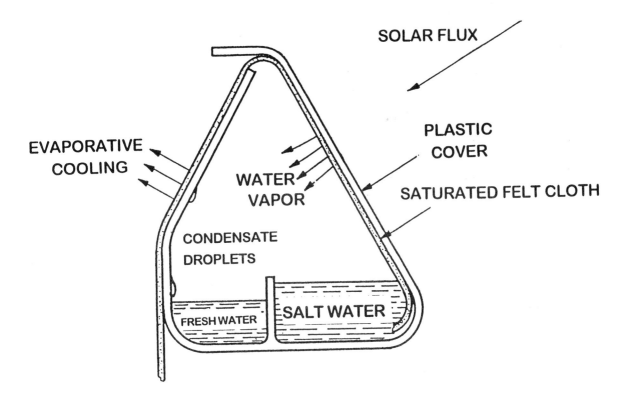

Fig. 8 Free form plastic covered still with black felt wick (after reference [8]).

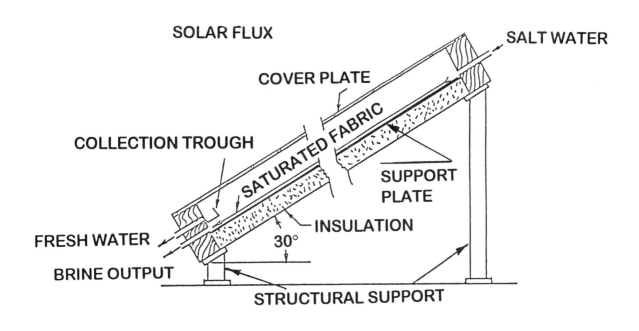

Fig. 9 Flat solar still with tilt and wick (after reference [10]).

REFERENCES

1. Meigs, P. <u>Reviews of Research on Arid Zone Hydrology Program</u>, Paris, UNESCO, 1953, pp.203-209.
2. Todd, D. K., <u>The Water Encyclopedia</u>, Water Information Center, Port Washington, New York, 1970, p. 559.
3. Dixey, <u>A Practical Handbook of Water Supply</u>, Thomas Murley Co., London, 1931, p. 562.
4. Patterson, W. L. and H. J. Lobb, Research Development Progress Report No. 519, Office of Saline Water, U. S. Department Interior, Washington, D. C. April 1970, p. 313.
5. Houghton, H. G., "On the Annual Heat Balance of the Northern Hemisphere," <u>Journal Metrology</u>, Vol. 11, No. 1, February, 1954.
6. Harding, J. "Apparatus for Solar Distillation," <u>Proceedings of the Institution of Civil Engineers</u>, (London), Vol. 73, 1883, pp. 284-288.
7. Telkes, M. <u>Solar Distiller for Life Rafts</u>, Office of Technical Services Research and Development Report No. 5225, U. S. Department of Commerce, Washington, D. C. 1945.
8. U. N., <u>Solar Distillation as a Means of Meeting Small Scale Water Demands</u>, United Nations Department of Economic and Social Affairs, 1970.
9. Howe, E. D., "Solar Distillation on the Pacific Atolls," <u>South Pacific Bulletin</u>, Sidney, Australia, April 1964.
10. Telkes, M., "Flat Tilted Solar Stills," <u>Proceedings of the International Seminar on Solar and Aeolian Energy</u>, Sunion, Greece, Plenum Press, New York, 1961.
11. Lof, G. O. G., <u>Demineralization of Saline Water with Solar Energy</u>, Saline Water Conversion Program Research and Development Progress Report No. 4 U. S. Department of the Interior, Washington, D. C., 1954.
12. Gomella, C., "Practical Possibilities for the Use of Solar Distillation in Under Developed Arid Countries," <u>Transactions of the Conference on the Use of Solar Energy</u>, Tucson, Arizona, University of Arizona Press, Vol. III, 1958, pp. 119-133.

EXERCISES

1. Write an engineering brief describing the regions in the U. S. that are either desert or semi-arid.
2. Prepare a unit conversion table that your team can use throughout the semester in dealing with the solar energy quantities measured in U. S. customary units or SI units.
3. Prepare a list of references that your team will explore in performing a literature search for solar stills.
4. Consider the six criteria that will be used to judge the quality of your solar still, and describe the strategy that your team will follow in addressing each criterion.
5. Complete the specifications shown in Table 2 by supplying numerical targets for all of the entries listed as open.
6. Write an engineering brief discussing the area of the solar still that your plans to develop. Justify the choice of this area.

CHAPTER 3

SOLAR ENERGY

HEAT

We usually produce heat by one of three different methods. By burning a hydrocarbon (fuel like gasoline), from controlled nuclear reactions (either fission or fusion), or by collecting solar energy from the sun. Most of the heat that we convert into energy to drive our autos or to produce electricity comes from burning a hydrocarbon such as coal, natural gas, or a petroleum product. We also produce electricity from fission type nuclear reactors located in about 120 power plants across the US and many more reactor installations found in other parts of the world. Solar radiation from the sun is also employed as an energy source, but its use is limited. Solar energy has two problems that severely constrain widespread application. First, is its availability. We can not be certain that solar energy will be there when we need it --- the sun may be out or it could be obscured by cloud cover. Second, the flux from the sun is not sufficiently high to deliver enough heat for commercial applications unless very large collectors and/or concentrators are employed.

Our sun is a star. Although it is 864,000 miles in diameter with a mass 330,000 times that of the earth, it is classified as a dwarf yellow star. A nuclear reaction is sustained in the interior of the sun where temperatures reach 20×10^6 °F. The surface temperature is much lower, only about 10,000 °F. The sun releases energy in the form of light (photons) that travel with a velocity of 186,000 miles per second. The photon travels the distance of 93 million miles between the sun and the earth in about eight minutes. The solar flux radiated by a hot "black" body (the sun) into space is given by:

$$F = q / A = ST^4 \qquad\qquad (1)$$

where

F is the solar flux (W/m^2).

q is the rate of heat transferred (W).

A is the area through which the heat is transferred (m^2)

T is the absolute temperature that is about 5800 $^\circ$ K for the sun's surface.

S is the Stefan-Boltzmann constant equal to 5.72 x 10^{-4} ($W/m^2 {}^\circ K$).

The solar flux F delivered to the earth, but in space outside the atmosphere is essentially constant at 1.353 kW/m^2 or 429.2 $BTU/(ft^2-h)$. This would be the energy or heat per unit area and per unit time delivered by photons that impinge on a solar collector, that is positioned with its surface perpendicular to the sun. Of course this delivery is based on the assumption that there is no atmosphere to interfere with the radiant heat transfer.

As the photons propagate through the earth's atmosphere, some of the solar energy is absorbed by the ozone, water vapor, and carbon dioxide present in the atmosphere. Still more photons are scattered and color the sky blue. As a result there is a loss of flux as the light passes through the atmosphere even on a clear day. Since the earth's atmosphere changes markedly from day to day, sometimes from hour to hour, so does the solar flux. The maximum flux, due to both scattered and direct radiation, that can be expected for a zenith sun over a desert location on a clear day is 1.05 kW/m^2 or 333 $BTU/(ft^2-h)$ [1].

Before we proceed, let's consider the magnitude of the energy involved in the maximum incident solar flux. Suppose we had an array of solar cells on our collector with an area of one square meter. Let's also assume that the solar cells convert the photons into electricity with an efficiency of 100 %. (This is a very poor assumption, but let's explore the possibilities). The output from our solar cell array would be slightly more than 1 kW. We could illuminate several rooms with the light from ten 100 W incandescent bulbs, or we could energize an electric motor producing over 1 ¼ horse power. Clearly, we have an abundance of power available from the sun even when we use relatively small solar collectors (our one square meter array of solar cells).

AVAILABILITY OF SOLAR ENERGY

Unfortunately there are two problems in the example described above. First the efficiencies of solar cells are relatively low --- only 10 to 20 %, which is not nearly the 100 % which we falsely assumed. Second, the magnitude 1.05 kW/m^2 of flux is rarely available. The flux decreases markedly with:

1. Cloud cover.
2. Time of day.
3. Time of year.
4. Latitude.

The availability of solar flux is a major deterrent in using solar energy for widespread applications. Clouds form, and very high concentrations of water vapor in them absorb and scatter the radiation from the sun. The solar flux penetrating the cloud cover is reduced significantly depending on the density of the clouds and the percentage of the sky covered.

We all know the intensity of the sun varies with the time of day. It is low in the early morning, high before and after noon, low again in the evening, and zero all night. The variation is dramatic, as indicated by the graph presented in Fig. 1, that shows the solar flux as a function of time before and after the solar noon. It is only when the sun is at its zenith, (solar noon) in the summer, that we receive the maximum solar flux of about 0.95 kW/m^2 or 300 BTU/(ft^2-h) at our latitude. The reduction in the solar flux is relatively small for the interval ± 3 hours of solar noon. However, for times t > 3 hours before and after noon the drop in the solar flux is pronounced.

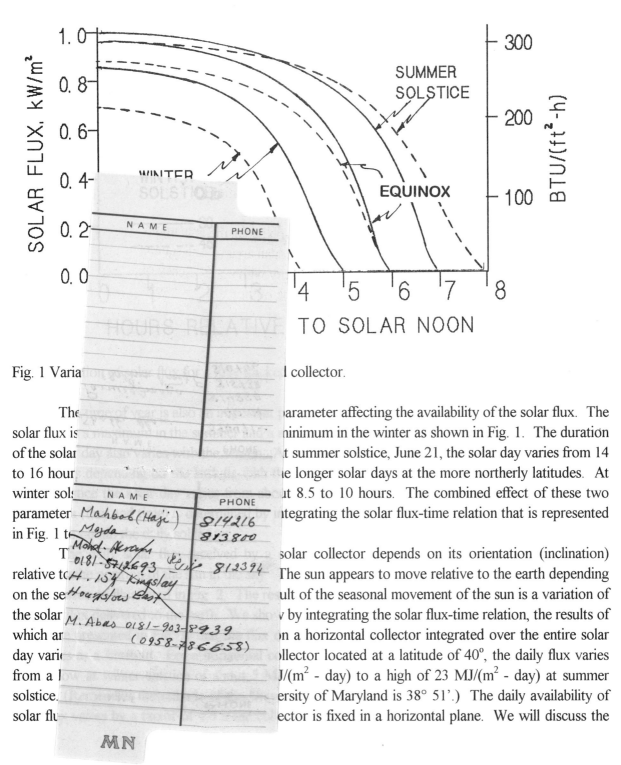

Fig. 1 Varia... collector.

The... parameter affecting the availability of the solar flux. The solar flux is ... minimum in the winter as shown in Fig. 1. The duration of the solar ... t summer solstice, June 21, the solar day varies from 14 to 16 hour... e longer solar days at the more northerly latitudes. At winter sol... t 8.5 to 10 hours. The combined effect of these two parameter... ntegrating the solar flux-time relation that is represented in Fig. 1 t...

T... solar collector depends on its orientation (inclination) relative to... The sun appears to move relative to the earth depending on the se... ult of the seasonal movement of the sun is a variation of the solar ... by integrating the solar flux-time relation, the results of which ar... n a horizontal collector integrated over the entire solar day vari... llector located at a latitude of 40°, the daily flux varies from a l... J/(m^2 - day) to a high of 23 MJ/(m^2 - day) at summer solstice. ... ersity of Maryland is 38° 51'.) The daily availability of solar flu... ector is fixed in a horizontal plane. We will discuss the influence of the angle of incidence of the solar collector in much more detail in the next section, since it markedly affects the daily solar flux available to the application.

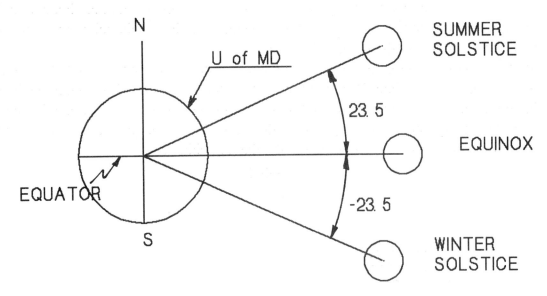

Fig. 2 Apparent motion of the sun with the seasons.

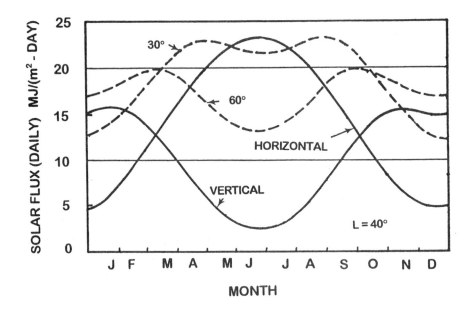

Fig. 3 Variation of daily solar flux received by a flat plate collector as a function of time of year and inclination angle. (Latitude 40°).

The final parameter affecting the incident solar flux is the latitude where the solar collector is located. As mentioned previously, the University of Maryland is located at a latitude of 38° 51', so the curves presented in Fig. 3 for a latitude of 40° represent a very good approximation for the daily solar flux that we can anticipate on our collector when the sky is bright and sunny.

The effect of latitude on the solar flux is complicated due to the fact that the earth is inclined with respect to its orbit about the sun by 23.5°. In the winter our northern hemisphere tilts away from the sun, and in the summer it tilts toward the sun as shown in Fig. 2. The north-south axis tilt of the earth's orbit causes the sun to appear to move back and forth across the equator. The movement in terms of the angle of declination is 47° (twice the tilt angle). The north-south axis tilt is responsible for the seasonal variations solar flux and the number of hours of sun light in the solar day, because the tilting axis of the earth changes the attitude of the sun

As the location of our solar collector moves in a northerly direction, the latitude increases. For instance, the latitude of Miami FL is about 25°, New Orleans, LA -- 30°, Albuquerque, NM -- 35°, Philadelphia, PA -- 40°, and Burlington, VT -- 45°. As we proceed in a northerly direction in the U. S., the sun's angle of elevation β, which is defined in Fig. 4, is smaller, and the solar flux is reduced. The angle of elevation β is sometimes called the solar altitude.

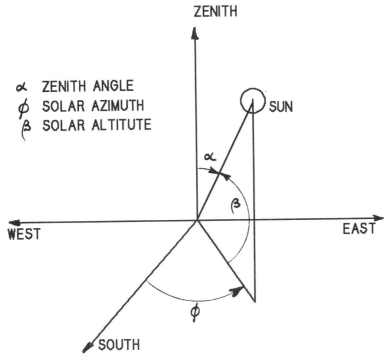

Fig. 4 Definition of several angles relative to the N, S, E, W and zenith (z) directions.

We can model the solar flux available on a flat plate collector by determining the zenith angle α, and the solar azimuth angle φ as a function of latitude, solar declination and time:

$$\cos\alpha = \sin L \sin D + \cos L \cos D \cos t \qquad (2)$$
$$\sin\phi = \cos D \sin t / \sin\alpha \qquad (3)$$

where

    L is the latitude angle (degrees).

    D is the declination angle of the sun (degrees).

    t is the hour angle of the sun (approximately 15°/h for each hour from noon).

Don't worry about evaluating Eqs. (2) and (3) at this stage of our development of the availability of solar energy. For those very interested in the topic, you will find the values of t, L and D may be determined from an ephemeris [4] for any day and any hour of the year. For those not evaluating Eqs. (2) and (3), we show the results of the analysis later.

A sketch showing the relation between the zenith angle α, solar altitude angle β, and azimuth angle ϕ of the sun is given in Fig. 4. Also, the zenith angle, α as determined from Eq. 2, is shown as a function of time of day in Fig. 5 for different seasons of the year and for latitude angles of 30° and 45°.

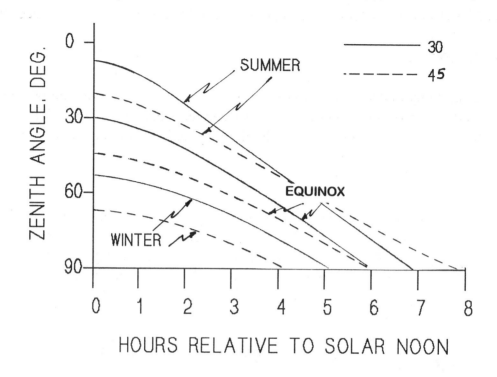

Fig. 5 Variation of zenith angle α with time of day for different seasons. Latitudes between 30°and 45°.

A relation for the solar flux on a flat collector inclined at an angle θ measured from the E -W axis (E positive) and inclined at an angle γ measured from the N-S axis (S positive) is given by:

$$F = F_0\{\cos\theta(\sin L \sin D + \cos L \cos D \cos t)$$
$$+ \sin\theta \cos\gamma [\tan L(\sin L \sin D + \cos L \cos D \cos t - \sin D \sec L)] \qquad (4)$$
$$+ \sin\gamma \cos D \sin t\}$$

where F_0 is the maximum solar radiation on a surface facing the sun, and the angles θ and γ are defined in Fig. 6.

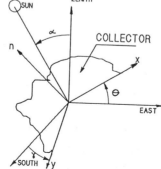

Fig. 6 Definition of orientation angles for a solar collector.

EFFECT OF ORIENTING THE COLLECTOR

We will use simplified versions of Eqs. 2 and (4) in the next paragraphs as we consider the effects of orienting the collector on the solar flux it receives. Of course, the idea is to increase the total flux received from the sun for the entire day by placing the solar collector at the best orientation.

CASE 1 $\theta = \gamma = 0$

The easiest way to deploy a solar collector is to place it flat on the ground with its surface horizontal and its outer normal pointing upward defining the zenith direction (see Fig. 6). In this orientation, $\theta = \gamma = 0$, and the relation for the solar flux at the collector F_c reduces to

$$F_c = F_0 \cos\alpha \qquad\qquad (5)$$

Accordingly, the variations of the solar flux at the collector F_c with time, season and latitude is given in Fig. 7. You should compare the solar flux on the horizontal flat plate (Fig.7) with that of a fully tracking collector (one that always keeps its face to the sun) as shown in Fig. 1. Do you notice the severe losses of available solar flux if the collector is deployed without inclination?

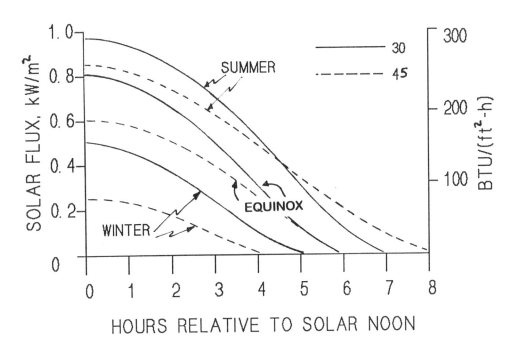

Fig. 7 Variation of solar flux (direct) on a horizontal collector as a function of time and season.

CASE 2 $\theta = 0$ and $\gamma = L$

What is the effect of tilting the collector so that it faces the sun at a more favorable angle than a collector that is horizontally deployed? Remember that in the northern hemisphere, the sun is always to the south. If we tilt the collector so that it faces south, we will reduce the angle between the sun and the outer normal vector from the collector. This reduction is particularly evident in the winter when the sun is far to the south (declination angle is -23.5° relative to the equator as shown in Fig. 2).

The idea of tilting the collector so that its surface face in a more southerly direction appears to be reasonable, but this thought leads us to the next question. How much should we tilt the collector? On of the common choices is to set the inclination (tilt) angle γ equal to the latitude $\gamma = L$ as shown in Fig. 8. In this case, the angle between the sun and the collector outer normal vector, ψ is:

$$\cos \psi = \cos D \cos t \qquad (6)$$

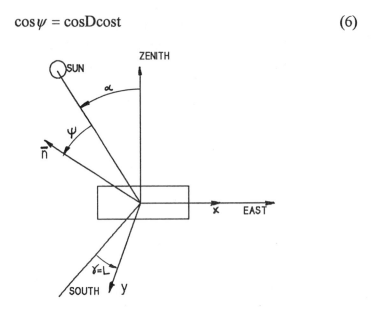

Fig. 8 S, E and zenith coordinate with oriented collector showing the angles γ and ψ.

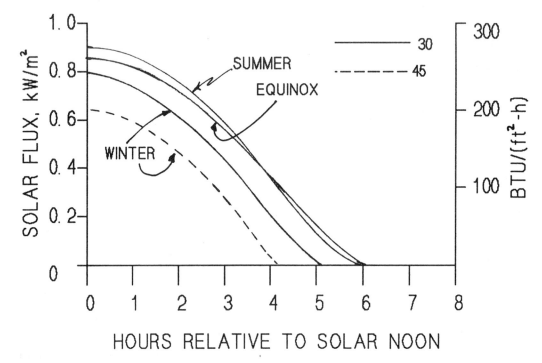

Fig. 9 Variation of solar flux for a fixed collector tilted at the latitude angle ($\gamma = L$) so that the collector faces south.

Since the angle ψ is much less than the angle α for a horizontal collector, we can anticipate an improvement due to the inclination of the collector. The magnitude of this improvement is ascertained by comparing the results of Fig 7 and Fig 9. During the summer, the inclination does not change the solar flux on the collector by a noticeable amount. However, the flux received during the equinox is modestly higher particularly at the more northerly latitudes. The significant gains are during the winter months when the sun is low in the sky. Inclining the collector during this season markedly increases the solar flux it receives. The disadvantage of the inclination is that the tilt causes a slight reduction in the duration of the sun day as seen by the collector in the summer. The overall increases in solar flux due to tilt angles of 30° and 60° are apparent by the comparisons shown in Fig. 2, for a collector located at a latitude of 40°. The effect of setting the tilt angle nearly equal to the latitude is to smooth out the seasonal variations, and to increase the overall performance when compared to a horizontally deployed collector.

CASE 3 $\theta = 0, \gamma = 90°$

The final case that we will consider is a vertical collector that faces south as illustrated in Fig. 10. In this instance, the angle ψ between the sun and the outer normal to the collector is:

$$\cos\psi = \sin L \cos D \cos t - \cos L \sin D \qquad (7)$$

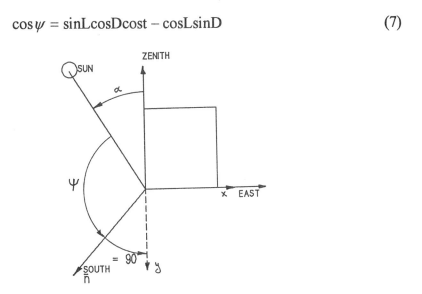

Fig. 10 Orientation of a vertical collector relative to the S, E and zenith coordinates.

This relation is markedly different than relation for the zenith angle given in Eq. (2). As a result, the solar flux curves presented in Fig. 11 are much different than those presented in Figs. 7 and 9. The very high angle between the sun and the outer normal vector ψ, in the summer, markedly reduces the flux input on a vertically oriented surface. On the other hand, during the winter the declination angle changes to reduce ψ significantly, and the south facing vertical collector (often a window) becomes very effective collector of solar energy.

These three case studies are sufficient to illustrate the fact that collector orientation is extremely important. We can increase or decrease the solar flux received by varying the orientation angle γ. For a fixed position (non tracking) collector, we can maximize the solar flux received by setting the angle γ equal to the latitude plus about 15 to 20 degrees.

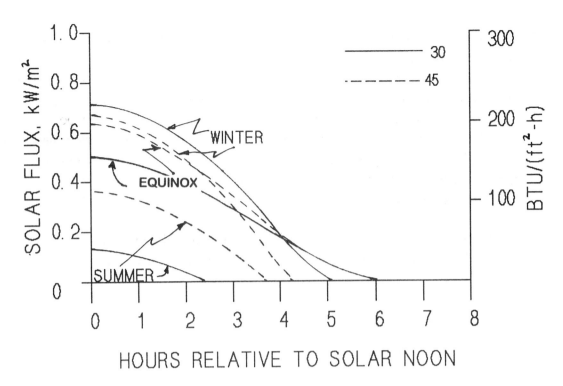

Fig. 11 Variation of the solar flux on a fixed vertical collector facing south.

TRACKING THE SUN

If we are willing to work occasionally after we install a solar collector, it is possible to make significant improvements in the performance of solar collectors. What if we adjust the tilt angle occasionally? The idea is to adjust the tilt angle so that the outer normal of the collector coincides with the zenith angle α at noon on the day of adjustment. This occasional adjustment of the tilt angle is remarkably effective if the adjustments are timed to coincide with the seasons. The results of these seasonal adjustments, presented in Fig.12, illustrates the marked improvements that are possible with this simple procedure.

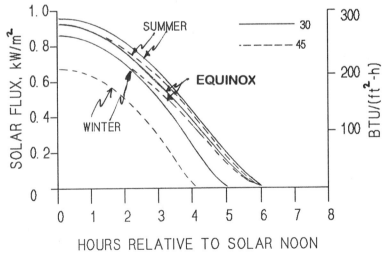

Fig. 12 Variation of solar flux for a collector that has been adjusted seasonally by orienting it toward the noon sun.

If seasonal adjustments of the tilt angle γ produce significant gains in the solar flux, should we consider continuous tracking? Let's look at the possibility of tracking, but as we do so remember that we are increasing the complexity of our collecting system. To track the sun continuously, we must rotate our collector, and this requires a mechanism that will turn the collector with time. The rotating mechanism will contain shafts, bearings, supports, gears, etc., and some power source (motor). This added complexity and inherent cost may represent a large price to pay for the addition solar energy received by a tracking collector. Before we can decide whether not it is worth the effort, we must explore the method used for tracking in more detail.

There are three common tracking methods:

1. East-West tracking with collector rotation about a N-S axis.
2. East-West tracking with collector rotation about the polar axis.
3. North-South tracking with collector rotation about the E-W axis.

These tracking methods are illustrated in Fig. 13.

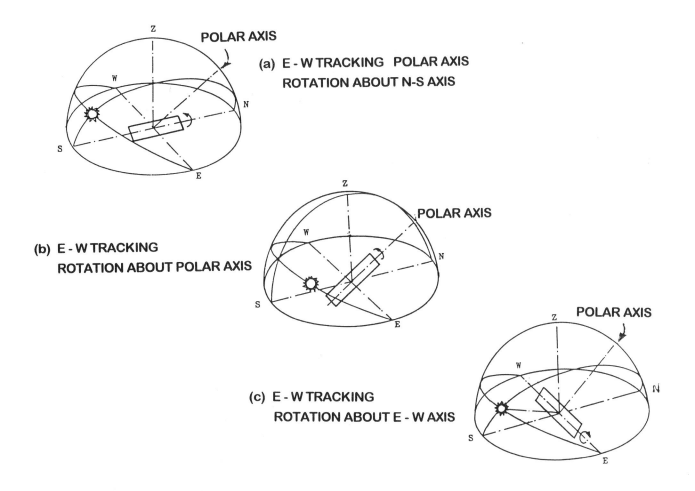

Fig. 13 Three common tracking methods.

Many different ways of orienting the solar collector have been investigated. These range from the most simple method (horizontal with no tracking) to the most complex (E-W tracking, with polar axis rotation). Let's examine the maximum possible energy received over an entire year by a flat collector for all of the different orientations described previously.

TABLE 1
Maximum Possible Solar Energy Received by a Flat Collector
Annual Yield

Configuration	Latitude Degrees	Energy 10^3 kW/(m²-year)	Ratio %
Fully Tracked (D)	45	2.85	----
	30	3.11	----
Horizontal (D)	45	1.64	57.5
	30	1.92	61.7
Horizontal (D + S)	45	1.92	67.4
	30	2.26	72.7
Fixed (+15°), (D + S)	45	2.03	71.2
	30	2.25	72.3
Polar EW Tracking (D)	45	2.80	98.2
	30	3.00	96.5
Horizontal EW Tracking (D)	45	2.30	80.7
	30	2.45	78.8
Horizontal NS Tracking (D)	45	1.70	59.6
	30	2.51	80.7

D......Direct radiation
(D + S) ......Direct and scattered radiation

The results of Table 1 indicate that E-W tracking with the collector rotating about the polar axis maximizes the annual energy to the collector. This tracking method produces an annual energy to the collector that is 98.2 % of that produced by a fully tracked collector. (Recall that a fully tracked collector requires rotation about two axes so that the outer normal vector of the collector is pointed to the sun at all times). The question that must be answered is whether or not the extra energy is worth the complexity and cost of building the rotating mechanism, the support structure needed for the polar orientation, and the motor to turn the mechanism. In many applications the answer to this question is a very clear and loud --- No! Tracking methods for very large collectors are often too costly to implement and maintain over their expected life.. In these instances passive (stationary) collectors are employed with a tilt angle that is:

$$\gamma = L + 20°, \qquad \theta = 0 \qquad\qquad (7)$$

CONCENTRATING THE FLUX

The flat collector is a very simple device that absorbs both direct and scattered sun light, and converts the photons received into either heat or electricity depending on the receivers incorporated in the collectors. In some applications, we find that the solar flux on a flat collector is not sufficient, and we seek ways of increasing (concentrating) the flux F. Solar flux can be concentrated by using either mirrors or lenses, although mirrors are more commonly employed because they are usually much less expensive and easier to fabricate than lenses.

LENSES

Let's begin by considering the convex lens presented in Fig. 14. We will consider the light rays from the sun to be parallel with the optical axis. A convex lens ground with two curved surfaces, diffracts the light and focuses all of the rays at the focal point. The concentration of solar flux is evident by examining the line density shown in Fig. 14. Indeed, if the lens was perfect, (but it never is) the flux at the focal point would approach infinity. Because of imperfections in producing the lenses and the scattering of light from the lens surfaces, the rays do not focus at a point but over a small circle of diameter d_0.

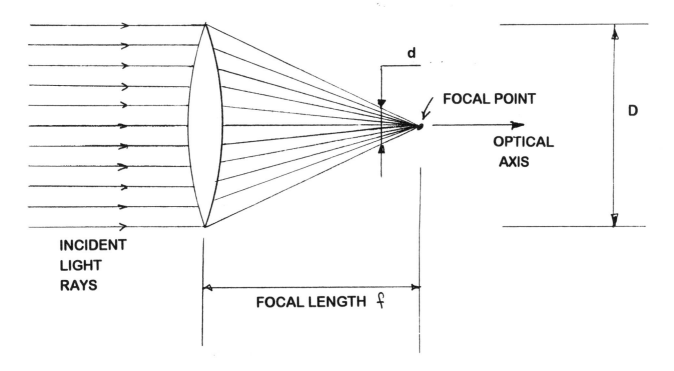

Fig. 14 Light focused by a convex at the focal point.

The concentrated solar flux in this small circular area at the focus is:

$$F_c = F_{in}(D/d_0)^2 \qquad (8)$$

where

F_c is the concentrated solar flux.
F_c is the concentrated solar flux.
F_{in} is the incident solar flux
D is the diameter of the lens
d_0 is the diameter of the focus spot

To examine the magnitude of the concentrated flux, consider a lens that focused so that

$$d_0 = D/20$$

In this instance,

$$F_c = 400\ F_{in}$$

Wow! The lens has produced a significant (400 fold) increase in the flux. If the incident flux was 0.8 kW/m^2, the concentrated flux would be 320 kW/m^2. This concentration is sufficiently high to be dangerous.

Lower concentrations of solar flux can be achieved in the lens arrangement of Fig. 11. If the energy converter is moved to the left from the focal point toward the lens, the diameter of the collected rays increases from d_0 to d. Replacing D with d in Eq. (8) gives:

$$F_c = F_{in}\ (d/d_0)^2 \qquad (9)$$

This relation shows that is it possible to vary the concentrated flux between F_{in} and F_c by positioning the solar converter[1] at some location between the lens and the focus point.

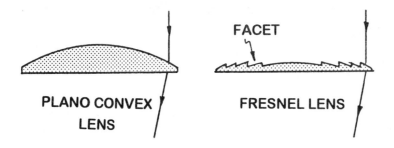

Fig. 15 A comparison of a Fresnel lens with a plano-convex lens.

---

[1] We use the term converter to indicate that the solar collector can convert photons to either heat or electricity depending on the application.

As mentioned before, the cost of the lenses is often prohibitive in solar energy applications particularly if the diameter D is large. A good rule of thumb is that the cost of a lens increases as a function of D^3 (double the lens diameter and you increase its cost by a factor of eight). There is one important exception to this rule, namely the Fresnel lens as illustrated in Fig. 15. The Fresnel lens is inexpensive in comparison to the more conventional convex or plano-convex lenses. It is relatively cheap, because it is fabricated by pressing a die with a stepped profile into a sheet of heat softened thermoplastic to produce the apparent curvature required to diffract the light.

The steps between the facets on a Fresnel lens produce some error in the focus and there is additional scattering due to the rounded corners at the edge of the facets. Nevertheless, the Fresnel lens is effective and in expensive in building relatively small solar systems where the collecting area is less than 2 to 3 ft^2.

MIRRORS

Mirrors are usually preferred for solar energy applications because they are:

1. Cheaper than lenses
2. Fabricated more easily
3. Available in larger areas
4. Amenable to many configurations.

Many years ago we made mirrors of glass because only a few plastics were available. Also we did not know how to coat plastics with thin metallic films to make them reflective. Glass mirrors were all flat, and the only question was whether the front or back faces of the glass were coated to make them reflective. However, in more recent years, we have learned to coat very thin and light plastic sheet with metallic films that have excellent reflective properties. Aluminized Mylar is an example. An additional advantage is that the thin plastic sheets can be formed with relative ease into a number of different shapes suitable for concentrators.

Let's consider three different types of mirrors that can be used to concentrate the solar flux, namely a flat booster mirror, the conical mirror, and the parabolic mirror. There are several other mirror configurations described by Meinel and Meinel [2], and you may find it useful to read this interesting and complete reference.

FLAT BOOSTER MIRRORS

Two configurations, presented in Fig. 16, illustrate the advantages of what we call flat booster mirrors. The symmetric booster mirror (Fig. 16a) increases the flux by a factor of two when the incoming rays are at normal incidence to the face of the collector. A single vertical west facing booster mirror nearly doubles the flux over most of the afternoon. The vertical booster mirror can be moved so that it is facing east to increase the flux due to the morning sun (Fig. 16b). The booster mirror concepts are easy to employ, and for small additional costs, the solar flux at the collector can be almost doubled.

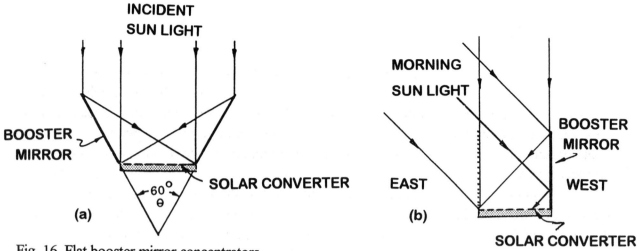

Fig. 16 Flat booster mirror concentrators.
  a. Symmetric equal size mirrors.
  b. West facing vertical booster mirror.

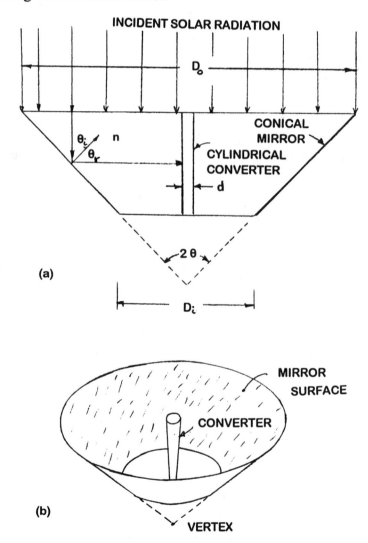

Fig. 17 Conical mirror solar flux concentrating system. $\theta = 90°$.
  a. Section view showing the reflection of incoming solar rays from the conical surface.
  b. Three-dimensional view showing the main features or the conical mirror converter system.

CONICAL MIRRORS

The conical mirror, presented in Fig. 17a, shows that the incoming solar rays are reflected from the conical surface. If the vertex angle of the cone is 90°, the rays of the light parallel to the axis of the cone reflect off of the surface and are directed toward the axis. We place the solar converter on a small diameter cylinder that is coincident with the axis of the cone as shown in Fig. 17b. The solar converter (solar cells or a photon absorber) is incorporated on the outside surface of this small diameter cylinder.

Let's examine Fig. 17a in more detail, and note that the apex angle of the cone $2\theta = 90°$. Because of this choice, the angle the incoming solar rays make with the outer normal to the surface is $\theta_i = 45°$ Recall Snell's law for reflection of light which states that the angle of incidence equals the angle of reflection.

$$\theta_i = \theta_r \tag{10}$$

We draw θ_r at the same 45° angle of θ_i in Fig. 17a, and observe that the conical mirror has reflected the light through a total angle $\theta_i + \theta_r = 90°$. The reflected rays travel on a horizontal plane and converge along the vertical axis at the center of the cone. The solar converter is placed in a region where the radiation converges.

We can determine the maximum value of the solar flux at the solar converter from:

$$F_c = F_{in} (A_p/A_s) \tag{11}$$

where

A$_p$ is the projected area of the cone perpendicular to the incident sun light.

A$_s$ is the surface area of the converter.

If we stand in the sky and look straight down at the cone, we see the projected area A_p and recall that it is determined from the relation:

$$A_p = (\pi/4)(D_0^2 - D_i^2) \tag{12}$$

where D_0 and D_i are defined in Fig. 17a.

We next determine the surface area of the central cylinder as:

$$A_s = \pi d L = (\pi d/2)(D_0 - D_i) \tag{13}$$

where d is the diameter of the solar converter.

Substituting Eqs. (12) and (13) into Eq. (11), and simplifying the resulting expression gives:

$$F_c = (D_0 + D_i) F_i /(2d) \tag{14}$$

To better understand the concentrating power of the conical mirror, consider an arrangement with dimensions ---- $D_i = D_0/2$, and $d = D_0/20$. Substituting these values into Eq. (14) gives:

$$F_c = 15 \, F_i$$

This result indicates that the conical mirror system with these dimensions gives a concentration factor CF = 15, which is a significant enhancement of the solar flux into the converter.

Before we move to the next topic, let us examine Equation (14) in more detail. This relation is more than a simple mathematical expression. It represents a design model for a conical mirror system. It is a model in the sense that it predicts the concentration factor for a defined geometry of a conical mirror arrangement. If we need a concentration factor CF different than 15 (as predicted in the above example), we examine the term that defines this factor:

$$CF = (D_0 + D_i)/(2d) \tag{15}$$

We can change the geometry (D_0, D_i and d) to increase the concentration factor CF. The power of analysis is that it makes design easier. More important, the effect of design changes are predictable. We reduce the trial and error approach to design by using good analysis that leads us to develop very helpful design models.

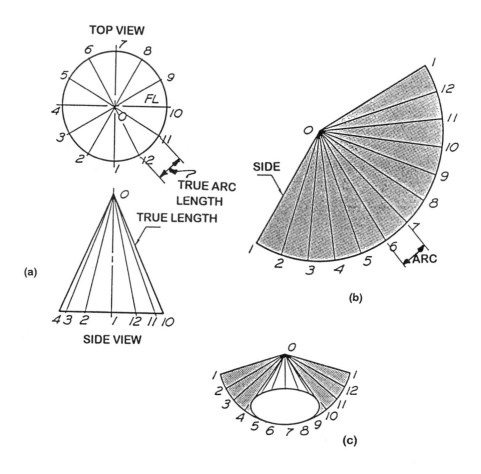

Fig. 18 Producing a cone from a sheet of paper, aluminum foil or plastic.
    a. Top and side views of the cone give the true lengths of the side and the arc.
    b. Lay-out of the developed surface.
    c. Rolling-up the fan to produce a cone.

The conical mirror has still another important advantage that involves ease of manufacturing. A conical surface is one that can be developed. What we mean by a developed surface is that a cone can be formed by cutting a sheet of material into the proper shape, and then made into a cone by rolling its ends together to form the conical form. The method of determining the "proper" two-dimensional shape is presented in Fig. 18. We begin by drawing (to scale) the top and front views of the cone as shown in Fig. 18a. We then draw the fan shape illustrated in Fig. 18b using the true length and the arc length established in the front and top views. Finally, we cut the fan shape from the sheet of material, roll it up to form the cone, and fasten the edges together to produce the conical mirror. It is easy to produce a cone using only a pair of scissors to cut a sheet of aluminized Mylar, and a roll of transparent tape to fasten the edges together.

PARABOLIC MIRRORS

The third and final mirror system that is discussed is the parabolic mirror. There are two different types of parabolic mirrors --- circular and cylindrical. To show the difference between them, let's begin with their common feature which is the equation for a parabolic curve:

$$x^2 = k z \qquad\qquad (16)$$

The curve generated by plotting z as a function of $\pm$ x is a parabola that is symmetric about z as shown in Fig. 17. Its vertex is at $x = y = z = 0$; its axis is 0z and its focus is at $z = k/4$. If we rotate the curve about the z axis, a three dimensional parabolic surface is generated that is called a circular paraboloid. We will not consider this circular paraboloid for this solar application because it is much more difficult to manufacture than the parabolic cylinder mirror described below.

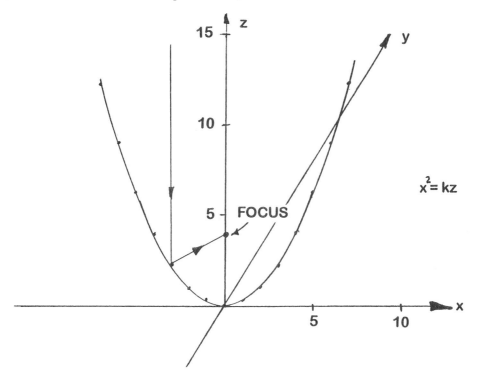

Fig. 19 A parabola that is symmetric about the z axis.

If we slide the parabola shown in Fig. 19 along the ± y axis, we generate a different three dimensional surface that is called a parabolic cylinder (see Fig. 20). It is the parabolic cylinder mirror that is often employed for concentrating flux in solar energy applications because it is easy and inexpensive to fabricate. The concentration factor CF for the parabolic cylinder mirror is given by rearranging Eq. (11) to give:

$$CF = F_o / F_{in} = A_p / A_s \qquad (17)$$

For a parabolic cylinder with a throat width W and a length L, the projected area A_p = WL. The cylindrical solar converter with a diameter d has a surface area A_s = πdL. Substituting these relations for the areas into Eq. (17) gives:

$$CF = 4 \, W / \pi d = 1.273 \, W/d \qquad (18)$$

This relation can be used to size the mirror and the solar converter to give a specified value of the concentration of the flux. Remember that the shape of the parabola is controlled by Eq. (16). We see that the throat width W = $2x_{max}$, and the location of the solar converter along the z axis determines the focal position (k).

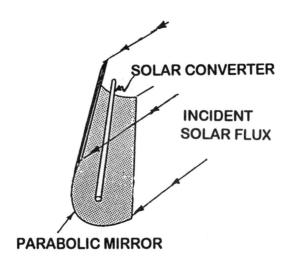

Fig. 20 A parabolic cylindrical mirror with a linear solar converter deployed along the focus.

CONCEPTS, TERMS AND UNITS

We have a lot of new terms that define engineering quantities that are somewhat abstract. We cannot see or feel heat, although we can feel the temperature increase or decrease that is caused by the addition or removal of heat from a body. Also, as we read literature on solar energy and heat transfer, we encounter many different units often associated with the same quantity. Let's try to clarify this subject by defining the terms and/or concepts and giving the units associated with each term.

HEAT

Heat is a difficult concept because we can not see, feel, taste, hear or smell it. However, when we add heat to a body, we increase its temperature, and when we remove heat from a body we decrease it temperature. We sense heat indirectly by feeling the temperature change. A unit of heat is the BTU (British Thermal Unit) which is the amount of heat required to increase a pound (weight) of water one degree Fahrenheit (°F). Another unit of heat is the calorie, which is the amount of heat required to increase the temperature of a gram (weight) of water by one degree Celsius (°C). We use the symbol Q to represent heat. Clearly, the two quantities BTU and calorie are related. The conversion factor need to change from one system of units to the other is given in Table 2.

In engineering applications we often work very hard to move large amounts of heat from on location to another. This simple act is so important, that we devote an entire course in the curriculum to a topic called "heat transfer". A trip to the library will show you that a large number of books have been written showing analytical methods to treat the three different mechanisms use to move (transfer) heat --- conduction, convection and radiation. We are going to discuss these mechanisms in more detail in a later chapter, but for now let's concentrate on defining the basic terms involved in moving (transferring) heat.

RATE OF HEAT TRANSFER

As we move heat from one location to another, we are concerned with the rate of the transfer. Sometimes we want to speed-up this process (bringing a tea kettle to boil). On other occasions, we want to slow the process (insulating our houses against the winter cold, and the summer heat). The rate of heat transfer q is the amount of heat moved per unit time from one location to another. In the U. S. Customary (English) system of units q is given in BTU/h and in the SI system q is expressed in Watts (W). Remember that a Watt is equivalent to a Joule per second (J/s).

RATE OF HEAT FLUX TRANSFER

One more layer of complexity before we close this topic. As we transfer heat from one location to another, we have some channel, conduit, or passage through which the heat passes. We can envision that this channel has a cross sectional area A. The rate of heat flow per unit area of the channel is defined as a flux F. In the U. S. Customary system of units F is given in units of BTU/ (h-ft^2) and in the SI system F is given in W/m^2. When we deal with heat transfer and solar energy, we encounter three quantities ---Q heat, q the rate of heat transfer, and F the heat flux. These quantities are often represented in different system of units. To help you deal with the conversion from one system of units to another we have included a list of conversion factors in Table 2.

TABLE 2

TABLE 2

Unit Conversion Factors

Symbol/Name	From	To	Multiply by
Q/ Heat	BTU	J	1.0548×10^3
	BTU	Cal	251.996
	BTU	ft-lb	778.3
	BTU	kWh	2.928×10^{-4}
q/Rate of heat transfer	BTU/h	cal/s	0.0700
	BTU/h	W	0.2931
	BTU/h	ft-lb/s	0.2162
F/Flux	BTU/(ft^2-h)	cal/(m^2-s)	0.7534
	BTU/(ft^2-h)	W/m^2	3.1524
	BTU/(ft^2-h)	kJ/(m^2-h)	11.345
	BTU/(ft^2-h)	L/min	4.521×10^{-3}
L/Langley	L	gram-cal/cm^2	1
	L	BTU/(ft^2-h)	221.2
	L	W/m^2	700

SUMMARY

We began our study of solar energy by recognizing that it was one of the three common sources of heat. The other two sources were nuclear energy and the burning of fuels. We showed an example indicating that the supply of solar energy was large. In spite of this large supply, the use of solar energy is limited because of the availability of the energy source. Sometimes the sun does not shine.

We go into significant detail in describing the solar availability covering the effects of cloud cover, time of day, time of year and latitude. Several graphs are given so that you can estimate the available solar flux for any time of the year at your location.

We covered the effect of the orientation of the solar collector on the solar flux. We treated the flat collector positioned horizontally with its outer normal pointed upward. We then consider two other cases of fixed collectors; one tilted toward the south and the other vertical with a face looking south. Clearly, the effect of the tilt to south enhances the solar flux received by an appreciable amount. We included the vertical collector to show you that windows facing south in the winter are excellent sources of heat for your home.

We also included a brief section on tracking the sun to increase the solar flux received by the collector. We found that east-west tracking with rotation about the polar axis was the most favorable case involving rotation about a single axis.

Since another limitation of solar energy is the relatively low flux levels[2], we discussed two optical methods for increasing the flux by concentrating the sun's rays. The concentrators incorporate either lenses or mirrors. We introduce the Fresnel lens and show methods to compute the concentration factor for lens type concentrators. We also describe three different ways of using mirrors to concentrate the solar flux. We recommended the use of mirrors for solar applications requiring concentration of the flux because they are inexpensive, easy to fabricate, and adaptable to large solar collectors.

Finally we discuss heat Q, heat transfer rates q, and heat flux F. A conversion table is given to aid in converting quantities expressed in U. S. Customary units to SI units and vice versa.

REFERENCES

1. Meinel, A. B. and M. P. Meinel, Applied Solar Energy, Addison-Wesley, Reading, MA 1976, p. 49.
2. Meinel, A. B., D. B. Kennedy, W. T. Beauchamp, NSF/RANN/SE/GI-41895/FR/75/7, NTIS, US Department of Commerce, Washington, D. C., 1975.
3. Rankins, W. H., and D. A. Wilson, Solar Energy Notebook, Lorien House, Black Mountain, NC.
4. Anon, Solar Ephemeris, Kauffel and Esser, 1962.

EXERCISES

1. What is the difference between absolute temperature and temperature? Which of these terms do you employ in Eq. 1?
2. What are the two principle constraints that limit the widespread application of solar energy?
3. What is the highest value of daily solar flux that you could anticipate if you conducted the test of your prototype still outdoors in an open field on May 10 th?
4. How would you orient your still to capture the maximum solar flux if you conducted the test described in exercise 3.
5. Determine the concentration factor CF for a lens concentrator with a diameter of 0.3 meters and a focus spot 0.8 mm in diameter.
6. Prepare a sketch of a booster mirror system to enhance the solar flux received by the solar still if it is tested outdoors at 9:00 am.
7. Design a conical mirror concentrator that provides a concentration factor of 200. In the design specify the apex angle, the outer and inter diameters of the cone, and the diameter of the concentrator.
8. Design a parabolic mirror concentrator that provides a concentration factor of 120. In the design specify the throat width and length of the mirror and the diameter of the concentrator. If you wanted concentrator/collector capable of 10kW at noon on a clear day in June at the College Park campus, what would be the length of the parabolic mirror. Consider a L/W ratio of 10.
9. Convert 1000 BTU to its equivalent value in terms of Joules. What is a Langley?

---

[2] We are thankful for this relatively low flux, because if the flux were more intense sun burn and skin cancer would be much more of a problem.

CHAPTER 4

ANALYSIS OF A SOLAR STILL

THEORY OF OPERATION

The analysis of the operation of a solar still is based on a heat balance. The solar heat transferred to the still is equal to the heat required for production of the water vapor and all of the heat losses from the still to the environment. As we perform the heat balance, you will act like an accountant keeping track of the incoming and outgoing heat transfer so as to maintain the process in balance. We introduce some new terms and some new concepts in this analysis, but please bear with us. We will explain each term and concept as they are introduced. You should also recognize that this analysis is not new. Many other folks have worked the problem, and references to their contributions [1-5] have been cited at the end of the chapter.

To begin the analysis, let's draw a picture showing the various components of heat transferred in and out of the still, as shown in Fig. 1. The definition of the symbols used in Fig. 1 are given below:

- F_s is the solar flux impinging on the cover of the still.
- $\tau_c F_s$ is the solar flux transmitted through the cover.
- $r_c F_s$ is the solar flux reflected from the cover.
- $\alpha_w \tau_c F_s$ is the solar flux transmitted through the cover and absorbed by the water.
- $\tau_c^2 r_w F_s$ is the solar flux that has been transmitted through the cover, reflected from the surface of the water, and then retransmitted through the cover.
- F_r is the heat transferred from the water to the cover by radiation.
- F_c is the heat transferred from the water to the cover by convection.
- F_e is the combined heat transfer from the water to the cover by the evaporation and condensation processes.
- $(F_{cover})_{out}$ is the heat lost from the cover to the environment.

- F_{base} is the heat lost from the basin to the ground below the still.

The units of all of these components of the solar flux are BTU/(ft²-h) in the U. S. Customary system or W/m² in the SI system.

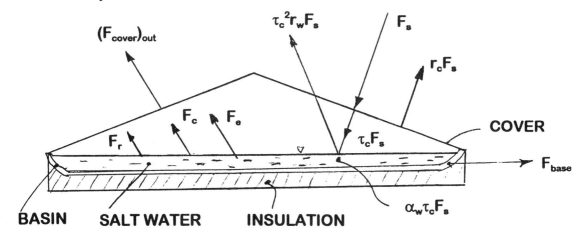

Fig. 1 Heat fluxes involved in the heat balance for a solar still.

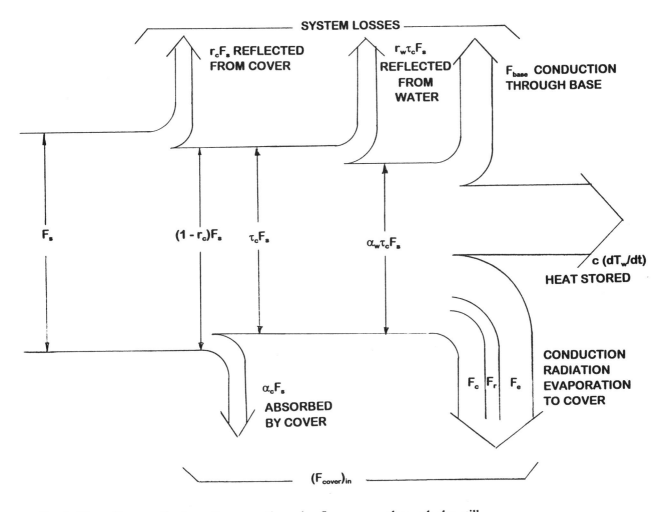

Fig. 2 Flow diagram for heat fluxes as the solar flux moves through the still.

Please don't turn off because of the large number of terms involved in the process of solar desalination. Remember that we will act like accountants and use a neat table to help us keep track of these terms in our heat balances. We will also use the heat flow diagram that is presented in Fig. 2, to aid in tracking the heat through the system. Examination of this illustration shows that we begin the solar distillation process with the solar flux F_s entering as the heat input to the system on the left side of the diagram. Flux losses from the system are represented by the broad arrows turned upward in the diagram. The heat flux into the cover, from four different mechanisms, is displayed by the broad arrows turning downward. This simple diagram is helpful in writing equations for heat balances so that control our analysis of the operation of the solar still.

A heat balance is a very simple concept with a simple relation given by:

HEAT IN = HEAT OUT + HEAT STORED (1)

Let's first look at the heat input to the still as depicted in Figs. 1 and 2. The heat input comes from the solar flux F_s, but not all of the solar flux gains entry to the system (our solar still). Part of the light from the sun is reflected from the cover of the solar still and is lost to the system. To better understand this fact, examine the behavior of light when it strikes some surface as shown in Fig. 3. Part of the light is absorbed, part is transmitted, and part is reflected. We represent this partitioning of the light in mathematical terms by writing:

$$\alpha + \tau + r = 1 \qquad (2)$$

where
α is the absorption coefficient
τ is the transmission coefficient
r is the reflection coefficient

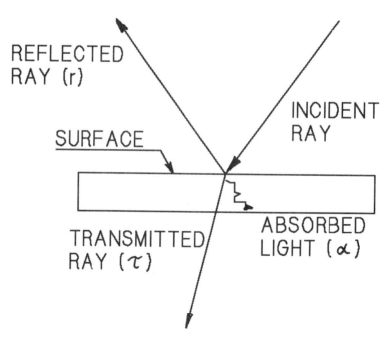

Fig. 3 Light interacting with a surface.

Let's examine F_s the flux (light) from the sun, and divide it into its three parts according to guidelines given in Eq. (2). First, some flux ($\tau_c F_s$) is transmitted through the cover into the still. Second, some flux ($\alpha_c F_s$) is absorbed by the cover of the still. Finally, some flux ($r_c F_s$) is reflected from the cover. Since this reflected portion of the flux is lost to the system, we will not consider it in the analysis. The transmitted flux enters the still and strikes the surface of the water. We are interested in that part of the transmitted flux that is absorbed by the water that is given by $\alpha_w \tau_c F_s$. The solar flux entered the still and was absorbed by either the cover or the water. These components represent the total solar energy delivered to the system, and are written as:

$$\textbf{HEAT IN} = \alpha_c F_s + \alpha_w \tau_c F_s = (\alpha_c + \alpha_w \tau_c) F_s \qquad (3)$$

where the subscripts c and w refer to the cover and water respectively.

Now that we have the heat input to the system, let's consider what happens to this energy. A part of this heat is stored by increasing the temperature of the water contained in the basin. We express the heat stored with the term $c(dT/dt)$. The remainder of the energy is eventually lost to the system. It is dissipated from the cover, lost from the base and the edges of the still, and part is reflected from the water surface out of the still. We denote these three quantities as F_{cover}, F_{base}, and F_{refl} respectively. Having defined these terms, we can write the right side of Eq. (1) as:

$$\textbf{HEAT STORED} + \textbf{HEAT OUT} = c(dT_w/dt) + F_{cover} + F_{base} + F_{refl} \qquad (4)$$

where

       c is the combined heat capacity of the water and basin per unit area 16 BTU/(ft^2-°F).

       T_w is the temperature of the water (°F).

The relation for the F_{refl} is given by:

$$F_{refl} = \tau_c{}^2 r_w F_s \qquad (5)$$

Now that the heat in and the heat out have been expressed, we can write the relation for the heat balance by combining Eqs. (1), (3) (4) and (5) to obtain:

$$F_s(\alpha_c + \alpha_w \tau_c) = c(dT_w/dt) + F_{cover} + F_{base} \qquad (6)$$

Equation (6) is important, but we need to express the terms F_{cover} and F_{base} in a useful form, before the relation aids in the prediction of the amount of water that we can process in the still.

Let's consider the energy lost from the basin through the insulation to the ground below the still. The heat is transfer out of the system by conduction through the insulation as shown in Fig. 1. Knowing that the heat is lost by a conduction mechanism, permits us to express the term F_{base} as:

$$F_{base} = K_b(T_w - T_g) \qquad (7)$$

where the subscripts g and w refer to the ground and water respectively and

K_b is the conductivity constant taken as 1 BTU/(h-ft²-°F) for a still with good insulation between the basin and the ground.

The temperature of the cover is very important because it serves as the condenser. The cover must be cool enough for the water vapor to condense converting it to water. Determining the cover temperature is complex, because several factors are involved. Let's solve for the temperature of the cover by writing an equation for $(F_{cover})_{in}$ that accounts for the components of heat transferred into the cover. We will treat for the heat lost from the cover to the environment $(F_{cover})_{out}$ later. The heat into the cover is shown by the downward curving arrows in Fig. 2. We express the four components in equation format as:

$$(F_{cover})_{in} = F_r + F_c + F_e + \alpha_c F_s \qquad (8)$$

where

F_r is the heat transferred from the water to the cover by radiation.
F_c is the heat transferred from the water to the glass by convection.
F_e is the combined heat transfer from the water to the cover by the evaporation and condensation processes.
$\alpha_c F_s$ is the solar flux absorbed by the cover.

Let's examine the relations, due to R. V. Dunkle [4], permitting us to determine the magnitude of these components. First, for the heat transferred by radiation:

$$F_r = 0.9 \, S[(T_w + 460)^4 - (T_c + 460)^4] \qquad (9)$$

where the emissivity $\varepsilon = 0.9$ has been take for water, and 460 has been added to T to convert the temperature scale from Fahrenheit to Rankine[1]. In Eq. (9), S is the Stefan-Boltzmann constant equal to 0.174 (10^{-8}) BTU/(h-ft²-°F⁴).

Next, the heat transferred from the water to the cover by convection is:

$$F_c = 0.128[(T_w - T_c) + (\frac{p_w - p_c}{39 - p_w})(T_w + 460)]^{1/3}(T_w - T_c) \qquad (10)$$

where p is the pressure of the water vapor in psi.

---

[1] We work with four temperature scales: Fahrenheit and Rankine in the English System of units and Celsius and Kelvin in the SI system of units. The Fahrenheit and Celsius scales are both relative since they are defined by the freezing and boiling points of water. The Rankine and Kelvin scales are absolute in that they define zero at a temperature of absolute zero. When dealing with heat transfer by radiation we use the absolute zero scales. Remember that °R = 460 + °F.

Heat is transferred to the cover when the water vapor condenses on its surface. The heat released during the condensation process is:

$$F_e = 0.0254[(T_w - T_c) + (\frac{p_w - p_c}{39 - p_w})(T_w + 460)]^{1/3}(p_w - p_c)h_w \qquad (11)$$

where h_w is the latent heat of vaporization of water (1025 BTU/lb)

Finally, we examine the heat lost by the cover to the environment $(F_{cover})_{out}$, and note that the losses are due to radiation to the ambient atmosphere and convection to the ambient air. These losses are expressed by:

$$(F_{cover})_{out} = 0.9S[(T_c + 460)^4 - (T_a + 460)^4] + h_a(T_c - T_a) \qquad (12)$$

where subscripts c and a refer to the cover and the air respectively.

h_a is the convection coefficient for heat transfer between the cover and the air. Its value depends on the velocity of the wind. For example, at a wind velocities of 5, 10 and 20 MPH (miles/h), $h_a = 2.6$, 4.1, and 7.2 BTU/(h-ft^2-°F) respectively.

For the cover, we consider the heat storage to be negligible and write the heat balance as:

$$(F_{cover})_{in} = (F_{cover})_{out} \qquad (13)$$

We have written many equations to describe all of the ways the heat is transfer from the sun into the still, more relations to describe how the solar energy is transferred within the still, and even more expressions to describe the heat dissipated from the still. In an effort to simplify the analysis (at least a bit), we have not included the heat flux reflected by the cover r_cF_s, because it does not enter the still. Also the heat flux $(\tau_c^2 r_w F_s)$ reflected from the surface of the water is assumed to be transmitted through the cover without secondary reflection or absorption. The reflected and absorbed parts of this energy remain in the system, but they are small and of secondary importance. As we examine these relations, it becomes apparent that there is not an easy (explicit) solution. It is necessary to solve the problem by trial and error. Fortunately we have a choice between two approaches:

1. We can program the controlling relations to solve for the temperature of the cover using an iterative approach.
2. We can use a graphical trial and error approach. We have the results of the extended analysis by Read and Morse [5] and the graphs that they produced to help us.

The graphical solution will be employed in this treatment as we proceed with a trial and error approach.

Let's examine the previous relations, and note the results of Read and Morse in the solution of several equations. From Eq. (11), F_e was determined as a function of cover temperature T_c with water temperature T_w as a parameter. For any pair of temperatures (T_c, T_w), we can determine F_e from the graph presented in Fig. 4. This result is very important, because F_e controls the amount of water produced by the still.

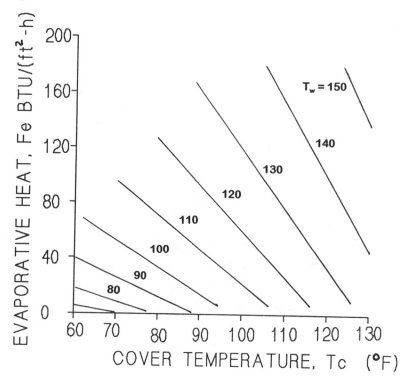

Fig. 4 Evaporative heat transfer as a function of cover temperature and water temperature.

Morse and Read also computed the heat transferred from the water to the cover by radiation F_r for the temperatures (T_c, T_w) from Eq. 9. In a similar fashion they determined the heat transferred from the water to the cover by convection F_c from Eq. (10). They next examined their solutions for F_c and F_r and plotted the values of F_e that occur when the sum ($F_c + F_r$) is equal to a prescribed constant. The results of this data selection process is given in Fig. 5.

They also determined the heat dissipated from the cover to the environment by radiation and convection by evaluating Eq. (12). They calculated $(F_{cover})_{out}$ as a function of cover temperature for different wind velocities and two different ambient temperatures as shown in Fig. 6. The curves shown in Figs. 4, 5 and 6 are used in a trial and error process to determine T_c so that $(F_{cover})_{out} = (F_{cover})_{in}$.

After determining T_c, we can compute separately the heat loss through the basin F_b. The numerical values for these quantities F_{cover}, F_{base}, and $F_s(\alpha_c + \alpha_w \tau_c)$ are substituted into Eq. (6), to give a numerical result for the heat storage term [$c(dT_w/dt)$]. We then determine the incremental increase in water temperature ΔT_w from:

$$\Delta T_w = \Delta t[F_s (\alpha_c + \alpha_w \tau_c) - F_{cover} - F_{base}]/c \qquad (14)$$

where the incremental quantities $\Delta T_w/\Delta t$ are used to replace the differential dT_w/dt.

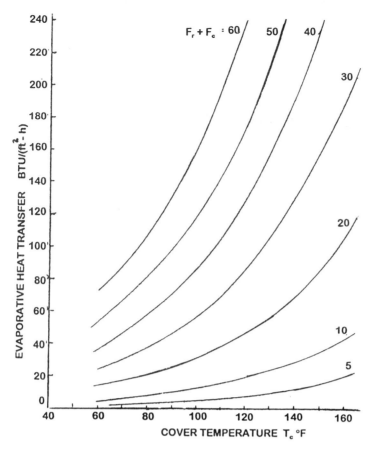

Fig. 5 Evaporative heat transfer as function of cover temperature and $(F_r + F_c)$.

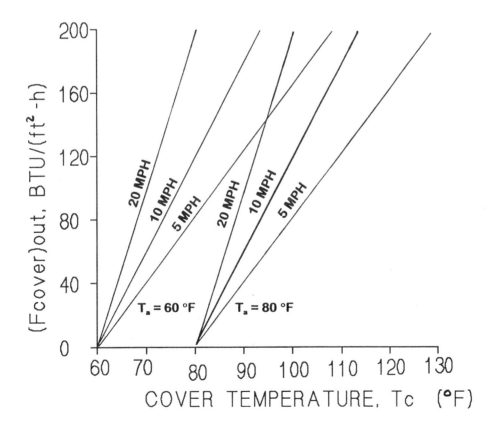

Fig. 6 Heat transfer from the cover to the environment.

The hourly values of F_e are given in Fig. 4 for specified T_c and T_w. These hourly values of F_e are converted to the water produced from:

$$(\Delta m / \Delta t) = F_e / h_w \qquad\qquad (15)$$

where $(\Delta m / \Delta t)$ is the rate of production of fresh water per unit area of the basin [lb/(ft^2 - h)].

Until equilibrium conditions are achieved (if ever) there is either a heat stored or heat lost term. This fact implies that the temperatures of the water and perhaps the cover as well change with time during both the day and the night. These changes require us to reevaluate all of the quantities involved in the distillation process periodically (usually on an hourly basis). The value of ΔT_w is added to $(T_w)_{old}$ to give $(T_w)_{new}$ for each new hour. The hourly values of F_e are summed over a 24 hour period, to give the quantity of water produced on a given day per unit area of the still.

We recognize that this is a difficult analysis that requires an iterative solution of complex equations. We do not expect that you will be able to perform independently a complete analysis. However, you should be able to follow the example solution that is given in the next section. Also you should be able to predict the output from the solar still developed by your team.

EXAMPLE SOLUTION

To illustrate the use of the graphs in obtaining a prediction of the amount of water that can be produced by a solar still, consider an example problem. Let's start with the listing of the important constants that affect the operation of the solar still.

- $c = 16$ BTU/(ft^2-°F) for a shallow depth of water in the still. The heat capacity increases with the depth of water and the size of the basin.
- $h_w = 1025$ BTU/lb is the latent heat of water at a temperature of 120 °F.
- $K_b = 1$ BTU/(h- ft^2-°F) is the conductivity constant.
- $T_a = 80$ °F is the ambient temperature.
- $T_g = 70$ °F is the temperature of the earth beneath the still.
- $\alpha_c = 0.1$ absorption coefficient for the cover.
- $\tau_c = 0.8$ transmission coefficient of the cover.
- $r_c = 0.1$ reflection coefficient of the cover.
- $\alpha_w = 0.9$ absorption coefficient for the water.
- $r_w = 0.1$ reflection coefficient for the water
- $T_w = 110$ °F at 11:00 hours.
- Wind velocity 5 MPH for the entire day.

We will consider the performance of the still for a period from 11:00 am until noon. The solar flux on a flat plate collector in the summer during this hour is essentially constant at 260 BTU/(h-ft^2).

To help keep track of all of the components of heat that are involved in the desalination process, a computational table with suitable headings is provided below:

TABLE 1
Solar Still Analysis

(1)	(2)	(3)	(4)
Step #1	Time	11:00 to 12:00	12:00 to 13:00
Step #2	F_s	260 BTU/(h-ft^2)	260 BTU/(h-ft^2)
Step #3	T_w	110 °F	116.3 °F
Step #4	$r_c F_s$	(0.1)(260) = 26 BTU/(h-ft^2)	
Step #5	$\alpha_c F_s$	(0.1)(260) = 26 BTU/(h-ft^2)	
Step #6	$\tau_c F_s$	(0.8)(260) = 208 BTU/(h-ft^2)	
Step #7	$r_w \tau_c F_s$	(0.1)(0.8)(260) = 20.8 BTU/(h-ft^2)	
Step #8	$\alpha_w \tau_c F_s$	(0.9)(0.8)(260) = 187.2 BTU/(h-ft^2)	
Step #9	T_c(1st est.)	95 °F	
Step #10	F_e(Fig. 4)	34 BTU/(h-ft^2)	
Step #11	$(F_{cover})_{out}$(Fig. 6)	63 BTU/(h-ft^2)	
Step #12	$F_c + F_r$	22 BTU/(h-ft^2)	
Step #13	$(F_{cover})_{in}$(check)	82 BTU/(h-ft^2)	
Step #9a	T_c(2nd est.)	98 °F	
Step #10a	F_e(Fig. 4)	28 BTU/(h-ft^2)	
Step #11a	$(F_{cover})_{out}$(Fig. 6)	73 BTU/(h-ft^2)	
Step #12a	$F_c + F_r$	19 BTU/(h-ft^2)	
Step #13a	$(F_{cover})_{in}$(check)	73 BTU/(h-ft^2)	
Step #14	T_c(final)	98 °F	
Step #15	F_e(final)	28 BTU/(h-ft^2)	
Step #16	(F_{cover})(final)	73 BTU/(h-ft^2)	
Step #17	F_{base}	40 BTU/(h-ft^2)	
Step #18	Heat Stored	100.2 BTU/(h-ft^2)	
Step #19	ΔT_w	6.3 °F	
Step #20	$(\Delta m / \Delta t)$	0.0273 lb/(h-ft^2)	
Step #21	$(\Delta m / \Delta t)$	0.419 oz/(h-ft^2)	
Step #22	$(T_w)_{12:00}$	116.3 °F	

Let's initially work Table 1 together. You should start with a clean sheet of paper and prepare a tabular format similar to that shown in Table 1. Start by entering the data for steps #1 to #3 using the parameters given in the initial description of the still. Steps #4 through #8 are computations of the various paths of heat flow, as shown in Fig. 2, by using the constants given in the initial description. Steps #9 through #15 include the iterative portion of the analysis. This part is a little tricky so let's begin with step #9 and cover the results determined in detail.

We begin the iteration process by estimating (an educated guess) the cover temperature T_c. This estimate need not be a wild guess because we know the water temperature is 110 °F and the ambient air temperature is 80 °F. Clearly, the cover temperature is between these two limits. Accordingly make your first estimate $T_c = 95$ °F, which is the midpoint between the limits. Read $F_e = 34$ BTU/(h-ft^2) from the intersection of the T_c and T_w points on Fig. 4. Recall that this value of F_e will be correct if and only if our initial estimate of T_c was accurate. To check if T_c and F_e are correct, you examine the heat balance for the cover, i. e. $(F_{cover})_{in} = (F_{cover})_{out}$. Combine Eqs. (6) and (8) to give:

$$(F_{cover})_{in} = F_r + F_c + F_e + \alpha_c F_s = (F_{cover})_{out} \qquad (16)$$

Taking $T_c = 95$ °F and knowing $T_w = 110$ °F, determine $(F_{cover})_{out} = 63$ BTU/(h-ft^2) from Fig. 6. Recall $\alpha_c F_s = 26$ BTU/(h-ft^2) from previous calculations in step #5. Substituting these two values into Eq. (16) gives:

$$(F_{cover})_{in} = F_r + F_c + 34 + 26 = (F_{cover})_{out} = 63$$

Next, employ Fig. 5 to determine $(F_r + F_c)$. Use the intersection point defined by $T_c = 95$ °F and F_e, $= 34$ BTU/(h-ft^2) to establish $(F_r + F_c) = 22$ BTU/(h-ft^2). OK! You have all of the terms involved in Eq. (16). Substitute them into the heat balance equation and see if it will balance:

$$(F_{cover})_{in} = 22 + 34 + 26 = 82 > (F_{cover})_{out} = 63$$

The heat flow into and out of the cover is not balanced, because the heat input is higher than the heat dissipated. This fact means that our first estimate of T_c was too low. As the cover temperature increases, the heat dissipated from the cover increases markedly as indicated in Fig. 6. Note also that the heat transferred to the cover by evaporation F_e is reduced as its temperature increases (see Fig. 4).

You need a second estimate of T_c. Try a small increase with $T_c = 98$ °F and repeat (iterate) the calculation to give results for steps 9a to 13a in Table 1. First read $F_e = 28$ BTU/(h-ft^2) from the intersection of the $T_c = 98$ °F and $T_w = 110$ °F lines. Note that this new result is appreciably lower than the value of 34 BTU/(h-ft^2) that you obtained in the first trial. This second value for F_e will be correct only if our second estimate of T_c is accurate. To check if both T_c and F_e are correct, use Eq. (16) again :

$$(F_{cover})_{in} = F_r + F_c + F_e + \alpha_c F_s = (F_{cover})_{out}$$

From Fig. 6 we determine $(F_{cover})_{out} = 73$ BTU/(h-ft^2), and recall $\alpha_c F_s = 26$ BTU/(h-ft^2) from step #5. Substituting these two values into Eq. (16) gives:

$$(F_{cover})_{in} = F_r + F_c + 28 + 26 = (F_{cover})_{out} = 73$$

Next, employ Fig. 5 to determine $(F_r + F_c) = 19$ BTU/(h-ft^2) from the intersection point defined by $T_c = 98$ °F and $F_e = 28$ BTU/(h-ft^2). You have all of the terms included in Eq. (16). Substitute them into the heat balance equation and see if it will balance:

$$(F_{cover})_{in} = 19 + 28 + 26 = 73 = (F_{cover})_{out} = 73$$

The heat flow into and out of the cover is in balance. The iteration process is complete. We next record our final and correct results for T_c, F_e and F_{cover} in steps 14, 15 and 16 in Table 1.

The remaining part of the analysis is much easier because we can solve the remaining equations directly, without the need to estimate a parameter and iterate the solution. We continue the analysis by solving Eq. (7) for F_{base}.

$$F_{base} = K_b(T_w - T_b)$$
$$F_{base} = 1(110 - 70) = 40 \text{ BTU/(h-ft}^2)$$

Enter this value for F_{base} in step #17, and proceed to determine the heat stored and ΔT_w. To accomplish this task, use Eq. (14) and the final numerical results from Table 1:

$$\Delta T_w = \Delta t[F_s (\alpha_c + \alpha_w \tau_c) - F_{cover} - F_{base}]/c \qquad (14)$$
$$\Delta T_w = 1\{260[0.1 + (0.9)(0.8)] - 73 - 40\}/16$$
$$\Delta T_w = 100.2/16 = 6.3 \text{ °F}$$

In this calculation, the increment of time Δt was taken as 1 (one hour) to correspond with a period during the day when the solar flux $F_s = 260$ BTU/(h-ft^2) can be treated as a constant. The term in the { } brackets 100.2 BTU/(h-ft^2) is the heat stored in the water contained in the basin. Record these results in Table 1 under steps #18 and #19.

Next, determine the amount of water produced from by condensing the water vapor on the cover. The heat flux F_e is transferred to the cover when the water vapor contacts the cover and is condensed to liquid droplets. If you use Eq. (15), it is possible to convert the flux F_e to the rate of production of fresh water condensed on the cover.

$$(\Delta m/\Delta t) = F_e/h_w \qquad (15)$$
$$(\Delta m/\Delta t) = 28/1025 = 0.0273 \text{ lb/(h-ft}^2)$$

Is 0.0273 lb/(h-ft^2) production of water a significant amount? We do not normally think of water in terms of weight but rather volume. To get a better idea of the amount of water let's convert the result shown above from pounds to a volume unit, say fluid ounces. We show this conversion below:

(0.273 lb) (1 US gallon/8.34517 lb) (8 pints/gallon) (16 ounce/pint) = 0.419 ounce

Expressing the result in terms of units which we understand helps us to appreciate the significance of the solution. You should now recognize that we get less than half of a whiskey shot glass of water from the still. Of course this amount is for each square foot of the basin area and for an hour of operation just before noon. Moreover, this result assumes that the still is 100 % efficient. Still efficiencies, shown in Fig. 7, usually range from 20 to 40 % with the higher efficiencies obtained on days when the solar flux is intense (greater than 2000 BTU/(day-ft^2)).

You have determined the water produced from 11:00 to 12:00 in this example problem. If you wanted to determine the amount of water produced from 12:00 to 13:00, you would need to know the temperature of the water in the basin T_w at noon. You establish the new water temperature from:

$$(T_w)_{new} = (T_w)_{old} + \Delta T_w \qquad (17)$$
$$(T_w)_{new} = 110 + 6.3 = 116.3\ °F$$

We record this result together with the amount of water produced in steps #20 to #23 in Table 1. We also record the new water temperature together with the new time in step #1 and #3 of the fourth column in the Table 1. If you think that you can perform this analysis, complete the fourth column in this table. In the analysis, covering the time from 12:00 to 13:00, assume the initial conditions of the still are the same. However, remember that $T_w = 116.3\ °F$, T_c will increase, and the rate of production of water will be larger. Good luck.

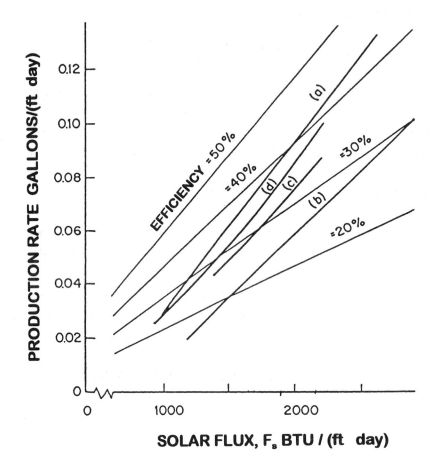

Fig. 7 Performance curves for solar stills after Howe [3].
    a. Small asbestos cement still, California.
    b. Saw-tooth still, California.
    c. Deep basin still, Florida.
    d. Inflated plastic covered still, Petit St. Vincent Island.

SIMPLIFIED STEADY STATE ANALYSIS

The analysis of the performance of the solar still presented above was complex because the distillation process was dynamic. The process is classified as dynamic when steady state conditions within the still had not been achieved. Under steady state conditions, the temperature of the various parts of the still are fixed or constant. In our previous solution, we found that the temperature of the water in the basin increased by 6.3 °F due to 100 BTU/(h-ft^2) of heat flux that was stored. The stored flux represented 38.5 % of the incident solar flux during the one hour of operation of the still. Clearly, with large amounts of the available flux going into storage, the water temperature in the basin increases significantly. The solar distillation process was dynamic in our example.

In some cases when the solar flux is nearly constant, the ambient temperatures change slowly, and the level of water in the basin is very shallow, the amount of heat stored is small. Under these conditions, the solar still is operating in thermal equilibrium. When thermal equilibrium is achieved, the heat balance presented in Eq. (1) simplifies to:

$$\text{HEAT IN} = \text{HEAT OUT} \qquad (17)$$

Under conditions of thermal equilibrium, the analysis of the solar still operation is simplified. The rate of production of fresh water depends primarily on the solar flux F_s with secondary effects due to convection to the environment and the ambient temperature. Anderson [6] gives an approximate relation for the fresh water production rate as a linear function of the incident solar flux:

$$(dm/dt)/A = 3.125 \times 10^{-4} \, F_s - 3.438 \times 10^{-5} \qquad (18)$$

where

(dm/dt) is the rate of fresh water production [kg/(m^2- s)].
F_s is the incident solar flux as previously defined but in units of (kW/m^2).

Equation (18) is an empirical relation derived from the results of a more complete set of solutions for which the wind velocity was 5 MPH. It will provide very good estimates of the production if the atmospheric conditions are reasonably constant and the depth of water in the basin is very shallow (25 to 50 mm or less).

We modified Eq. (18) in predicting the rate of production of fresh water from a solar still in a later chapter on EXCEL. The modification involved replacing the rate term dm/dt) with (Δm/Δt). We also changed the time scale in the equation from seconds to minutes. Making these modifications to Eq. (18) yields:

$$\Delta m/A = (0.01875 \, F_s - 0.002063) \, \Delta t \qquad (19)$$

where

Δm is the water produced in kg.
A is the area of the basin in the still in m^2.
F_s is the incident solar flux in kW/m^2.
Δt is the time of operation under steady state conditions in minutes.

Try your hand at estimating the production of a solar still. Explore conditions where you have achieved thermal equilibrium. Also find those conditions where the solution is dynamic, and you need to employ the more complex approach to obtain solutions with the necessary accuracy.

SUMMARY

We have introduced you to a subject called heat transfer in describing the analysis of the performance of a solar still. We begin the chapter by drawing a picture of the still identifying the various components of heat that are important in the solar desalination process. Another picture is presented that shows the flow of the heat fluxes in the process. Understanding these two pictures is paramount in following the heat transfer analysis to predict the rate of production of fresh water from the still.

Many equations are introduced without derivation to show methods for computing the various components of heat. In presenting these equations we introduce you to basic concepts of heat transfer including, conduction, convection and radiation. We make no attempt to solve these equations. Instead we present the graphs due to Read and Morse that give the results of their extensive computations.

An example solution is presented for a solar still operating under non steady state (dynamic) conditions. The solution is iterative in nature and complex considering the experience of an entering freshman student. To aid in the solution a table with 22 steps has been introduced. Use the table as a worksheet as you duplicate these results.

A simplified approach for determining the rate of fresh water production based on a steady state solution is also presented. While this approach utilizes an empirical relation, the results provide reasonable estimates if the temperature of the water in the basin is not changing rapidly.

REFERENCES

1. G. O. G. Lof, J. A. Eibling and J. W. Bloemer, "Energy balances in solar distillers," Journal of the American Institute of Chemical Engineers, Vol. 7, 1961, p.646.
2. S. G. Talbert, J. H. Ebling and G. O. G. Lof, Manual on Solar Distillation of Saline Water, Research and Development Progress Report No. 546, Office of Saline Water, U. S. Department of the Interior, 1970.
3. Howe E. D., "Solar Distillation," Transactions of the Conference on Solar energy, Tucson, Arizona, Vol. 3, 1955, p. 159.
4. Dunkle, R. V., "Solar water distillation: The roof-type still and a multiple effect diffusion still," International Developments in Heat Transfer, papers submitted to the International Heat Transfer Conference, University of Colorado, Denver, 1961, Part 5, pp.895-902.
5. Morse, R. N. and W. R. W. Read, "The Development of a Solar Still for Australian Conditions," Mech. Chemical Engineering Transactions, Institute of Engineers, Australia, May 1967, pp. 71-80.
6. Anderson, E. E., Fundamentals of Solar Energy Conversion, Addison-Wesley, Reading, MA, pp. 376-377, 1983.

EXERCISES

1. Draw a schematic illustration of a solar still and show all of the components of heat flux that are involved in the desalination process.

2. The illustration presented in Fig. 2 is for a dynamic heat transfer process where heat is stored by increasing the temperature of the water in the basin of the still.. Prepare a modified illustration for the case when the process is in thermal equilibrium and no heat is stored in the system.

3. For an incident solar flux of 180 BTU/(h-ft^2) determine the heat input to a solar still. Consider the absorption coefficients of the cover and water to be 0.1 and 0.9 respectively and take transmission coefficient of the cover as 0.85.

4. Perform a dynamic analysis of a solar still using the format presented in Table 1. Consider the input conditions as shown below:
    - $c = 14$ BTU/(ft^2-°F) for a shallow depth of water in the still. The heat capacity increases with the depth of water and the size of the basin.
    - $h_w = 1025$ BTU/lb is the latent heat of water at a temperature of 120 °F.
    - $K_b = 1.2$ BTU/(h- ft^2-°F) is the conductivity constant.
    - $T_a = 87$ °F is the ambient temperature.
    - $T_g = 68$ °F is the temperature of the earth beneath the still.
    - $\alpha_c = 0.1$ absorption coefficient for the cover.
    - $\tau_c = 0.85$ transmission coefficient of the cover.
    - $r_c = 0.05$ reflection coefficient of the cover.
    - $\alpha_w = 0.9$ absorption coefficient for the water.
    - $r_w = 0.1$ reflection coefficient for the water
    - $T_w = 160$ °F at 13:00 hours.
    - Wind velocity 10 MPH for the entire day.
    - $F_s = 180$ BTU/(h-ft^2).

5. Repeat the analysis of exercise 5, except assume that steady state conditions exist and the system is in thermal equilibrium. In using Eq. (19), recall that the units are not consistent with those presented in the problem statement.

6. Why is it dangerous to drink the water produced in your solar still if the temperature of the water did not exceed about 170 °F in the basin?

PART II

ENGINEERING

GRAPHICS

CHAPTER 5

THREE-VIEW DRAWINGS

INTRODUCTION

Engineering graphics is a broad term that is used to describe a means of communication. We normally think of communication in terms of writing and speaking, because they are more commonly employed in the normal course of our life. However, when we try to communicate design ideas, we find writing and speaking insufficient to express our thoughts. A more visual way to communicate is needed. It more effective to present our ideas by means of drawings, sketches, pictures, graphs of many different types, etc.. Visuals aids, such as drawings, convey our ideas quickly and with remarkable precision. It is easier to transmit information, and it is easier to receive information if it is conveyed in the form of drawings, sketches or graphs.

The objective of this part of the textbook is to introduce you to methods of communication using visual aids. You should understand the advantages of presenting information in drawings, sketches and graphs, and that these are very common techniques used by engineers to communicate very complex ideas quickly and with precision. You will begin to learn how to prepare orthographic projections, isometric drawing, sketches and several different types of graphs. There are two general approaches used in preparing drawings and graphs. The first is a manual approach. We draw the visuals by hand using a few simple drawing instruments. The second is using a computer and suitable software to aid in the preparation of the drawing or graph. In this chapter we will cover the manual methods for preparing drawings and graphs. In separate chapters we will introduce KEY CAD Complete, which is a software program for preparing engineering drawings. In another chapter we will cover EXCEL, which is a spread sheet program that permits us to produce a several different types of different graphs.

VIEW DRAWINGS

Let's begin by considering the block like object shown in Fig. 1. We could describe this as a rectangular block with a slot cut out of its top. However, this written description is vague because we haven't conveyed the relative proportions of the block, the precise location of the slot, or the size of any of its features. We need to communicate proportion, exact location, and size of every feature so that the object can be reproduced by anyone capable of reading a drawing. We use pictorial drawings and/or multi-view drawings to quickly convey this information to the reader. The drawing shown in Fig. 1 is a pictorial, that we will initially use to help us describe multi-view drawings.

The pictorial (isometric) drawing in Fig. 1 is shown with three arrows. These arrows represent the directions of viewing, which isolate the front, top and side views. When taken individually, each view is a two dimensional rendering of the three dimensional object. Of course, two-dimensional drawings are incomplete, because they show only the information in one of many possible views. Nevertheless, the two-dimensional views are important because we can draw objects to true scale on a sheet of ordinary paper. We avoid the problem of incomplete information inherent in two-dimensional drawings, by presenting a sufficient number of views to completely locate and size all of the features of the object.

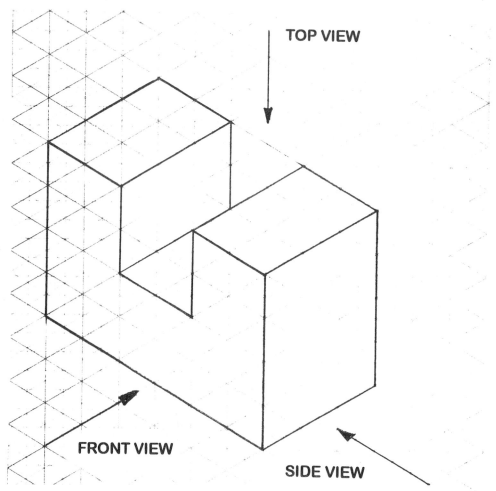

Fig. 1 Pictorial drawing showing a three dimensional rendering of a rectangular block with a slot. The three directions of viewing give the front, top and side views.

A three-view drawing of the block presented in Fig. 1 is illustrated in Fig. 2. The single pictorial drawing of the block is now represented with three different two-dimensional drawings representing the front, top and side views. These three drawings completely define the proportions of the block, its size and the location and size of the principle feature (the slot).

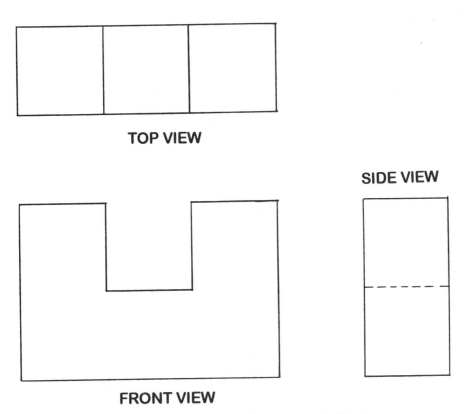

TOP VIEW

SIDE VIEW

FRONT VIEW

Fig. 2 A three-view drawing of the object shows the front, top and side views.

The arrangement of the views is important. The front view is placed in the lower left corner of the paper, the top view is directly above it, and the side view is directly to the right of the front view. This arrangement permits us to prepare the three-view drawing using orthographic projection. In orthographic projection, we project dimensions from one view to another. For example, we measure and draw the front view and project lines upward to the top view. The width of the object is shared in both the top and front views. We also project construction lines to the right from the front view, to give the height of the side view. The front and side views share the height dimensions of the block. We can also project from the top view to the side view if we draw a 45° construction line from the right hand corner of the front view, as shown in Fig. 3. We then project lines to the right from the top view until they intersect the 45° construction line, and then we turn them downward to show the depth of the object on the side view. All of the construction lines used to prepare Fig. 2 are illustrated in Fig. 3. Remember, orthographic projection will save you time in preparing your drawings. It reduces the number of time consuming measurements that you must make in preparing the different views necessary to completely describe any given part. The construction lines also help you in visualizing the feature locations on the adjacent views.

One more point to make before we leave Fig. 2. Did you notice the dashed line on the side view? Why were all of the lines solid except that one? We have a convention in engineering drawing for the use of line styles and line weight. Solid lines represent edges of features that we can see in a given view. As we look at the top of the block shown in Fig. 1, we can see the four sides of the rectangle, and we can see the two edges of the slot. We use solid lines then to represent all six edges that we can see in the top view. However, when we view the object from the side, we can only see the four edges outlining the rectangle. Looking from the right side, we cannot see the slot. If we look at the pictorial, or the top and front views, we know that the slot exists. To show it on the side view, we use a dashed line to represent a line hidden from view. Drawings differ from photographs in that we can show hidden features on the appropriate view by using dashed lines.

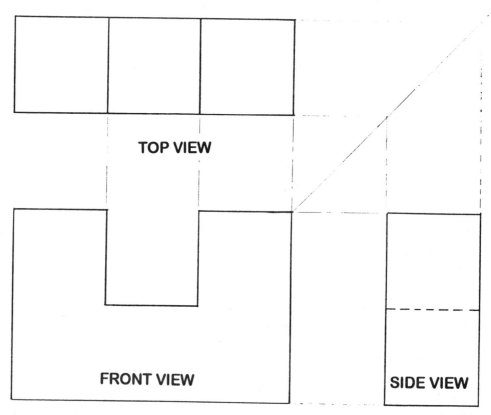

TOP VIEW

FRONT VIEW

SIDE VIEW

Fig. 3   Construction lines used to convey dimensions from one view to another in orthographic projection.

LINE STYLES

We use different line styles and different line weights (thickness and darkness of the lines) in preparing engineering drawings. The seven different line styles shown in Fig. 4 include:

1. Heavy weight solid lines to represent the edges of the object visible in each view.
2. Heavy weight dashed lines to represent hidden lines in appropriate views.
3. Medium weight long dash then short dash lines to represent centerlines in appropriate views.
4. Light weight solid lines used in dimensioning select views.
5. Very thin and light lines used in construction.

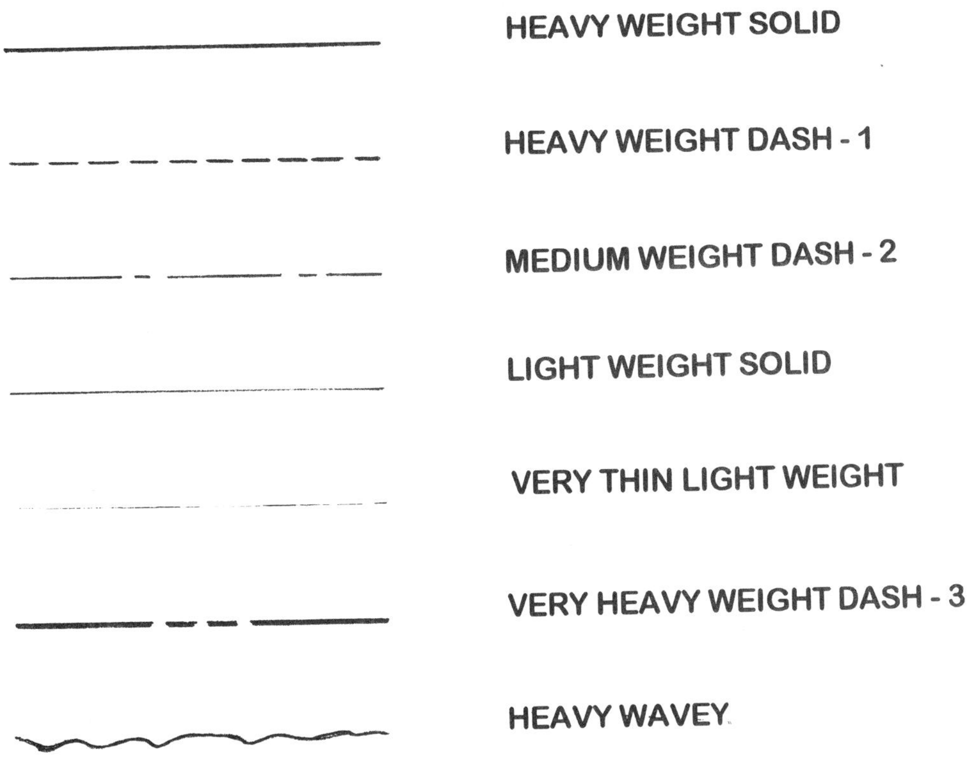

HEAVY WEIGHT SOLID

HEAVY WEIGHT DASH - 1

MEDIUM WEIGHT DASH - 2

LIGHT WEIGHT SOLID

VERY THIN LIGHT WEIGHT

VERY HEAVY WEIGHT DASH - 3

HEAVY WAVEY

Fig. 4 Different line styles used in view drawing.
   a. Heavy weight solid lines representing edges
   b. Heavy weight dashed lines representing hidden lines.
   c. Medium weight long dash then short dash lines for centerlines.
   d. Light weight solid for dimensioning.
   e. Very thin light lines for construction.
   f. Very heavy weight dashed lines for section cuts.
   g. Heavy wavy lines to indicate a break in the view.

We use 4H to 6H lead with a very sharp point to draw construction lines. These lines are so light and thin that they will not show when the drawing is reproduced. Light weight dimension lines are drawn so they will remain visible when the drawing is copied. We use an H or F lead to give the correct relative darkness, and use a sharp point with a very slightly rounded tip. Medium weight centerlines are drawn with a HB or B lead with a rounded point. Heavy weight lines, both solid and dashed, should be drawn with B or 2B lead with a rounded point.

The very soft leads --- 3B to 6B are usually employed by artists to prepare sketchings, but not by engineers preparing multi-view drawings. Engineers handle a completed drawing much more than an artist handles a completed sketch. In handling the soft leads smear, degrade the appearance of the drawing, and detract from the quality of the copies that are usually made from the originals.

We recognize that many of you will be short on pencils, but perhaps the team members can get together and share resources. Please do not use ball-point pens for drawing. There are two problems with ball-point pens. First, you have no control over the width of the line as it is determined by the diameter of the ball in the pen. Second, you will probably make several mistakes as you prepare the drawing. The lines drawn with a ball-point cannot be erased, and you eventually finish a drawing that is very sloppy and hard to read. Work in pencil and use a clean, white, vinyl eraser to eliminate all traces of your errors. Strive hard to produce an accurate, clean, and error-free drawing.

While we are on the topic of pencils and erasers, let's list some other simple tools that you will want to acquire.

1. Transparent ruler with scales in both inches and millimeters.
2. Triangles ---30/60 and 45/45 degrees.
3. Protractor
4. Compass
5. Templates circles, ellipses, etc.

This is a short list. We have not included a complete set of drawing instruments or a drafting board with T-square. Our purpose is not to teach drafting, but to introduce you to the essentials of engineering graphics, and you do not need a complete set of drafting tools to learn the early lessons in graphics. We encourage you to invest the small sum needed to acquire the items listed above. You will find them useful in many other courses that you will take during your program in engineering.

Finally, a suggestion for the paper that you use in preparing your drawings. We recommend National Brand engineering paper 8-1/2 by 11 in size. It is light green in color to relieve the strain on your eyes. It also has a grid (five squares to the inch) on the back side of each sheet. The grid shows through to the front side providing guidelines that are helpful in projecting the construction lines needed to prepare three-view drawings. The paper erases well, produces good copies, and is punched for a three ring binder.

Now that you are equipped with the proper pencils, eraser, tools and paper you are ready to begin to learn how to draw several different features normally encountered in preparing multi-view drawings of engineering components.

REPRESENTING FEATURES

We will demonstrate the techniques for drawing various features in three-view drawings. The examples selected include a block with a slot and a step, a block with a tapered slot, and a block with a step and a hole.

BLOCK WITH SLOT AND STEP

The rectangular block in Fig. 1 had one feature, namely a slot. We encounter many different geometric features in depicting parts that we design, including holes, curved boundaries, steps, and tapers. A pictorial of an object with both a slot and a step, presented in Fig. 5 serves as our next example. Let's prepare a three-view drawing of this object using the methods of orthographic projection. Look at the pictorial, and start with the front view.

As you examine the front view in Fig. 5, visualize the outline of the block. Even with the step and the slot, the outline of the block (the outside edges) is a rectangle. Draw that rectangle representing the outline of the front view in the lower left hand corner of your quadrille paper. We will not worry about exact dimensions of the rectangle at this stage; however, try to maintain the proportions shown in Fig. 5. When drawing the rectangle in the front view, extend the vertical lines

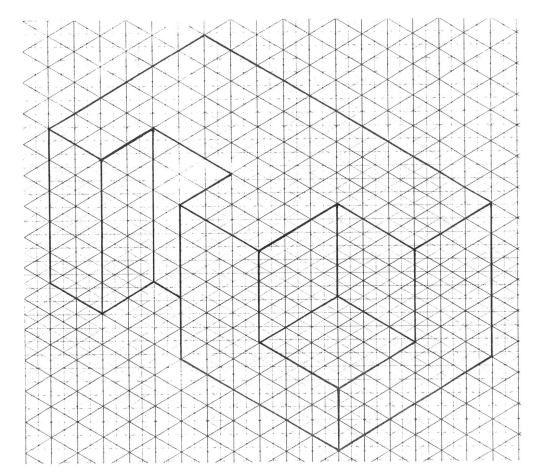

Fig. 5 A pictorial drawing of a block with a slot and a step.

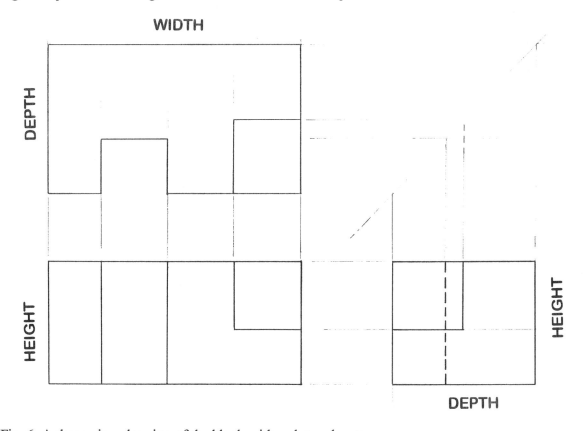

Fig. 6 A three-view drawing of the block with a slot and a step.

upward into the region of the top view, and the horizontal lines to the right into the region of the side view. These are construction lines, and you should keep them thin and light. Now look at the step that is in the upper right of the front view of the block. Note the intersection of the planes defining the step with the front plane of the block. Those intersections produce two new edges that you can see in the front view. Draw the location of these edges with the horizontal and the vertical lines shown in the upper right hand corner as indicated in Fig. 6. Extend the lines used to locate the step in the front view upward and to the right. Finally, locate the slot on the left side of the pictorial drawing in Fig. 5. Note again the planes that define the slot, and observe that they intersect the front plane to form two vertical edges. We draw two vertical lines in the proper location to represent these edges. Project these lines upward into the region of the top view using construction lines. OK! We have completed the front view, and are ready to move on to the top view.

Look down on the pictorial drawing. Again, the outline that you see is rectangular in shape, but in this view the rectangle is not perfect. The rectangle is interrupted by the slot. Looking downward, the edge defining the outline of the rectangle across the slot is missing; We can see through the block at the location of the slot down to the bottom plane. Draw the outline of the rectangle in the location of the top view of Fig. 6. Use the construction lines that exist at the location of the top view to help with the width dimensions. There should be an open section in the rectangle at the location of the slot. Next, show the depth of the notch in the top view by drawing the three lines that represent the edges formed by the three vertical planes of the slot with the top plane of the block. Finally, examine the step. The step has two vertical planes that intersect the top plane to form the defining edges. We draw those two lines in our drawing to complete the top view. If you have made full use of the construction lines projected from the front view into the region of the top view, it was easy to draw the top view. You only had to locate the position of three horizontal lines that defined the depth of the slot, step and block. We carry these depth dimensions to the right with construction lines.

The final view is the (right) side view. We could also do a left side view, but convention calls for us to draw the right view. After having completed the front and top views, including the orthographic projection of construction lines, the side view is easy to prepare. Draw a construction line at 45° so that it cuts the horizontal construction lines from the top view. Then draw a second set of construction lines downward from these intersection points into the side view. The side view now contains seven construction lines. The three horizontal lines projected from the front view give the height of the step and the block. The four vertical lines projected from the top view give the depth of the slot, step and block. We have the location and dimensions of all of the lines in the side view from our orthographic projections. All that we need to do to complete the side view is to darken select portions of the construction lines that represent edges. Again, look at the side of the pictorial drawing in Fig. 5 and observe that the rectangular outline of the block is completed. Also note the edges produced by the intersections of the planes forming the step with the plane of the right side of the block. Draw these two edges in the upper left corner of the side view. From a visual perspective, our drawing of the right side is complete; however, a multi-view drawing often carries more information than what we can visualize. We know from the front and top views that a slot exists. Our projection lines from the top view to the side view show the depth of the slot. Even though we cannot "see" the slot in the side view, we represent its presence and its location with a dashed (hidden) line. Our three-view drawing of a block containing a slot and a step is complete as illustrated in Fig. 6.

BLOCK WITH TAPERED SLOT

Let's consider drawing still another feature, namely a block that incorporates a tapered slot as illustrated pictorially in Fig. 7. Begin a three-view drawing with the front view in the lower left corner of your drawing paper as shown in Fig.8. Look at the front view in Fig. 7 and observe the edges produced by all of the planes that intersect the front plane. Drawing these edges gives us four vertical lines and three horizontal lines. The tapered surface intersects the front plane giving an edge shown in the front view. The top surface is represented by still another edge visible in the front view. We project all of these lines into the remaining two views with construction lines.

Examine the top view and observe that the rectangular outline of the block remains intact. Observe three edges inside the rectangular outline. The edge due to the intersection of the taper plane with the top surface produces a horizontal line, and the two vertical planes intersect the top surface to produce two vertical lines in the top view. Project the horizontal lines in the top view to the right so that they intersect the 45° construction line shown in Fig. 8. Then project these three lines downward from the intersection points on the 45° line into the side view.

The six construction lines projected into the side view give us most of the information needed to complete this view. Clearly, it is evident from Fig. 7 that the rectangle outlining the side view is intact. In fact as we view the right side, a simple rectangle formed by the four edges is all that is visible. The information regarding the tapered surface that is evident in the pictorial drawing, and the front and side view is not visible in the side view. We add information showing the location of the tapered surface on the side view by using the dashed (hidden) lines.

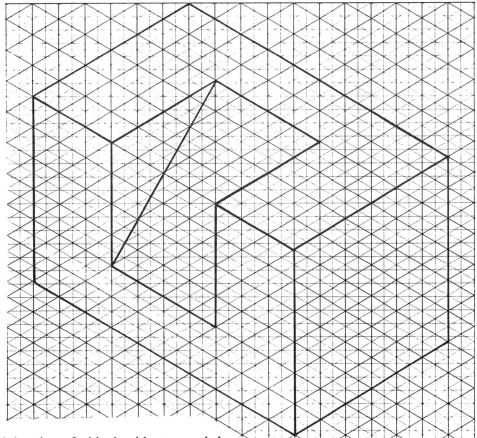

Fig. 7 A pictorial drawing of a block with a tapered slot.

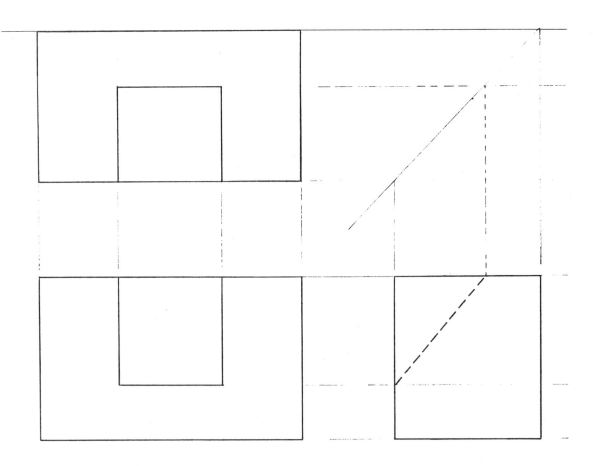

Fig. 8 A three-view drawing of the block with a tapered slot.

BLOCK WITH STEP AND HOLE

A pictorial drawing of a block with a step and a hole is illustrated in Fig. 9. We have prepared the three-view drawing of this object and have presented it in Fig. 10. The purpose in showing the fourth example of a three-view drawing is to illustrate how holes and curved boundaries are represented in engineering drawings. Assume in this discussion that you understand enough based on the previous examples to draw the outlines of the three-views. The only question concerns drawing the curved boundary that outlines the step and the hole that is drilled through the step.

The circular boundary outlining the step is evident only in the top view. The front and side views give no evidence of the presence of a curved boundary, because the vertical curved surface does not produce intersections (edges) on the front or side planes in either of these two views. Produce the curved surface in the top view using a compass with its point located in the center of the hole. The radius is set on the compass, so that the circular arc is tangent to the horizontal lines forming the outline of the block in the top view.

The compass is also employed to draw the hole in the top view. Note the two orthogonal lines that define the center of the hole. These are center lines that locate the position of the hole relative to some other feature on the block. The presence of the hole is also depicted in the front and side views even though it is not visible in either view. Use dashed lines (hidden) to locate the edges of the holes. Also locate the centerline of the hole in the front and side views. Note the long dash, short dash line used to denote the centerlines in all three-views. The centerlines are very important when we dimension the drawings, because we dimension holes to their centerlines and not to their edges.

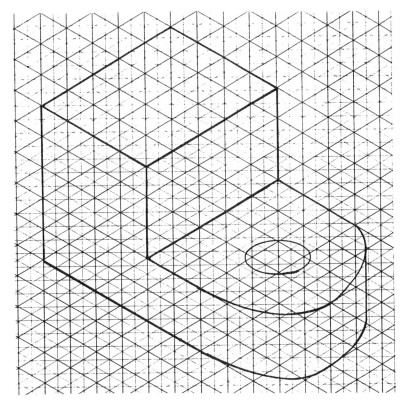

Fig. 9 A pictorial drawing of a block with a step and a hole.

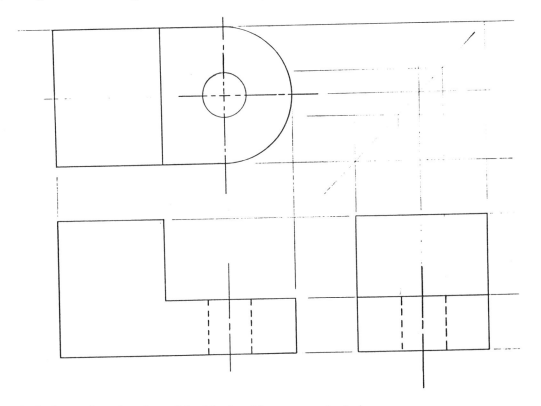

Fig. 10 A three-view drawing of the block with a step and a hole.

DIMENSIONING

In the previous section, we prepared our three-view drawings maintaining proportionality, but without concern for the dimensions. This approach was a simplification that we took to clarify the discussion of three-view drawings. In practice, the dimensions are critical because they control the size of the component and the location of all of its features. Let's examine dimensions from two different points of view. First as the individual preparing the drawing, you must know (or decide) on all of the dimensions required to completely define the component. If you are a designer of a new component, you start with a blank sheet of paper and assign the dimensions that you believe will optimize the design of the component. If you are redesigning an existing component, you will start with the drawing of that component and modify existing dimensions to refine the design. The point here is that you (as the person preparing the drawing) know the dimensions. It is your responsibility to include on your drawing all of the dimensions necessary for someone else to fabricate the component.

Next consider the second point of view, that of the person using the drawing. This person may manufacture the part, may assemble the product that incorporates the part, or may repair the product. Engineering drawings serve many purposes and are used by several other people that are not involved with design. The three-view drawing defines this component without ambiguity. The dimensions precisely give its size. The component as defined by the drawing, and its dimension can be made by anyone in the world with complete interchangability.

Let's begin to learn about dimensioning by adding dimensions to the drawing of the block with a slot that is shown in Fig. 2. We have copied this drawing, and have added dimensions as presented in Fig. 11. Examine the front view of this drawing noting that we have given the width of the block as 3. This dimension is inserted in a break in the dimension line. No units are given except for a notation in the drawing block that all dimensions are in inches, mm, ft, etc.. The dimension line is terminated by arrowheads that point to the two extension lines. The arrowhead is long (about 1/8 in.) and thin. The extension lines are separated from the view drawings by a small gap (about 1/16 in.).

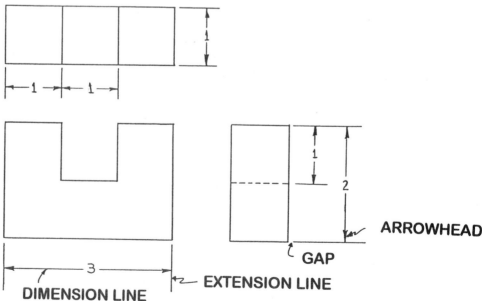

Fig. 11 Dimensioning example showing the dimension line, extension line, arrowhead and gap.

In the example presented in Fig. 11, we have dimensioned the block using inches as the unit of measure. The fact that we have defined the width as 3, indicates to the person manufacturing the block that the width can be 3 ± 1/64 in. The tolerance on the width is implied or is given in the drawing block. If you, as the designer, want to specify a block manufactured with more precision, you would specify the dimension using decimals. For example if you wrote 3.00, the person manufacturing the part would understand that the width of the block would have to be between 3.00 ± 0.01 in. If you need still more precision specify the dimension as 3.000 and the block must be produced with a width between 3.000 ± 0.005 in.. Remember there is a great difference between 3, 3.00 and 3.000 in the precision and tooling required to manufacture the components. There is also a great difference in the cost. As we tighten the tolerances, the cost of manufacturing a part increases significantly.

Let's return to Fig. 11 and examine the dimensioning of the top and side views. We have already shown the width on the front view, but we need dimensions for the depth and height of the block and the location and size of the slot. Remember that the top view is used to give dimensions for the width and depth, and the side view is used to give dimensions for the height and depth. In the top view of Fig. 11, we have specified the depth as 1. We have also specified the location of the slot and its width on this view. The height of the block and the height of the slot are given on the side view.

We have completed the dimensioning of the block and the slot. Every dimension necessary to manufacture the component has been specified in the drawing. Also the drawing has not been over dimensioned. (We have not specified the same dimension twice). The choice of where we place the dimensions is somewhat arbitrary. We can dimension the width on either the front or top views, the depth on the top or side views and the height on the front or side views. Two choices for each dimension are possible. We usually select one view or the other for a given dimension to keep the drawing clear and uncluttered..

DIMENSIONING HOLES AND CYLINDERS

To demonstrate techniques for dimensioning either holes or cylindrical boundaries, let's add dimensions to the drawing shown in Fig. 10. Again start with the front view, and locate the centerline of the hole as 3.20 from the left edge of the block. Holes are always located by the dimension from an edge to a centerline. Use the centerlines, because the drill employed to make the hole is inserted into the component at the point where the center lines cross.

We choose not to dimension the width in the front view, because we want to specify the radius of the curved (cylindrical) boundary in the top view. Going to the top view, we indicate the radius of the curved boundary as 1.20 R. The R is added to the dimension to indicate that it is given in terms of the radius and not the diameter. Note that once the radius R is specified, we have in effect given the width of the block as the sum of 1.20 + 3.20 = 4.40. To have specified the total width of the block in the front view would have been over dimensioning.

We show the location of the step from the left edge of the block as 2.00 in the top view. The height dimensions are given in the side view. We have indicated the total height of the block as 2.50 and the height of the step as 1.00 from the bottom edge of the block. Note that we have dimensioned the diameter of the hole in the side view as 0.75 DIA. We dimension holes in terms of diameter because the drill sizes used in manufacturing the holes are given in terms of their diameter, and not their radius.

Have we completed the dimensions as shown in Fig. 12? You might question if we have specified the depth of the block since it has not been indicated in the side view. Well, we specified the depth when we called out the radius of the curved boundary in the top view. The depth is equal to two times the radius R or 2.40.

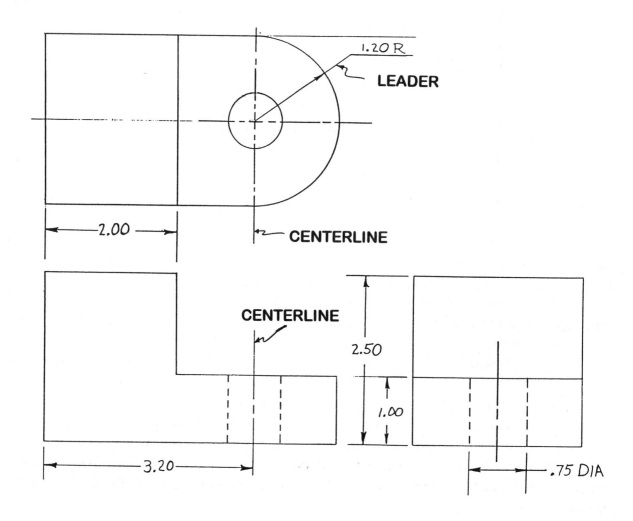

Fig. 12 Dimensioning example showing centerlines, leader, and radius and diameter indicators.

Again we have not shown units in the dimensioning. The units are defined in the drawing block along with other common information pertaining to the component. The use of two standards for units, the U. S. Customary and the SI systems, cause some difficulty in preparing and reading drawings. Some drawings are prepared using U. S. Customary units of in. or ft, and others are prepared using the SI system with units given in mm or m. Sometimes when the drawing is to be used by many people from different countries, both systems are employed in the dimensioning. An example of dual dimensioning is given in Fig. 13. In this case we do not break the dimension line because the U. S. Customary unit is placed above the line, and the SI unit is placed below the line and enclosed with parentheses.

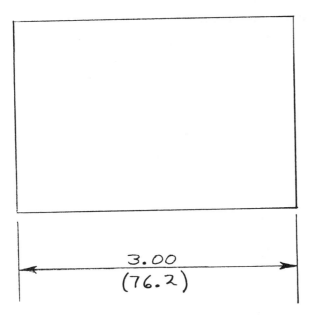

Fig. 13 Illustration of a convention used for dual dimensioning.

DRAWING BLOCKS

It is time to discuss the drawing block, because it serves a very important function on an engineering drawing. In the previous section we referred to the fact that the units for the dimensions were specified in the drawing block. The unit used in the drawing is only one of the many facts presented in the drawing block. As illustrated in Fig. 14, the drawing block is located in the lower right hand corner of the drawing, just inside the border. A typical drawing block conveys important information, some of which are common to all drawings produced by a certain company, and some which are unique to the individual drawing. Information commonly shown in the drawing block include:

1. Name of the company issuing the drawing.
2. Name of the part that the drawing defines.
3. Scale used in preparing the drawing.
4. Tolerances to be employed in manufacturing the part.
5. Date of the completion or the release of the drawing.
6. Material to be used in manufacturing the part.
7. Heat treatment of the part after manufacturing.
8. Units of measurement to be used in manufacturing the part.
9. Initials of the individual preparing the drawing.
10. Initials of the individual checking the drawing.
11. A drawing number which uniquely identifies the drawing.

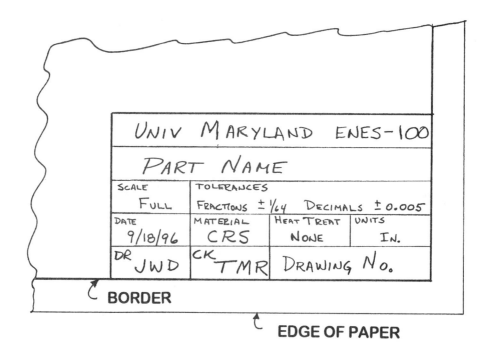

Fig. 14 An example of the information presented in a drawing block.

Let's examine each of these items. The name of the company is self evident. We illustrate it in Fig. 14 with the University of Maryland --- ENES 100. In designing a part, you will identify it with some name such as bracket, support, shaft, etc., and include this name on your drawing. The part name should be brief (no more than three or four words).

Next you will indicate the scale used in preparing the drawing. The example shown in Fig. 14 indicates that we used full scale in drawing the three-views of the part. The scale that we select depends on the size of the part and the size of the paper that is used for the drawing. In this class we are constrained to standard size copy paper (8-1/2 by 11 inches), because our laser printers are limited to this size. Suppose the part that you are designing is 12 inches wide, 6 inches high and 1 inch deep. Will the three-view drawing of this part fit on this standard size paper? The answer to this question is a clear NO. We need to scale down the part dimensions on the drawing so that it will fit on a single sheet of paper. In this case you would probably use ¼ scale. With ¼ scale the front view of the part would be 3 inches wide by 1 ½ inches high. You would dimension the drawing using the actual sizes of the part (i. e. you would show the width as 12 inches, although it is only 3 inches on the scaled down drawing). You indicate to those reading the drawing that you have reduced the size of each view by a scaling factor of ¼.

Tolerances that are to be employed in manufacturing the part are called out in the drawing block. Many companies have standardized their tolerances, and these limits are preprinted in drawing blocks that are incorporated on the company's drawing paper. The date of completion of the drawing is also shown. In some instances the drawing release date is used instead of the completion date. The release date identifies when the design engineers turn over the ownership of the design of a product to the operations (production) function which is responsible for producing the product.

The material from which the part is to be fabricated is often identified in the drawing block. In the example shown, the abbreviation CRS indicates that cold rolled steel will be used in manufacturing the component. Sometimes the heat treatment of the component, if required, is identified in the drawing block. Heat treatment is a multi-step process employed to enhance the strength and hardness of a component. Usually heat treatment follows the machining of a part, and we indicate whether or not it is required to assist those folks in charge of operations in controlling the flow of parts in the production process.

The units used in the drawing are given in the drawing block. We can use U. S. Customary units, SI units, or dual units. We cannot use mixed units (Note the difference between mixed and dual units). U. S. Customary units are in terms of inch (in.) or foot (ft). SI units are in terms of millimeter (mm) or meter (m).

Those responsible for the drawing are identified. The individual, who has prepared the drawing, signs the block with his or her initials. The drawing is checked for completeness and accuracy, and the individual checking the details also initials the drawing block. Finally, the drawing is given a number. In a large company, which may release thousands of drawings each year, the drawing numbers are controlled by the engineering records department. This department maintains a numbering system which insures that each part or component has a unique drawing number. The engineering records department also organizes the numbering system to group together all of the drawings needed to build a specific product.

ADDITIONAL VIEWS

Some of the parts that we design are complex and addition views may be needed to ensure that the drawings are properly interpreted. We are not restricted to three-view drawings. For very simple parts, we can adequately describe the object with one or two views. There is no need to waste time drawing additional views. For complex parts that are more difficult to visualize, we can provide additional views clarify the drawing. These extra views can show either external surfaces or internal sections. If it helps to visualize the object, we can add back, bottom and left side views to the more commonly employed front, top and right side views. To draw these additional external views, we simply rearrange the layout of the views on the drawing as shown in Fig. 15. This drawing shows five views of a multiply tapered block, illustrates the proper arrangement to show additional external views, and maintains the advantages of orthographic projection. Clearly, the extra views help us visualize the complex shape of this block.

An addition internal (sectional) view is often more useful in clarifying a drawing than an additional external view. The concept of a sectional view requires us to mentally cut the object with a cutting plane. We then divide the part into two and view the internal section revealed by the cut. An example of the technique used is illustrated in Fig. 16 where we have modified Fig. 8 by adding a sectional view. On the front view drawing in Fig. 16, we show a very heavy dashed line to indicate the location of the cut. The cut line is turned through 90° at both ends, and arrowheads are drawn to indicate the direction of the view. The arrowheads are labeled with the letter A. In this case, we are viewing the section cut from the right side. Accordingly, we expect the section view to closely resemble the right side view. We then draw the section that is revealed by the cut.

The section view may be placed at any convenient location on the drawing. We have placed it in the open space in the upper right hand corner of the drawing. The section view is usually encircled with a wavy line to distinguish it from the usual three-views. We also match the section view with the cut by using the letters A-A for identification. In some drawings, we might make several cuts each revealing different sections with each sectional view identified by A-A, B-B, C-C, etc. In the sectional view, we show the view revealed by the cut with cross hatching. The remaining part of the view (outside the cut section) is drawn without cross hatching. Try to prepare a section view of the component shown in Fig. 12. Make the section cut along the centerline through the hole in the top view, and then look at the section from the right side.

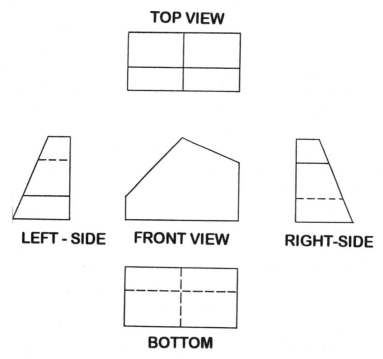

Fig. 15 A five view drawing of a complex block.

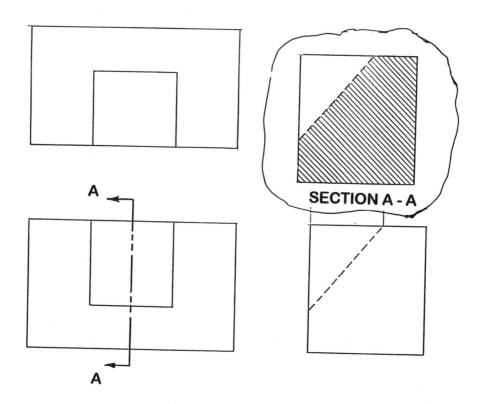

Fig. 16 A section cut and the corresponding section view.

SUMMARY

We have introduced engineering graphics by describing techniques for preparing multi-view drawings. Multi-view (usually three-view) drawings are used to communicate the relative proportions of a component and the exact size of all of its features. The drawing techniques are covered in detail with a few simple examples. We hope that you will take the time necessary to learn these techniques, because learning to draw and read three-view drawings is extremely important in engineering.

Dimensioning is a significant part of preparing an error free drawing. All of the dimensions must be included so that the part can be manufactured from the drawing. Often the part is manufactured in another city, or state or even another country. The person manufacturing the part does not know you and cannot ask you questions to clarify the ambiguities in your drawing. The drawing and all of its dimensions must completely define the component. An important implication of the dimensioning are the tolerances required in fabricating the part. As you write the numbers for the dimensions, you implicitly assign the tolerances. There is a great difference between 3, and 3.000 in the precision required in manufacturing and in the cost of the component.

We introduced drawing blocks and indicated the type of information that they normally convey. Remember drawing blocks are not unique and you will see differences in the information presented by different companies. We also introduced the concept of scale in this section. The scale used in preparing a drawing is your decision. Select the scale factor so that the three-views fit the paper without crowding. Sometimes you will scale down the view drawings so they will fit on the sheet. Other times you will scale up the views of a very small part, so that you can see its very small features.

The coverage of three-view drawings presented in this chapter is very brief. If you need to learn more, we recommend the very complete textbook by James Earle [1] for your additional reading.

REFERENCES

1. Earle, J. H., Engineering Design Graphics, 4th edition, Addison Wesley, Reading, MA 1983.

EXERCISES

1. Prepare a three-view drawing similar to the one shown in Fig. 2 except change the width of the notch from 1 inch to 1 ½ inch.
2. Take a piece of clay or foam plastic and use a razor knife to manufacture a block with the shape shown in Fig. 6.
3. Prepare a three-view drawing of a block with a taper notch like that shown in Fig. 8. Select the dimensions yourself, but be consistent from one view to another with these dimensions.
4. Prepare a three-view drawing similar to that shown in Fig. 10 except increase the diameter of the hole to 1 ¼ inch.
5. Dimension the drawing that you prepared for exercise 1.

6. Dimension the drawing that you prepared for exercise 3.
7. Dimension the drawing that you prepared for exercise 4.
8. Design a drawing block that your team can employ with their drawings of the solar still.
9. Prepare a five view drawing of the object shown in Fig. 9.
10. Prepare a drawing with a section view for the block defined in Fig. 1.

CHAPTER 6

PICTORIAL DRAWINGS

INTRODUCTION

Pictorial drawings are three-dimensional illustrations of a component or an object. For a person trying to visualizing an object, the pictorial drawing is the most effective means to convey its size and shape. Some folks have difficulty putting the three standard (front, top and side) views together to "see" the object. Pictorials drawings assemble the three-view s on a single sheet giving a three-dimensional view, that facilitates visualization. Because pictorials are so easy to visualize, they are often used for catalogs, maintenance manuals, and assembly instructions.

Three different types of pictorials are in common usage:

- Isometric
- Oblique
- Perspective

A simple cube with three different types of pictorials is illustrated in Fig. 1. The isometric pictorial is drawn with its three axes spaced 120° apart. The term isometric means "equal measurement" indicating that the sides are all scaled by the same factor relative to their true length. Parallel lines defining edges on the object are also parallel on the isometric drawing. Drawing paper with isometric axes is available in good office and drafting supply stores. We encourage you to use it, because it greatly facilitates the preparation of an isometric pictorial.

Oblique pictorials are drawn with the front view in the x-y plane. We project oblique lines, which represent the z axis, at some angle often 45°. The angle used for the oblique lines can vary from 0 to 90°. Parallel lines defining edges on the object are also parallel on the oblique drawing. If the true length of the lines is employed in scaling all three sides, we call it a cavalier oblique pictorial. The cavalier oblique style is frequently used, but the resulting pictorial is a distorted. The distortion is due to the depth dimension which appears to be too long.

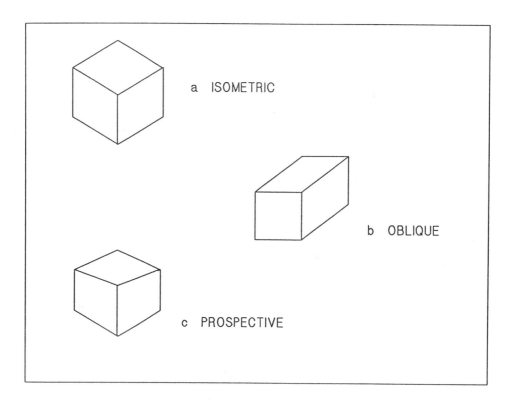

Fig. 1 A cube represented with isometric, cavalier oblique, and perspective pictorials.

The perspective is a pictorial drawing that represents what we actually see. Artists draw or paint using perspective style. Engineers sometimes represent their designs in this style; however, this is the most difficult of the three types of pictorials to master. In perspective drawing, we do not have a well defined coordinate system. Parallel lines tend to converge to a vanishing point as they recede from the observer. Scales on the different axes are different in order to shorten the lines located some distance from the picture plane. The use of converging lines instead of parallel lines and the foreshortening of select dimensions gives the drawing perspective. The prospective drawing looks like the object that we see.

ISOMETRIC DRAWINGS

In our discussion of the three forms of pictorial drawings, we will introduce the axes used to frame the drawing, the direction of viewing the three-dimensional object, and the dimensions used for the width, height and depth. Let's begin with the isometric pictorial, shown in Fig. 2, that employs axes which make 120° with each other. The axes divide the paper into three zones that are utilized to present three-views. If the axes make a Y with the vertical line directed downward from the two branches, we are looking downward at the object. From this perspective, we visualize the top view in the region between the branches of the Y as shown in Fig. 2. The front view is displayed in the region to the right of the vertical axis, and the left-side view is drawn in the region to the left of this axis.

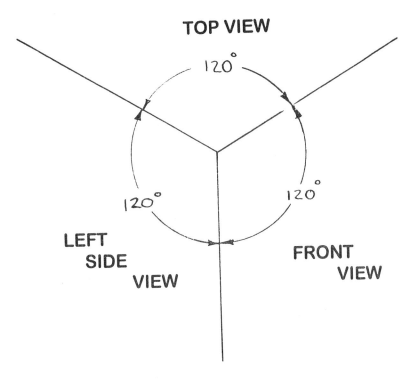

TOP VIEW

120°

120°

120°

LEFT SIDE VIEW

FRONT VIEW

Fig. 2 Isometric axes at 120° angles give three regions for the front, top and left-side views.

OK! We have defined the axes and the direction of viewing the object in Fig. 2. Let's discuss the dimensions that we use on the drawing for the width, height and depth. Isometric means equal measurement, so its clear that we will use the same scale along all three axes. To illustrate the techniques used to prepare isometric drawings, consider a simple rectangular block with width W, height H, and depth D. We have prepared an isometric pictorial of this block in Fig. 3. To draw this isometric pictorial:

1. Use a 30° triangle to draw the isometric axes identified with the numbers 1, 2, and 3 as shown in Fig. 3.
2. Use your scale and measure down the vertical a length equal to H, and establish point A.
3. From point A draw two more lines (numbers 4 and 5) that are parallel to lines number 1 and 2.
4. Along line 5, measure the width W, locating point B. Similarly measure the depth D along line 4 to give point C.
5. From points B and C, draw the vertical lines 6 and 7 that intersect lines 1 and 2, and locate points E and F.
6. From point F, draw line 8 parallel to line 2. From point E draw line 9 parallel to line 1.
7. Lines 8 and 9 that intersect at point G complete the isometric drawing.

The isometric pictorial that we have drawn shows the left-side view, the top view, and the front view, because we are viewing the object from above looking from the left to the right. The origin of the isometric coordinates is positioned at the upper left hand corner of the rectangular block. The procedure for preparing isometric drawings is easy to follow. All of the lines are parallel to the isometric axes, and all of the measurements are to the same scale.

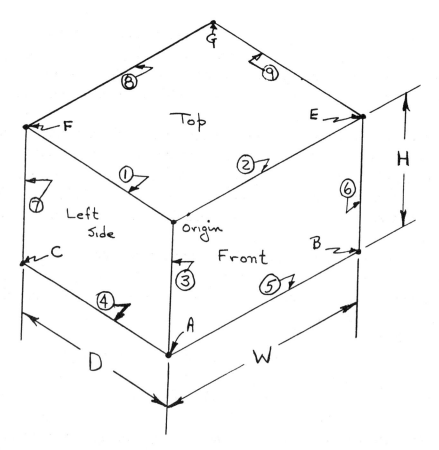

Fig. 3 Isometric pictorial of a rectangular block.

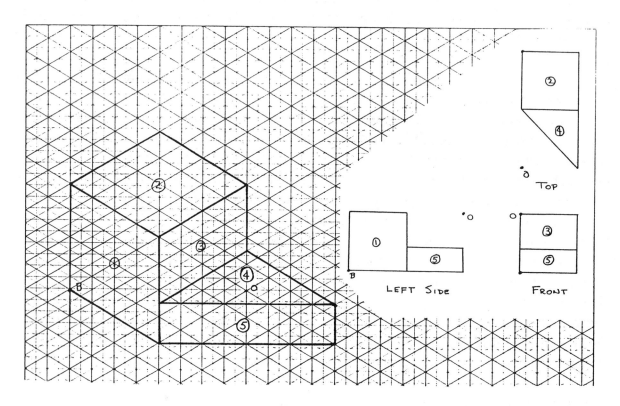

Fig. 4 Isometric pictorial of a block with a step and a tapered side.

The rectangular block was too easy. Let's try a more complex geometry as shown in Fig. 4. Look first to the inset of Fig. 4, that shows a three-view drawing of an odd shaped block. It is an unusual three-view drawing in that it presents the left-side view rather than the right-side view. The three-view drawing is presented in this manner, because the isometric drawing gives the same three-view s.

For the simple rectangular block, we placed the origin of the isometric axes at the upper left hand corner of the block. However, in this case that location is not recommended as a point to begin our pictorial, because it is located out in space in our three-dimensional representation. This fact is evident, if we locate the origin by the point O in the three-view insert of Fig. 4. In this example, it is easier to work from some other point. Let's try point B located in the left rear corner as a point to start your drawing.

The isometric pictorial, presented in Fig. 4, is drawn on isometric paper with only a straight edge to guide the lines. If you have a steady hand, you can sketch the lines without the straight edge. Isometric paper gives many evenly spaced lines parallel to the isometric axes eliminating the need for the 30° triangle and the scale. We begin at point B and draw plane 1 in the region of the left view. We do not draw the entire left-side view, because there is a taper to the block that complicates this view in the isometric representation. We leave the left-side view incomplete, and move to the top view and draw plane 2. Both planes 1 and 2 are clearly defined in the three-view drawing and are easy to construct on the isometric pictorial. Again we do not complete the top view, because the step and the taper complicate the geometry. We move next to the front view and add plane 3 which defines the depth of the step. We can now go back to the top view and draw plane 4 as shown in Fig. 4. Now that the top view is complete in the isometric drawing, and we know the height of the step, it is easy to draw plane 5. Note that plane 5 is on the surface formed by the taper. It does not lie in a plane formed by the isometric axes. We locate this non-isometric plane by first drawing all four of the isometric planes on the pictorial. It is then clear from the location of planes 1 and 4, where plane 5 is positioned.

You now understand how to draw simple rectangular blocks, and more complex blocks with both a step and a taper.

Let's next consider a cylinder of diameter D and height H, and illustrate it with an isometric pictorial. To draw the cylinder, lay out two isometric axes located a distance H apart using light construction lines as indicated in Fig. 5. On the upper set of axes, draw a square in the top plane with the length of the sides of the square equal to the diameter of the cylinder. Then select an isometric ellipse (35° - 16') from an ellipse template, and draw an isometric ellipse so that it is tangent to each side of the square drawn in the top plane. (If you do not have one of these handy templates, sketch the ellipse in by hand). Note that the ellipse is tangent to the isometric axes at four points as indicated in Fig. 5. Move down to the second set of isometric axes which represent the bottom plane. Take the handy template and draw isometric ellipse again. This time draw only the front half of the ellipse, since that portion is all that is visible when we view the cylinder from above. The two ellipses are joined with vertical lines at their outside points to complete the cylinder. The construction lines in Fig. 5 remain, to help you understand the procedure used in this drawing. To finish the drawing, erase the construction lines and shade the cylinder to enhance the visual effect of a three-dimensional object. Shading and shadows will be discussed later in this chapter when we refer to this isometric drawing of a cylinder again.

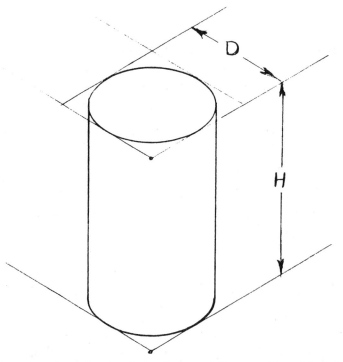

Fig. 5 Isometric pictorial of a right circular cylinder of diameter D and height H.

OBLIQUE DRAWINGS

Oblique pictorials and isometric pictorials are similar because both use parallel lines in constructing the three views. The difference between isometric and oblique pictorials is in the definition of the axes. In oblique drawings, we use a x,y, z coordinate system as shown in Fig. 6. The three coordinate axes divide the sheet into three regions for drawing the front, top and right-side views. With the axes defined as shown in Fig. 6, we are viewing the object from above looking from right to left. The z axis, which is the receding axis in Fig. 6, is drawn with a 45° angle relative to the x axis; however, other angles such as 30° or 60° are often employed.

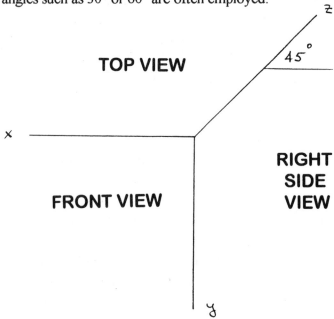

Fig. 6 Oblique axes use the x, y, z coordinate system.

Three different types of oblique drawings are frequently used for pictorials. They are illustrated in Fig. 7:

1. Cavalier oblique can be drawn with the receding axis at any angle from 0 to 90°, but the measurements along all three axes are the same scale.

2. Cabinet oblique can be drawn with the receding axis at any angle from 0 to 90°, but the measurements along this axis are half scale.

3. General oblique can be drawn with the receding axis at any angle from 0 to 90°, but the measurements along all this axis varies from half to full scale.

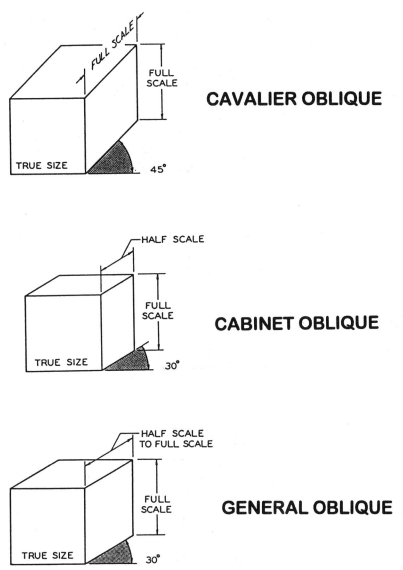

Fig. 7 A pictorial of a cube drawn with cavalier, cabinet and general oblique techniques.

If we examine the cube represented by the three types of oblique drawings in Fig. 7, it is evident that full scale (true length) measurements are used in the front view in all three types of oblique pictorials. The difference among them is the scale used along the receding axis. In cavalier oblique, the full scale measurements are made along the receding axis. This scale produces a drawing that looks out of proportion. The cube does not look like a cube.

In cabinet oblique half scale measurements are made along the receding axis. The resulting drawing is in better proportion than the cavalier oblique, but sometimes it appears that the depth dimension along the receding axis is too short. We prefer the general oblique where the measurement on the receding axis can be varied from ½ scale to full scale to give what appears to the eye to be the correct proportions.

To illustrate the procedure followed in drawing an oblique pictorial, examine the three-view drawing of a pair of connected rectangular blocks as shown in Fig. 8. To begin our oblique pictorial, draw the x, y, z axes using the lower left hand corner as the origin (point O). First draw the part of the front view (plane 1) that corresponds to the front of the large block. Then draw part of the top view (plane 2) of the large block. In drawing the front view, use true lengths (on plane 1) to measure the width and height of the large block. On the top view, establish the depth of the large block, maintaining perspective by using a scaling factor of ¾.

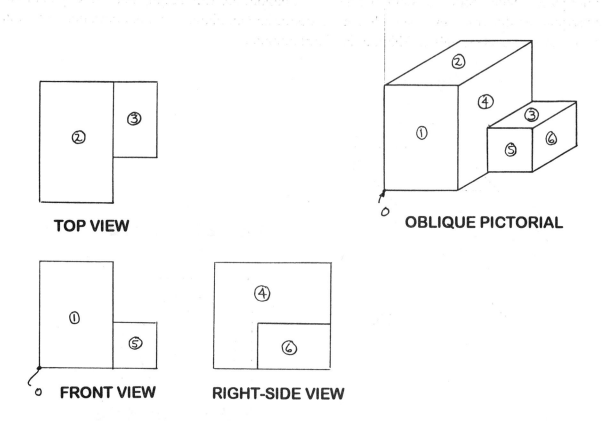

Fig. 8 Three-view drawing of a connected pair of rectangular blocks together with an oblique pictorial of the same object.

Note that the right-side view of the large block is obstructed by the smaller block. We handle this obstruction by drawing the small block. Using the information in the three-view drawing we can place plane 3 on the oblique pictorial. Plane 3 is located by working from the back edge in the top view. The width and height measurements required to locate and size plane 3 in the oblique pictorial are true lengths, but the depth is again scaled by ¾.

After we have drawn plane 3 locating the small block in the pictorial, it is easy to draw plane 4 by referring to the right-side view in the three-view drawing. Complete the drawing of the small block by dropping vertical lines down from three corners in plane 3 and closing the sides that form planes 5 and 6.

The resulting oblique pictorial clearly captures the relative proportions, and the positioning of the two blocks. A comparison of the pictorial with the three-view drawing demonstrates the advantages of the pictorial in visualizing the object. The pictorial is much more effective in visualizing the component. The three-view drawing is better for more precise definition of size and location. We dimension the three-view drawing and use it in the shop for manufacturing. Usually the pictorial is not dimensioned, and it is not use it as a detail drawing intended for the person manufacturing the component.

As final examples of preparing oblique pictorials, consider the drawing of a cylinder or a block with a circular hole as shown in Fig. 9. It is easy to draw a cylinder or a circle on an oblique pictorial, providing the required circles are placed on either the front plane or any plane parallel to the front plane. Since both the width and height dimensions are true length, and the x, y axes are orthogonal on the front view, the circle is not distorted into an ellipse. We can drawn the circle with a compass or a circle template. This is a significant advantage.

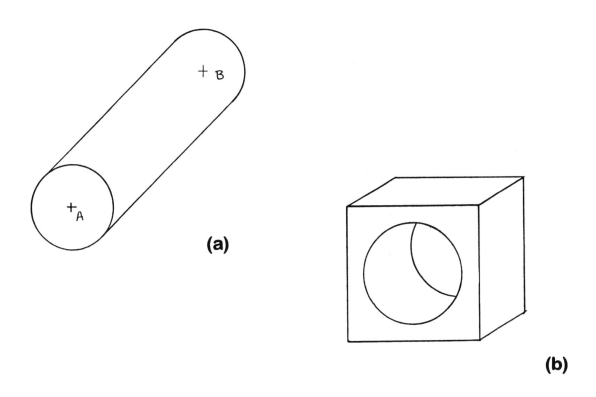

Fig. 9 Examples of oblique pictorials.
(a) Right circular cylinder. (b) Rectangular block with circular hole.

To represent the cylinder shown in Fig. 9a, we draw two circles centered at points A and B. Points A and B lie on the z (receding) axis which has been drawn at a 45° angle to the x axis. The circles are drawn in with construction lines, and the spacing of the two circles is scaled at a factor of ¾ relative to the length of the cylinder. The diameter of the circles are full scale. Place two lines parallel to the z axis are drawn tangent to the circles to give the sides of the cylinder. Draw the front circle with a heavy line, and darken the top right portion of the back circle. The resulting pictorial shows a somewhat distorted cylinder, The distortion is due to the fact that we have drawn the back circle with the same diameter as the front circle. Looking at a real right circular cylinder, the back circle would "appear" to be smaller than the front circle. We will address the apparent difference in the size of features located in different planes in the next section on perspective drawing.

The final example of oblique pictorial, presented in Fig. 9b, shows a simple rectangular block with a central hole. We have drawn the block so that the circle of the hole is see in its entirety in the front view. The question is how to draw the circle in the back plane. Draw the square locating the back plane in the pictorial using light construction lines. Then find the center of this square and draw the circle with the same diameter as the front circle. Note that the two circles intersect, and that only a portion of the circle on the back plane is visible. Darken the construction lines on the back circle, over that part of the arc that is visible through the hole. The resulting pictorial is an effective three-dimensional drawing showing the appearance of a hole through a rectangular block. Our artist friends would critique us, because it too distorts the visual image of the object. The scale in the back plane and the front plane are the same and that produces distortion of the image. Usually this distortion is acceptable in engineering drawing, but we can improve our pictorials by preparing perspective drawings.

PERSPECTIVE DRAWINGS

Perspective drawings are pictorials that represent what we see either with our eyes or with a camera. This method of illustration is critical to the success of an artist making either sketches or paintings. Engineers also use perspective drawings, particularly when preparing visuals for folks who are not trained to read our more conventional three-view drawings. The tools used are the same as those described previously, except for adding a thumb tack and a piece of string to the list.

There is one very significant difference between perspective drawings and isometric or oblique drawings. In isometric or oblique drawings, the lines defining the edges (say top and bottom) are parallel to the axes; however, in perspective drawing, the lines defining some of the edges may not parallel. Drawing parallel often lines distorts the drawing, because we see parallel lines appearing to converge as they recede in space. The best illustration of this fact is a pair of railroad tracks, shown in Fig. 10. Looking down the tracks, you see that the tracks converge to a point and that the railroad ties appear to get shorter. The poles lining the track also appear to get shorter. Now everyone knows that the tracks are parallel. What's going on?

To understand what is going on, we need to define four terms that are used in describing prospective drawing.

1. Picture plane is the surface (i. e. the sheet of paper) of the pictorial. The edges of the paper represent the window through which you "see" a three-dimensional object that is the subject of the perspective drawing.
2. Horizon line divides the sky and the land or the sea if you are outdoors. In Fig. 10 this line is just below the level of the bridge that crosses the railroad tracks. The horizon line is at the level of your eyes and will change with your elevation. In a room where you cannot locate the true horizon because the walls of the block our view, we assume a horizon line at about the elevation of your eyes.

3. Viewing point and direction of view depends on the location of eyes relative to the object. You can look directly at the object, from left to right , right to left, downward, upward, etc. What you see changes markedly depending on these parameters. Look out a window at an object, and change where you stand and the direction of your view. Does the view of the object change?

4. Vanishing point is where parallel lines converge to a point as they recede into the distance. You can clearly identify the vanishing point in Fig. 10 where the tracks appear to meet.

Fig. 10 Photograph of railroad tracks showing the visual effect of convergence of parallel lines and foreshortening of objects in a distance.

ONE-POINT PERSPECTIVE

Depending on the view, an object can be represented by using one, two, or three-point perspective. Let's start with the simple one-point perspective and illustrate the approach by drawing a rectangular block. In one-point perspective, you place the front view of the block in the picture plane and show its true width and height as illustrated in Fig. 11. Then you draw a construction line to represent the horizon. The location of this line depends on the viewing point and the viewing direction. In Fig. 11, you are viewing the block straight on (not from the right or the left); however, you are above the block. Your eyes look downward and see the top surface of the block. The elevation is taken into account by raising the horizon line. Next, locate the vanishing point on the horizon line at the center point behind the front view, because we are looking straight on at the block. Draw construction lines from the vanishing point to the top corners of the block in the front view as shown in Fig. 11. The back edge on the top view is drawn parallel to the front top edge to establish the depth of the block. Note that the back edge is much shorter in length than the front edge. The shortening of the lines on the recessed planes give the illusion of the third dimension. The edges at the side are darkened to complete the pictorial. These edges are converging, again to give the illusion of depth on the two dimensional sheet of drawing paper.

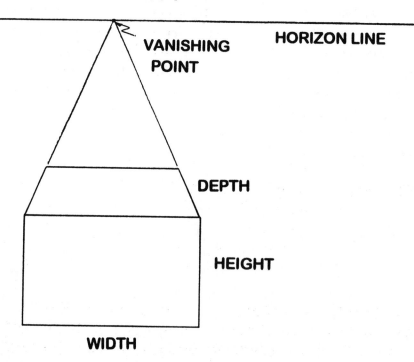

Fig. 11 Example of pictorial drawing with one-point perspective.

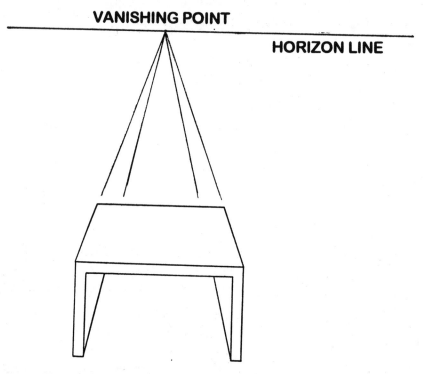

Fig. 12 One-point perspective drawing of a coffee table.

Another example of one-point perspective is the drawing of a coffee table presented in Fig. 12. The front of the table is drawn to scale in the picture plane as in Fig. 11. The width and height dimensions are true length. Coffee tables are low, so we stand looking downward, but straight on toward the top surface of the table. Draw the horizon line at eye level aligning the vanishing point with the center of the table. Next, draw light construction lines from the top outside corners or the table to the vanishing point. We also draw construction lines from the lower inside corners of the table legs as shown in Fig. 12. These construction lines define two triangles. We use the larger of these two triangles to draw the back top edge of the table, and then its edges to complete our perspective rendering of the top view. We use the smaller of the two triangles to draw in the bottom edge of legs that are visible under the table.

In a normal perspective drawing we would erase the construction lines, the vanishing point and the horizon line. We have not erased them in Fig. 12, because they were used to illustrate the procedure followed in making a one-point perspective drawing.

TWO-POINT PERSPECTIVE

The one-point perspective is useful when we view an object straight on so that its front view lies in the picture plane. However, if the object is rotated so that neither the front or side view is in the picture plane, as illustrated in Fig. 13, a two-point perspective is required. Again consider a rectangular block to illustrate the approach followed in drawing a two-point perspective pictorial. From Fig. 13, it is evident that only one edge of the block lies in the picture plane, so we will start with that fact ands proceed step by step to draw the block.

- Draw a vertical line, as indicated in Fig. 14, to establish the edge between left-side view and the front view.
- Draw the horizon line to reflect the fact that we are standing above the block, looking downward at an angle onto the top surface.
- Place two vanishing points on the horizon line. We have spaced the vanishing point located to the right of the vertical line (VP - R) farther from the vertical line than the vanishing point on the left-side (VP - L), because we are viewing the block at a slight angle from the right toward the left.
- Measure the true length of the vertical line (line 1) and label its ends with the letters A and B.
- Draw four construction lines connecting points A and B with VP - R and VP - L.
- Draw vertical lines (2 and 3) to locate the back edges of the left-side and the front of the block. The ends of these lines are located by the construction lines have been labeled (C, D) and (E, F).
- Draw top edge lines (4, 5) by connecting points F, A and D.
- Draw bottom edge lines (6, 7) by connecting points E, B and C.
- Draw construction lines from point F to VP - R, and from point D to VP - L, and locate point G at the intersection of these two lines.
- Draw sides (8, 9) by connecting points F, G, and D.

The two-point perspective drawing of the rectangular block is complete as shown in Fig. 14. The procedure may seem long when we outline it in steps, but it is not difficult. Once you understand the basic concepts of establishing the true length of the vertical line in the picture plane and the vanishing points on the horizon line, all of the other steps are routine.

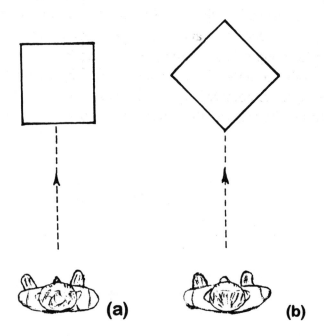

Fig. 13 Directions of viewing control the number of points used in perspective drawing.
    a.   Straight on --- one-point perspective.
    b.   Angle view --- two-point perspective.

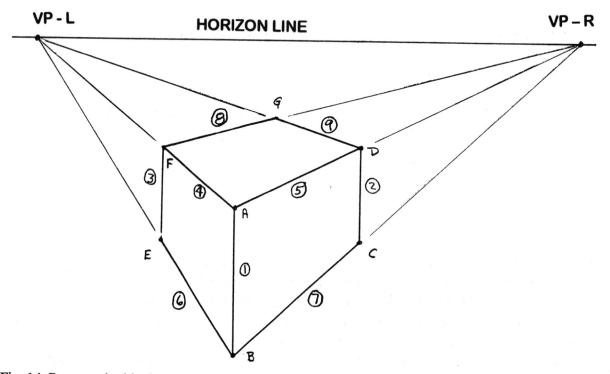

Fig. 14 Rectangular block represented with a two-point perspective drawing.

To complete the discussion of the two-point perspective, return to the example of the coffee table. This time, you will use two-point perspective to draw the table. Begin by placing the leg of the table in the picture plane as indicated in Fig. 15. The length of the leg is shown in true length on the vertical line that represents the edge of the leg. Establish the horizon line and the vanishing points to give the direction of the view that you want to represent. Draw construction lines from the ends of the vertical line to the vanishing points. Vertical lines are drawn to give the width and the depth of the table. The position of these vertical lines is not established by measurement, because the both the width and depth dimensions are not true length in the two-point perspective. Place the vertical lines in a position that maintains, "to the eye," the correct proportions of the table.

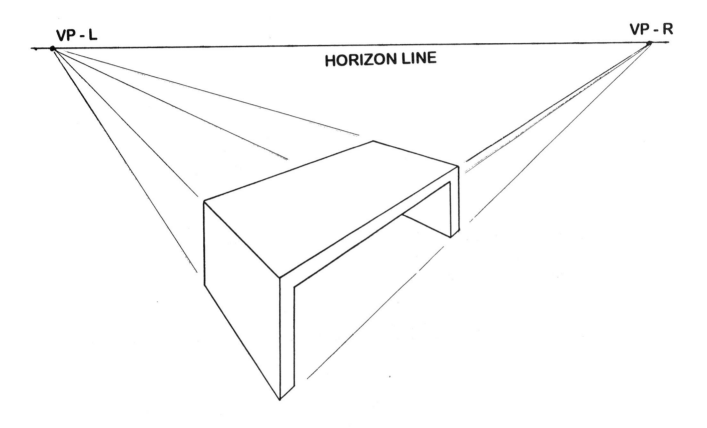

Fig. 15 Two-point perspective drawing of a coffee table.

Once the vertical lines that bound the left-side view and the front view are drawn, the remainder of the drawing is easy complete. Construction lines are drawn from the ends of the vertical lines to the vanishing points. The construction lines outline the table. It is necessary to darken only those segments of the construction lines that define the visible edges of the table.

Three-point perspectives are used when the object is very tall. Architects drawing a city view with skyscrapers would use three-point perspectives and taper the building as it extends into the sky. Engineers usually deal with smaller objects that usually can be represented in pictorials with either one or two-point perspective drawings. For this reason, we will not describe the methods used in preparing three-point perspectives. However, if you are interested in learning much more about perspective drawing, we recommend the excellent book by Powell [2].

SHADING AND SHADOWS

Add shading and shadows to our pictorial drawings makes them appear more realistic. Let's first distinguish between shading and shadow. If you light the object, some surfaces are exposed to this light and other surfaces are in the shade. There is a difference in the intensity of light reflected from these surfaces. Those in the shade are darkened slightly. A shadow is produce when an opaque object blocks the light. The shadow occurring in this region is shown as a dark area in the drawing. We show an example of shading and shadowing of a right circular cylinder in Fig 16. In this example, parallel light rays are illuminating the cylinder from the upper left. (They are included on the drawing only to show the logic for determining the shade and shadow regions). The right half of the cylinder is in the shade and is darkened slightly. The shadow is cast on the plane of the floor on which the cylinder rests. The depth of the shadow is the same as the depth of the cylinder as shown on the isometric pictorial. The length of the shadow is dependent on the direction of the parallel rays of light. Extending the lines representing the light rays helps define where the edge of the shadow forms on the floor.

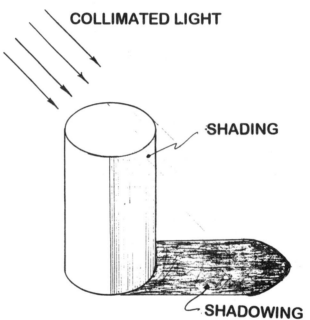

COLLIMATED LIGHT

SHADING

SHADOWING

Fig. 16 Shading and shadowing of an isometric pictorial of a right circular cylinder.

Let's consider another example of shading and shadowing in a two-point perspective drawing of a cube. The drawing, presented in Fig. 17, is similar to that shown in Fig. 14, so we will assume that you can draw the cube in the two-point perspective pictorial.. In Fig. 17, we show the construction technique for determining the exact size of the shadow when the light is coming from a point source.

Suppose you have completed the two-point perspective drawing of the cube and are ready to shade and shadow the drawing. The process is first to select the location of the light source. It is your choice, but you will place the light source well above the horizon either to the left or the right of the cube. Second, you must select the vanishing point for the shadow. Again it is your choice as long as it is directly below the light source and in the ground (floor) plane. The reasons for these two constraints are evident. The shadow must vanish when the light source is directly overhead, and the shadow must always lie on the ground (floor) plane. You selected the vanishing point of the shadow on the horizon line; but it could have been placed anywhere on the ground plane under the light source.

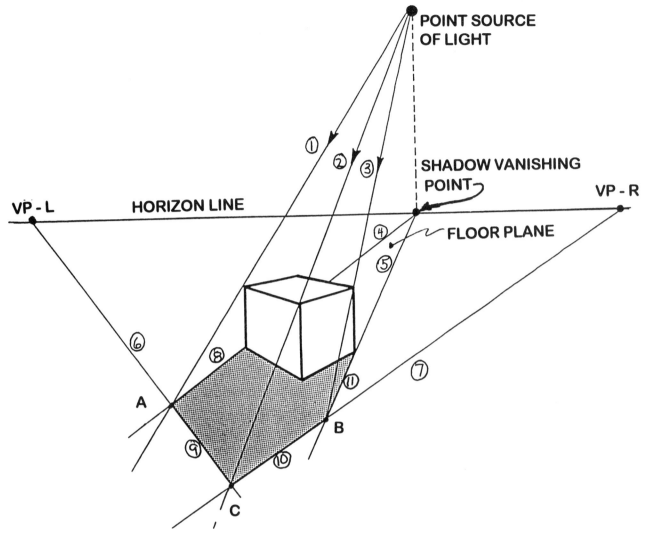

Fig. 17 Technique for determining shadow outline on a two-point perspective drawing.

Let's go though a step by step procedure for locating the shadow outline shown in Fig. 17:

1. Draw the light rays (1, 2, and 3) from the source through three of the top corners of the cube.
2. Draw two construction lines (4 and 5) from the vanishing point of the shadow through the two bottom external corners.
3. Locate points A and B at the intersections of the lines (1 and 6) and (3 and 7).
4. Draw lines 6 and 7 from the left and right vanishing points through points A and B.
5. The intersection of lines (6 and 7) locates point C.
6. Darken segments of the construction lines (8, 9, 10 and 11) to give the shadow outline.
7. Erase all of the construction lines and darken the shadow region within the outline.

We have completed the shadow, but the front and left-side views of the cube are in the shade. To complete the pictorial these two sides should be darkened slightly to indicate that they are in a shadow.

SUMMARY

Three different pictorial drawings, isometric, oblique and perspective, have been introduced. Both isometric and oblique pictorials are widely used in engineering to present three-dimension illustrations on a two-dimensional format (a sheet of drawing paper). The isometric and oblique pictorials are easy to draw because lines are parallel, and most if not all of the measurements are to scale. However, exact scaling of dimensions and parallel lines tend to distort these three-dimensional illustrations. The eye or camera "sees" dimensions to scale, and parallel lines as parallel only if the view depicted is on the picture plane. If the view is on any other plane behind the picture plane, the dimensions are foreshortened. If the parallel lines are on views containing the receding axes, they tend to converge. We ignore these distortions in engineering drawings when we prepare isometric or oblique pictorials.

Perspective drawings provide a more realistic representation of three-dimensional objects. Artists almost always use perspective concepts in their sketches or paintings. In engineering we usually employ one-point or two-point perspectives to produce realistic three-dimensional drawings that are used in catalogs and maintenance manuals. The techniques of perspective drawing require that we understand four quantities: the picture plane, the horizon line, vanishing point or points, and viewing direction. The techniques for drawing perspectives with converging lines and foreshortened dimensions follow directly from the definitions of these four quantities.

Shading and shadowing is an added technique for making pictorial drawings even more realistic. We have indicated methods for determining the outline of shadows either from point light sources or collimated light sources that produce parallel light rays.

REFERENCES

1. Franks, G. Pencil Drawing, Walter Foster Publishing, Laguna Hills, CA 1988.
2. Powell, W. F. Perspective, Walter Foster Publishing, Laguna Hills, CA 1989.
3. Earle, J. H., Engineering Design Graphics, Addison Wesley, Reading, MA 1983.

EXERCISES

1. What are the three types of pictorial drawings? Why do we use pictorial drawings in engineering applications?
2. Prepare an isometric pictorial drawing of a rectangular block 10 mm wide by 15 mm deep by 50 mm high. What scale should you use in preparing this drawing? Why?
3. Prepare an isometric pictorial drawing of the solar still that your team is developing.
4. Prepare an oblique pictorial drawing of the solar still that your team is developing.
5. Prepare a prospective pictorial drawing of the J. M. Patterson building. View the building from the intersection of the two frontage streets.
6. Draw a pictorial of a sphere with shading and shadowing.

CHAPTER 7

TABLES AND GRAPHS

INTRODUCTION

On many occasions we find ourselves with a collection of numerical data that we must present at a meeting, or in an engineering report. At other times, we may have results from a mathematical relationship that must be presented or reported. We have two choices in presenting numerical data. We can show the numbers in tabular form, or in a suitable graph. Both methods of presentation, the table or the graph, have advantages and disadvantages. The method that you choose will depend on your audience, the message that you are reporting, and the purpose of your presentation.

In this chapter, we will describe how to list data in a table using Microsoft's Word 7 as the word processing program. In a different chapter, we describe data entry into a spreadsheet which is also suitable method for preparing tables. We then introduce five common methods for representing data in the form of graphs which include:

1. Pie charts
2. Bar charts
3. X - Y graphs.
4. Semi-log graphs
5. Log - log graphs

Each type of graph is used for a different purpose and selection of the proper type of graph is essential in communicating effectively. For instance, the pie chart is used to show distributions (who gets the most and the least). The bar chart is used to compare one set of data with another set. X - Y graphs, the most frequently used type of graphing in engineering, show how Y varies with X.

When Y varies by very large amounts with small changes in X, we often use semi-log graphs which are capable of covering a very large range of Y values. When both X and Y vary over very large ranges, we display the results using a log-log graph representation.

TABLES

In Chapter 1 we described the responsibilities of Mechanical Engineers in their first position and presented statistical data in a table. Let's reproduce that table data, to show you how it is easy to use Word to prepare a table. We prepare the table heading, by selecting the center alignment, then identify the table number, and type the title. We often use a bold font for the table heading, to attract the reader's attention.

TABLE 1
Responsibilities of Mechanical Engineers in Their First Position

---

OK, we are now ready for the body of the table. Point the mouse to the menu row and select "Table". We have a choice of whether or not we want to show grid lines in the table. Let's click on the "Gridlines" label to use the grid lines to guide us as we enter the data. If we don't like them they can easily be removed at any time by clicking again on this label. Next, click on "Insert Table". The new menu that appears on the screen, requires some information about our table. We need to know beforehand the arrangement of the table (how many columns and rows). Let's say we want three columns and 15 rows. We can always add or delete either columns or rows later if we find that we were not correct in specifying the initial configuration. Finally, we select auto-format, and let Word initially control the width of the columns. Click back on the text, and the outline of the table appears. If the grid lines are dotted and light when the table first appears on the screen, they will not print as they are intended only to guide your typing. If you want the grid lines to show when the table is printed, click on Format/Borders and Shading. A new menu appears on the screen, and you click on the "Grid" button to choose the thickness of the grid lines that you want to outline each cell. The result of our first trial after we have typed the data into the correct cells is shown on the next page.

The result of our first attempt is fair, but it could be improved. The auto-format selection divided the width of the page into thirds for the width of the columns. This partitioning is not the best choice, considering the wasted space associated with the numerical entries and the double rows needed to accommodate the assignments. The first column titled ASSIGNMENT needs more width and the 2nd and 3rd columns are too wide. Let's modify the table by changing the column widths. We accomplish this by clicking on Table/Cell Height and Width. Select the column tab and adjust the width of the first column (3 in.), and click the Next Column button and adjust the width of both column 2 and 3 to 1 inch. The Table looks much better, and requires less space on the page, but it is not centered. To center it, click Table/Cell Height and Width and select the Rows tab. From the Rows menu select center alignment. The improved table is shown on the lower half of the next page. As a result of our modifications, it looks very professional.

ASSIGNMENT	% TIME	% TIME
Design Engineering		40
Product Design	24	
Systems Design	9	
Equipment Design	7	
Plant Engineering/ Operations/ Maintenance		13
Quality Control/ Reliability/ Standards		12
Production Engineering		12
Sales Engineering		5
Management		4
Engineering	3	
Corporate	1	
Computer Applications/ Systems Analysis		4
Basic Research and Development		3
Other Activities		7

TABLE 1

Responsibilities of Mechanical Engineers in Their First Position

ASSIGNMENT	% TIME	% TIME
Design Engineering		40
Product Design	24	
Systems Design	9	
Equipment Design	7	
Plant Engineering/ Operations/ Maintenance		13
Quality Control/ Reliability/ Standards		12
Production Engineering		12
Sales Engineering		5
Management		4
Engineering	3	
Corporate	1	
Computer Applications/ Systems Analysis		4
Basic Research and Development		3
Other Activities		7

Tables are effective in presenting precise numerical data. We do not need to estimate crudely a number by reading from a curve on an X-Y graph. If we have a reason to show our results with six significant figures, it is very easy to do so. A government agency that probably produces the most widely read tables in the United States is the Internal Revenue Service. They prepare tax tables each year that precisely show our tax obligations. We will present another example later that shows the advantage of a table in conveying numerical data with many significant figures. We will also show how spreadsheets can be employed to produce both graphs and tables in another chapter.

GRAPHS

We use graphs to visualize the data in both reports and presentations. The graphs are not intended to give precise results since we use tables for that purpose. The graphs show our audience a trend, a comparison, or a distribution quickly and effectively. There is no need for the audience to study the data to develop an understanding. Your graph shows the bottom line, and eliminates the time and effort required for the reader to analyze the data.

There are many different ways of presenting numerical data in a graphical format. Distribution of goodies are usually shown with pie charts, because we all quickly relate to getting a good size share of the pie. Comparisons are made with bar charts, with the height of each bar indicative of the magnitude of the quantity being compared. Linear graphs, where we plot a dependent parameter Y as a some function of an independent parameter X, is frequently employed. The data plotted can be generated with mathematical functions when we know the function Y(X). However, if the mathematical relation is not known, we conduct experiments and measure Y as we systematically change X. In both cases, the X-Y graphs represent the numerical data, and show a trend (increasing, neutral or flat, decreasing, oscillating, etc.). In some instances, the variations in X, Y or both of these quantities is extremely large, and it is not possible to clearly show the trends over the entire range of either X or Y on a graph with linear scaling. In these cases, we use a non-linear format, namely semi-log or log-log to present the widely ranging data. Let's consider five types of graphs and learn how to prepare them manual techniques. In a later chapter, we will show how to prepare these same graphs by using a spreadsheet.

PIE CHART

A pie chart is used to show how some quantity is distributed. In Table 1, we showed the various assignments for Mechanical Engineers starting there careers. Let's represent this same data in a pie chart as shown in Fig. 1. We begin by drawing a circle to represent our pie, and then we decide what fraction of the pie corresponds to each assignment. This determination is easy, if we remember that the whole pie contains an included angle of 360°. The slice of pie representing design engineering is a fraction of the whole pie, i. e. (360°)(0.40) = 144°. The size of the pie slices in terms of degrees for all of the engineering assignments are listed below:

1. Design engineering .... (360°)(0.40) = 144°.
2. Plant engineering, operations and maintenance .... (360°)(0.13) = 47°.
3. Quality Control, reliability and standards .... (360)(0.121) = 43°.
4. Production engineering .... (360)(0.121) = 43°.
5. Sales engineering .... (360)(0.05) = 18°.
6. Management .... (360)(0.04) = 14°.
7. Computer applications and systems analysis .... (360)(0.04) = 14°.
8. Basic research and development .... (360)(0.03) = 11°.
9. Other activities .... (360)(0.07) = 25°.

We construct the pie chart by using a protractor to lay out these angles on the circle. The pie slices are then labeled as shown in Fig. 1. When we examine the pie chart, we can visualize the importance of design because the design slice is huge. We can also see the importance of producing product since these activities plant operations, quality control, and production combine to produce still another huge slice. The remainder of the pie, which is less that a quarter, is divided between, sales, management, computers and systems, research and development and other activities. These activities are important, but they represent opportunities for a much smaller fraction of the engineers beginning their careers. Compare the effectiveness of the data as presented in Table 1 and the pie chart of Fig. 1. The pie chart quickly leads the reader to the conclusion that design and production are where most of the opportunities exist for entry level positions in Mechanical Engineering.

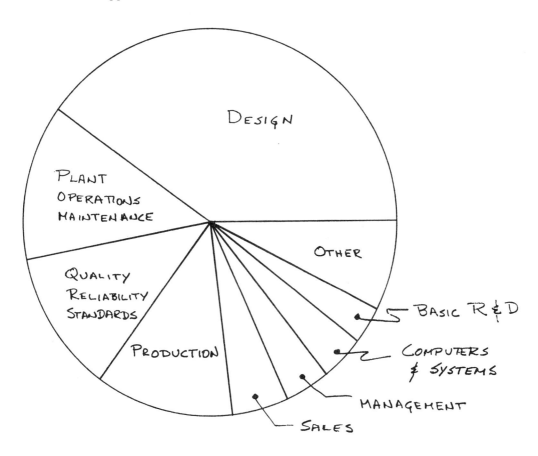

Fig. 1 A pie chart showing the type of initial assignments in industry for beginning engineers.

BAR CHART

Bar charts can also be used to show distribution, but they are better suited for illustrating comparisons. As an example of a bar chart, consider the results of a study by the Council of Chief State School Officers on the percentage of high school students graduating with three or more years of secondary mathematics and science in 1982 and 1994. We have prepared a bar chart showing the comparison in Fig. 2. The visual effect enhances the comparison. At a glance, we can see that a lot more students were taking mathematics and science in 1994 than in 1982. The second glance indicates that only about a third of the students were in math and science in 1982, while more than half of them were taking math and science in 1994. Finally, we can note that math seems a bit more popular than science in both 1982 and 1994. Three quick glances and the reader understands the data, because you have presented it in a visual format that effectively carries the message.

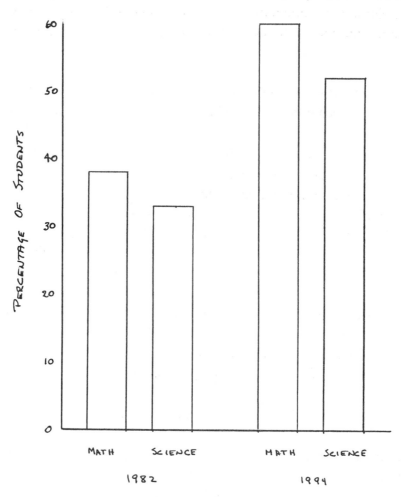

Fig. 2 A bar chart showing the percentage of high school students taking math and science in 1982 and 1994.

The preparation of the bar graph is easy. We used an engineering paper with a barely visible grid that facilitated establishing a suitable scale along the ordinate. A straight edge was employed in drawing the bars, and the grid lines visible on the engineering paper were used to scale each bar. The time to prepare the bar chart was about 10 minutes.

LINEAR X-Y GRAPHS

X-Y graphs are probably the most frequently employed graph used in engineering because it illustrates trends. The curves are produced by plotting Y the dependent variable along the ordinate as a function of the independent variable X which is displayed along the abscissa. Connecting the points with a curve or line segments indicates the trend in Y with changes in X. Graphing X-Y can be accomplished using linear scales for both X-Y, a linear scale for X and a log scale for Y, or log scales for both X and Y. We will cover all three of these methods of producing X-Y graphs.

We are going to need numerical results for our examples in discussing X-Y graphs. We will generate our numerical data using a very important equation that relates to money, and how you may choose to accumulate it, or spend it. Let's begin by assuming that you are going to accumulate some money. Sounds good? Suppose your rich uncle purchased a mutual fund for you at your birth. Your uncle plans to give you the proceeds of the fund on your 21st birthday. How much will you have accumulated when the big day arrives. The sum S accumulated is given by the following relation:

$$S = P(1 + i)^n \qquad\qquad (1)$$

where

S is the sum accumulated.

P is the amount of the initial investment.

i is the interest rate for the compounding period.

n is the number of periods over which the interest accumulates.

Suppose your rich uncle invested P = $5000 in a mutual fund that guaranteed an annual interest rate I = 10 %, and the interest is compounded semi-annually. We will also assume that uncle avoided the tax collectors (Federal, State and Local). Avoidance is not possible, but it does simplify the analysis. Let's calculate exactly how much money you can expect to collect on your 21st birthday. We need to compute S in Eq. (1) knowing that P = $5000. The number of compounding periods that will occur from your birth until you are 21 years of age is 42, because the fund compounds the interest earned twice each year. The interest rate I = 10% on an annual basis, but the interest rate i is only 5% per the semi-annual compounding period. Substitute these numbers into Eq. (1) to obtain:

$$S = \$5000(1 + 0.05)^{42} = \$5000(7.761587) = \$38,807.94$$

Wow! This is wonderful. You can buy a very nice car on the good uncle, or you can defer this option, and continue to compound interest accumulating an even larger sum. We have evaluated Eq. 1 in a spreadsheet (Excel) for a total of 80 periods. The results are shown in Table 2 on the next page.

In examining Table 2, we find that the uncle's $5,000 has grown over the years. The table gives accurate values at the end of each compounding period. For example, at the end of the 20th period, your tenth birthday, the principal in the mutual fund was $13,266.49. Note that the table conveys the exact numerical value with as many significant figures as required. If you maintain the fund until you are 40 years old, accumulating interest for 80 periods, you would have a total of $247, 807.21. Quite a growth from the $5,000 seed money planted by uncle.

Table 2

Accumulated Sum from a Initial Investment of $5,000
at annual interest rate of 10%
interest compounded semi-annually
no taxes paid on interest earned

Periods	Multiplier	Sum	Periods	Multiplier	Sum
0	1.0000	$ 5,000.00	40	7.0400	$ 35,199.94
1	1.0500	$ 5,250.00	41	7.3920	$ 36,959.94
2	1.1025	$ 5,512.50	42	7.7616	$ 38,807.94
3	1.1576	$ 5,788.13	43	8.1497	$ 40,748.33
4	1.2155	$ 6,077.53	44	8.5572	$ 42,785.75
5	1.2763	$ 6,381.41	45	8.9850	$ 44,925.04
6	1.3401	$ 6,700.48	46	9.4343	$ 47,171.29
7	1.4071	$ 7,035.50	47	9.9060	$ 49,529.86
8	1.4775	$ 7,387.28	48	10.4013	$ 52,006.35
9	1.5513	$ 7,756.64	49	10.9213	$ 54,606.67
10	1.6289	$ 8,144.47	50	11.4674	$ 57,337.00
11	1.7103	$ 8,551.70	51	12.0408	$ 60,203.85
12	1.7959	$ 8,979.28	52	12.6428	$ 63,214.04
13	1.8856	$ 9,428.25	53	13.2749	$ 66,374.74
14	1.9799	$ 9,899.66	54	13.9387	$ 69,693.48
15	2.0789	$ 10,394.64	55	14.6356	$ 73,178.15
16	2.1829	$ 10,914.37	56	15.3674	$ 76,837.06
17	2.2920	$ 11,460.09	57	16.1358	$ 80,678.92
18	2.4066	$ 12,033.10	58	16.9426	$ 84,712.86
19	2.5270	$ 12,634.75	59	17.7897	$ 88,948.50
20	2.6533	$ 13,266.49	60	18.6792	$ 93,395.93
21	2.7860	$ 13,929.81	61	19.6131	$ 98,065.73
22	2.9253	$ 14,626.30	62	20.5938	$ 102,969.01
23	3.0715	$ 15,357.62	63	21.6235	$ 108,117.46
24	3.2251	$ 16,125.50	64	22.7047	$ 113,523.34
25	3.3864	$ 16,931.77	65	23.8399	$ 119,199.50
26	3.5557	$ 17,778.36	66	25.0319	$ 125,159.48
27	3.7335	$ 18,667.28	67	26.2835	$ 131,417.45
28	3.9201	$ 19,600.65	68	27.5977	$ 137,988.32
29	4.1161	$ 20,580.68	69	28.9775	$ 144,887.74
30	4.3219	$ 21,609.71	70	30.4264	$ 152,132.13
31	4.5380	$ 22,690.20	71	31.9477	$ 159,738.73
32	4.7649	$ 23,824.71	72	33.5451	$ 167,725.67
33	5.0032	$ 25,015.94	73	35.2224	$ 176,111.95
34	5.2533	$ 26,266.74	74	36.9835	$ 184,917.55
35	5.5160	$ 27,580.08	75	38.8327	$ 194,163.43
36	5.7918	$ 28,959.08	76	40.7743	$ 203,871.60
37	6.0814	$ 30,407.03	77	42.8130	$ 214,065.18
38	6.3855	$ 31,927.39	78	44.9537	$ 224,768.44
39	6.7048	$ 33,523.76	79	47.2014	$ 236,006.86
40	7.0400	$ 35,199.94	80	49.5614	$ 247,807.21

Let's represent the data shown in Table 2, as an X-Y graph. We first decide that the sum S is the dependent variable to be represented along the ordinate (the Y axis), and that your age is to be the independent parameter displayed along the abscissa (the X axis). We draw the X and Y axes on our engineering paper (which has a the faint grid), and apply a scale to each axis, as shown in Fig. 3. Scaling is very important because it determines the size of our graph. If the scale is too small, the graph looks like a postage stamp on your paper, and you have wasted an opportunity to show the graph to full advantage. However, if the scale is too large, we can not fit all of the data on the paper. To scale properly look at the range of the data to be covered for both the X and Y variables. In this case, the range for X varies from 0 to 21, and Y varies from $5,000 to $38, 807.94. We selected a scale of 1 inch equal to 5 years along the X axis, and a scale of 1 inch equals $5000 along the Y axis. The range displayed for X varied from 0 to 25, and for Y from 0 to $40,000. We add numbers to each axis, beginning with zero at the origin and incrementing in steps of 5 along both axes. Captions to both axes are added to remind the reader of the definitions of X and Y. These choices give the graph shown in Fig. 3, that is approximately 5 by 8 inches in size, which fits nicely on a single page with sufficient room for the figure caption and the margins.

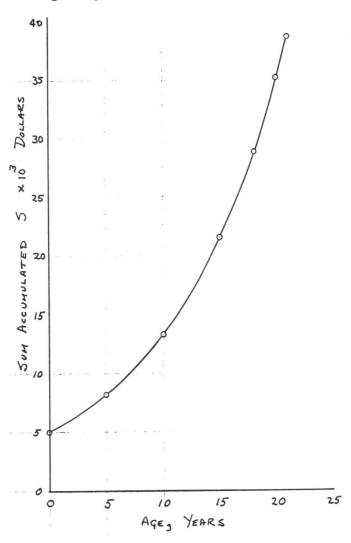

Fig. 3 A X-Y graph illustrating the sum accumulated with time from an initial investment of $5,000.

The data consisting of X and Y coordinates, shown in Table 2, locate the points that are plotted on the graph. We have used a drop compass to draw the small points, but, if you don't have this instrument, the points can be place by free hand. We have only plotted seven points to establish the curve. The number of points that are plotted depends on the function being graphed. In this case Y varies monotonically with respect to X. We can draw the curve accurately with only six to eight points when the function is relatively smooth and does not exhibit peaks or valleys.

Inspecting Fig. 3 clearly shows the trend of the accumulation sum S with respect to time (age). The sum increases continuously with time, and the rate of the increase (slope of the curve) is also increasing. The visual effect of the X-Y graph is dramatic. You know at a glance that you are getting rich. The only question is how rich? If we look at the ordinate and abscissa, we can estimate the sum accumulated for a given age, but the estimate may be in some error. The faint grid lines that we used in plotting the data do not show in the copy presented in Fig. 3. We lose accuracy in reading our graph without grid lines.

If we seek to prepare an X-Y graph that can be used to show both trends, while retaining some accuracy in reading the scales, a good quality graph paper with a fine grain grid should be employed. An example of this graph, plotted to the same scale on a graph paper with grid 20 lines to inch, is shown in Fig. 4. With these fine pitch grid lines, we can read the scale to $\pm (1/20)(5) = \pm 0.4$ years of age or $\pm \$400$ for the sum S. The resolution of the scale, that is possible with good quality graph paper, is a big improvement over the graph without visible gridlines as shown in Fig. 3. However, the best accuracy in reporting numerical data is obtained by using tables.

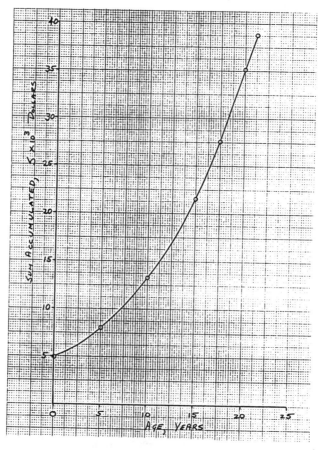

Fig. 4 A X-Y graph with fine pitch gridlines used for showing trends and reporting numerical values.

X-Y GRAPHS WITH SEMI-LOG SCALES

The results presented in Table 2, indicate that you can accumulate some very serious money from a relatively small initial investment if it is invested for a long time. If we try to plot the larger numbers associated with the sum S in Table 2 on the linear graph of Fig. 4, we would go off-scale. We could re-scale, but we would lose resolution particularly along the ordinate where the range in S is very large. A better approach is to use semi-log paper in preparing the graph. Semi-log paper, shown in Fig. 5, has a linear scale (in this example along the X axis), and a log scale (along the Y axis). Looking closer at the Y axis indicates that the graph paper is scaled with three log cycles over the 10 inches of the paper which are ruled. We have selected three log cycles, because it gives the range that we need to cover the range of values for the data given in Fig. 2. Of course, semi-log graph paper is commercially available with several different numbers of cycles on the log scale.

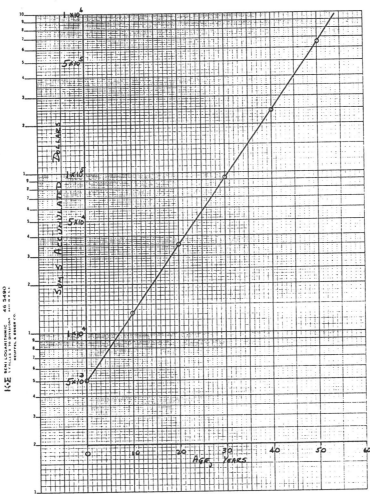

Fig. 5 A semi-log representation of the sum S accumulated with time.

Let's scale both axes on our semi-log graph paper. The X axis is scaled with one inch equal to 10 years, covering the range from 0 to 50 years. The Y axis scale is imposed upon us by the selection of the paper. (Remember that we selected three cycle paper, so we can cover a range of three decades). We label the first decade in thousands, the second in tens of thousands and the third in hundreds of thousands. Zero can not exist on a log scale, because the $\log_{10}(0)$ is not defined. In our graph in Fig. 5, we have placed the origin at Y = $2000 and have provided for a margin at the bottom of the semi-log paper. It follows that the maximum value of Y which we can show on our three cycle paper is $1,000,000.

We have labeled the Y scale at locations of 1 and 5 as designated on the log scale of the preprinted graph paper. The number is multiplied by 10^3 or 10^4 or 10^5 depending on the cycle involved. Next we place points on the graph at the coordinate locations defined in Table 2. In this example, we can draw a straight line through the data points. The reason for the linearity of the relation for the sum S on a semi-log graph paper is evident, if we take the log of both sides of Eq. (1) to give.

$$\log_{10}(S) = \log_{10}(5000)(1 + 0.05)^n = \log_{10}(5000) + \log_{10}(1 + 0.05)(n) \qquad (2)$$

Examination of the right hand side of Eq. (2) shows that $\log_{10}(S)$ is linear in the number of periods of accumulation (n). The intercept of the straight line with the Y axis (when n = 0) is $5000. The slope of the straight line is $\log_{10}(1 + 0.05)$, which is the coefficient of n.

The use of semi-log paper has two advantages. First, it permits us to cover a very large range in the quantity represented along the Y axis. We have used a three cycle paper which covered a range from 2000 to 1,000,000. If the need existed, we could cover even a larger range by selecting a semi-log paper with more log cycles. The second advantage of semi-log representation is that it converts certain non-linear (exponential) functions, like Eq. (1), into linear relations that are much easier to interpret and to extrapolate.

X-Y GRAPHS WITH LOG-LOG SCALES

When you encounter power functions of the form:

$$Y = AX^k \qquad (3)$$

it is advantageous to represent both X and Y on log scales in preparing a X-Y graph. If we take the log of both sides of this power function we obtain:

$$\log_{10}(Y) = \log_{10} A + \log_{10} X^k = \log_{10} A + n \log_{10} X \qquad (4)$$

With the logarithmic form of the function $Y = AX^k$, the use of log-log graph paper is ideal. Representing both X and Y on a log scale gives us the opportunity to visualize the constants A and k in the power function. To illustrate this fact, we have taken as an example the function $Y = 2X^{1.4}$, and plotted it in Fig. 6. We cover values of X from 0.1 to 100 and values of Y from 1 to 1000. We have also shown the scales for $\log_{10} Y$ and $\log_{10} X$ in Fig. 6, to emphasize the difference between the two quantities.

There are three advantages for using log relations and log-log scales on graphs:

1. The linearization of non-linear power functions that often arise in engineering.
2. The ability to plot wide ranging numerical data.
3. Plotting a power relation on a log-log graph gives a straight line that is easy to interpret.

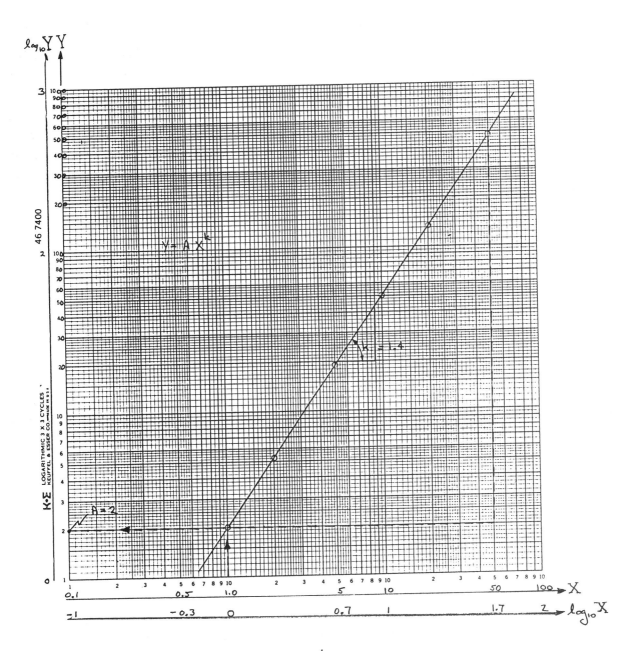

Fig. 6 A log-log graph of a power function $Y = AX^k$.

If the data is from experimental studies, it is often necessary to establish the constants A and k in a power relation like that shown in Eq. (3). The graphical procedure for determining these constants is given in Fig. 6. We find the constant A by setting X = 1, and reading the corresponding Y value as indicated with the dashed lines in Fig. 6. We find the constant k by determining the slope of the line. Remember in finding this slope, that it is necessary to work with the small numbers taken from the log scales. Accordingly, the slope k is given by:

$$k = (\log_{10} Y_2 - \log_{10} Y_1)\big/(\log_{10} X_2 - \log_{10} X_1) = (2.68 - 0.30)\big/(1.7 - 0) = 1.40. \qquad (5)$$

The log or log-log graphs are very important because many processes, that are widely used in engineering, exhibit non linear behavior that can be modeled with either exponential or power functions. The behavior of these processes are usually best represented by graphs with either one or both scales in terms of logarithms.

SPECIAL GRAPHS

There are many special graphs that have been developed to help the reader quickly absorb and understand numerical data. This brief chapter on Tables and Graphs does not permit a complete description of the many special and clever graphs that have been devised. However, we will introduce one of these, namely the geographical graph, which is based on a map of the world, the U. S., or some state. Superimposed on the map are contour lines dividing the entire geographical region into sub regions. The contour lines or sub regions are labeled to give the geographical distribution of some quantity across the mapped region. An example of a geographical graph, presented in Fig. 7, shows the weather prediction for the U. S. for November 13, 1996.

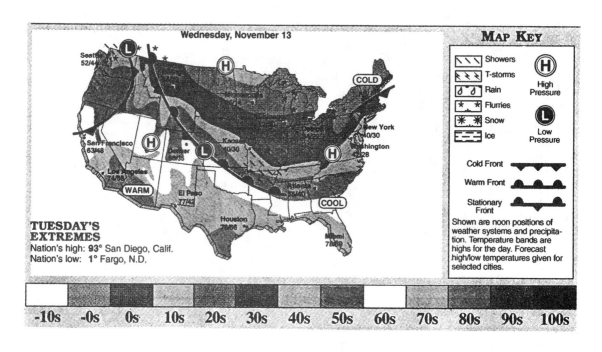

Fig. 7 A geographical graph showing the weather prediction for the U. S. for November 13, 1996.

EXERCISES

1. Write a memo for a group of young engineers starting their careers with your company that explains the policy of the engineering department relative to reporting data with tables or with graphs.

2. Prepare a table using a word processing program that shows the SAT scores for entering freshman at your College of Engineering for the time period from 1980 to 1996. Report both the math and verbal scores for women and men. Also tabulate the number of women and men in each class. The Dean of the College should be able to provide you with the data that is needed.

3. Use the data from exercise 2 to construct a bar chart comparing the scores of women and men for the years 1985 and 1995.

4. Use the data from exercise 2 to construct two pie charts showing the percentage of men and women enrolled as freshmen in the College of Engineering in 1985 and 1995.

5. Prepare a table like that shown in Table 2 showing the sum S with time. Use P = \$1000, I = 8%, with interest compounded quarterly. Determine the Sum after each compounding period for a total of 20 years.

6. Prepare a X-Y graph showing the sum S with respect to time using the data generated in exercise 5.

7. Prepare a semi-log graph showing the sum S determined in exercise 5 on the log scale and the time on the linear scale.

8. Evaluate the power function $Y = 1.8 \, X^{1.75}$, and plot the result on a log-log graph. Let X vary from 1 to 100. Try to find log-log paper with a suitable number of cycles for both axes. Confirm that A = 1.8 and k = 1.75 from your graph.

PART III

SOFTWARE

APPLICATIONS

CHAPTER 8

KEY CAD Complete

DOS Version

INTRODUCTION

KEY CAD Complete is a Computer Aided Drawing (CAD) program that has been selected for your use in ENES 100. It is an entry level program, that is available to the student at a modest cost. The program is also relatively easy to learn to use, and a beginning student can produce high quality three view and isometric drawings. All CAD programs have the advantage that they remove the requirement of manual dexterity from the drawing process. If you never learned to print, you can breath a sigh of relief because you type printed matter in KEY CAD as text. If you can point with the mouse and learn to exercise the menu commands, you will be able to produce first rate drawings in KEY CAD.

We will introduce you to the KEY CAD screen, the menu, the icon buttons, and the drawing pad. This introduction will be brief, because it is easier to learn by clicking than by reading. We also describe many of the more important menu items, and the lists of features available to you under each item. To illustrate the features of KEY CAD, we consider some simple examples, and show how to produce engineering drawings. The examples will demonstrate how to prepare:

- A drawing block.
- A three view drawing of a notched rectangular block.
- Dimensioning a three view drawing.
- A three view drawing of a more complex object.
- An isometric drawing

THE KEY CAD SCREEN

When KEY CAD is loaded, the screen that is displayed is shown in Fig. 1. It is relatively simple. A menu bar is located along the top edge of the screen, and icon button pad is located on the upper right side. The main portion of the screen is dedicated to a drawing pad. A rectangle already drawn on this pad, defines the border of the drawing. There is a ◀ ▶ button at the right side of the menu bar, that serves as a toggle for turning the icon button pad on and off. The file name of the drawing will appear in the square brackets at the lower right corner of the screen after you save the file.

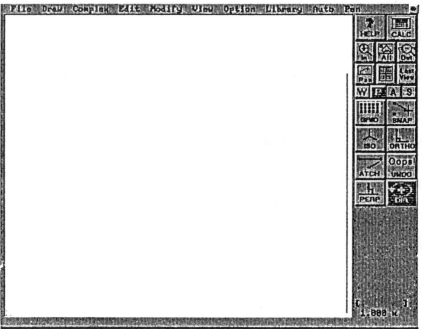

Fig. 1 The KEY CAD screen displayed on your monitor.

It is possible to move the cursor around the screen with the arrow keys on the key board, but the speed is so slow that we don't recommend using the keyboard for cursor placement. Instead, use the mouse to position the cursor. When the cursor is in the work area, it appears as the intersection of two lines (cross hairs), one vertical and the other horizontal. However, when you move the cross hairs to the menu bar or the icon button pad, the cursor changes to a pointer.

The menu bar contains the following headings:
- File...for handling the files, printing output, and quitting.
- Draw...for drawing objects and typing text.
- Complex...to draw very complex shapes using splines, and freehand.
- Edit...editing features such as copy, move, erase, etc.
- Modify...change attributes such as style, fill, hatch and units.
- View...image viewing features such as redraw, window, last, half, etc.
- Option...global default settings such as grid and enable.
- Library...group and name objects to use as symbols.
- Auto...determines lengths and angles to dimension objects.
- Pen...select active layer of drawing, set colors, etc.

Each menu heading has a pull down list. Use the mouse, point to a menu item, click the left mouse button (LMB), and a pull down list of selections is displayed on the screen. Click the right mouse button (RMB) and it disappears. Explore the menu bar, clicking on the various menu items until you begin to understand the features and options available to you in KEY CAD. Recognize that the LBM acts the same as the Enter key on the keyboard, and the RMB acts the same as the Esc key. We will start learning to draw with KEY CAD, by using the mouse as our pencil, and the features and options available on the menu bar and the icon button pad.

OPERATIONS

As the menu suggests, KEY CAD has many capabilities and usually there are several options for each menu item. We will cover some of the most important capabilities such as drawing, editing, modifying and printing. After learning about these capabilities, you will be able to prepare high quality three view and isometric drawings. We will make no attempt to cover all of the possible capabilities and/or features of KEY CAD. For a more complete treatment, we refer you to the instruction manual [1].

DRAW

Click on Draw and the pull down lists indicates several choices including line, rectangle, circle, arc, text, etc. These choices are all that are necessary to quickly prepare quality drawings for 99.9 % of engineering applications. As you study this chapter, try to duplicate the drawings shown here by following the directions provided in the descriptions for the drawings. Load KEY CAD and use each of the available drawing options.

LINES

Select Draw/Line and you are set to draw a line. If the line is to be either vertical or horizontal, click on the ORTHO (orthogonal) icon, which eliminates the possibility of inclined lines. To begin drawing a line, click the LMB at the starting point, move the cross hairs with the mouse to the end point of the line, and click the LMB again. If one line is all that is required, click the RMB to complete the line operation and return to the Draw pull down list. However, if you want to draw several lines connected at their ends, continue to position the end point of each line with the mouse and click the LMB at each corner. To stop drawing lines you must click the RMB.

Try drawing an inclined line without activating the ORTHO icon. Remember that the icon buttons all toggle. Make sure that the icon button is not engaged (light colored), if you want to deactivate the feature it controls. After you have drawn an inclined line, activate the ORTHO feature and draw horizontal and vertical lines, as individual line segments and as a group of connected lines. You will notice an ✗ mark at each location where you clicked the LMB. These marks are to aid you in feature identification should you need to edit the drawing later. The marks are not printed and they will not clutter your neat drawings. Don't worry about drawing anything at this stage of the learning process. Play and learn the hand-eye coordination and mouse actions necessary to draw lines.

RECTANGLES

Select Draw/Rectangle and you are ready to draw a rectangle or square. It is easy and quick. Place the cross hairs at any corner of the rectangle, click the LMB, and pull the rectangular shape with the mouse to the opposite corner. The shape of the rectangle is displayed on the screen as you move the mouse. Click the LMB again, the rectangle is completed, and you are automatically returned to the Draw listings. Try making a rectangle and a square.

CIRCLES

Select Draw/Circle and a selection box appears with choices of Place and Set Up. In KEY CAD, we can draw the circle using three different techniques, namely Radius, Diameter, and Point. The default setting is Radius. With Radius selected, click on Place, and you are set to draw the circle. Locate the center of the circle with the cross hairs, click the LMB, then move the mouse to form a circle of the correct size. Click the LMB again, and the circle is completed, and you are returned to the Draw pull down list.

If you select Diameter under Setup, the circle is drawn by locating two diametrically opposite points on its circumference. For the Points option, the circle is drawn by locating any three points that are located on its circumference.

TEXT

Select Draw/Text and you are ready to place printed matter on the drawing. The pull down list has three choices, namely Place, Set Up, and Edit. Select Place and you are prompted to locate the starting point for the text message. Click the LMB with the cross hairs at this location, and an Enter Text Box becomes available for you. After you have typed your note on the line available in this box, click the LMB, and the note is placed on the drawing. You are returned to the Enter Text Box, but if you click the RMB the box disappears and you are returned to the Draw listings..

The size of the letters in the note can be changed by clicking on Set Up. A Text Defaults Box appears and you can specify the height and the width of the letters for the text. This is an important feature particularly when dimensioning the drawing. If you are dimensioning a short length, it may be necessary to reduce the size of the letters to fit in the space available between the dimension leader lines.

If you mess up typing the note on the drawing, it is easy to correct. Choose the Edit option, and a small rectangle appears to help you select the item to be edited. Place the small rectangle anywhere on the message, and click the LMB. The message changes color and the Enter Text Box appears with the incorrect message. Edit the message, click the LMB, and the correct note is displayed. Always click the RMB to return to the previous list or menu.

CIRCULAR ARCS

Select Draw/Arc and you are ready to draw a circular arc. The prompt seeks the location of the center point for the circular arc, and the two end points. In the default settings, the arc with be drawn from the beginning point in a clockwise direction to the end point. The direction for drawing the arc, clockwise or counterclockwise can be changed with the DIR icon button located at the lower right corner of the icon button pad. If the icon button is depressed (dark), the arc is drawn in the clockwise direction. If the button is up (light), the arc is drawn in the counterclockwise direction. Fortunately, the screen shows the arc as you are setting the end points, and if the direction is not correct simply click on the DIR icon and reverse it.

MULTIGON AND BEZIER

The pull down list under the Draw command also contains Multigon and Bezier selections. Try them and see if you might be able to use them to advantage someday.

EDIT

The pull down list under Edit contains 18 selections. There are many ways to correct and improve a drawing using this command. We will discuss five of these choices to get you started, and then you can explore independently the remaining choices. When you select the Edit command, you are prompted to select the feature or features that you want to change or correct. The selection can be made in two different ways. If the P (point) icon button is depressed, a small rectangular box becomes the cursor that is placed over the feature selected for editing. If the W (window) icon button is depressed, you will draw a rectangle around the feature or features to be edited. In both cases, click on the LMB, after you have marked the feature. If you are in the point selection mode (small rectangular box), you select the features one by one. In the window selection mode, you select a group of features. When you have selected all of the features that you want to change, click the RMB to end the selection process.

ERASE

Let's suppose that you want to erase one or more features (line, circles, rectangles, etc.) from your drawing. You select Edit/Erase and mark all of the features to be erased. Click the RMB, and a screen appears for you to confirm your selection. Click on the ERASE button and all of the features that you had selected are gone. Sometimes you may want to improve the quality of the screen after significant erasures. Click on View/Redraw and the drawing is renewed with missing grid dots restored and unnecessary ✕ marks eliminated.

COPY

Select Edit/Copy and you are ready to duplicate some object in your drawing. Mark the features that you want to copy, click the RMB, and you will be prompted to indicate a reference point on the drawing that is to be copied. Position the cross hairs on a suitable reference point, click the LMB, and the object to be copied is shown in a different color. Move the cursor and the new colored object moves with the cross hairs to a new location of you choice. Click the LMB to place a copy of the object at its new location. If you want more copies, keep moving the mouse and click the LMB for each copy. Click the RMB, to complete the copy operation and return to the Edit list.

MOVE

Select Edit/Move and you are ready to reposition some feature from one location to another on your drawing. Mark the object to be moved, click the RMB, and then locate a convenient reference point on it. Click the LMB and the object changes color. As you move the mouse to the new position for the object, you can observe its position. When the object is in the correct location, click the LMB to place the object in its new position and return to the Edit list.

SCALE

Select Edit/Scale and you are set to change the size of one or more objects on your drawing. To illustrate the scale command, we drew a circle and then copied it to give two equal circles on our drawing. We selected the second circle to be scaled. Upon exercising the LMB, a scaling screen appeared with several scaling choices. We changed the scale readings for the X and Y axes to read X = 1.000 and Y = 0.500. We then defined the center of the selected circle as the reference point and clicked the LMB. The circle was rescaled with the ratio of two X for one Y. The result, shown in Fig. 2, is the conversion of a circle into an ellipse with a major axis twice as large as the minor axis.

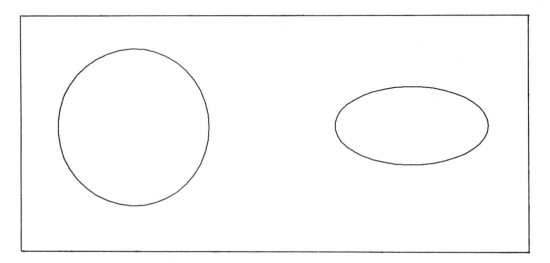

Fig. 2 Example showing the conversion of a circle into an ellipse with the Scale command.

BREAK

The final edit option that we will describe in this section is the break command. Select Edit/Break and mark the feature to be edited. You will be prompted to locate the starting and ending points for the break. When you click the LMB after locating the end point, the line between the two break points disappears. The break command permits you to erase part of a feature such as a line or rectangle, without erasing the entire object.

There are many more options available on the edit list. Try to master them as you extend your CAD skills.

MODIFY

Modify is very much like the Edit command in the sense that you mark some object on the drawing and change it. When selecting Modify, you have four choices, --- Style, Fill, Hatch and Units. Select Style, mark the object, and click the RMB. A box appears that has a listing of 11 different line styles. You can change the default setting for a solid line to a line style of your choice. After you select the line style, you are given a choice of the width of the line, --- slim, thick or fat. We usually use slim lines for drawings, and thick lines for borders. Fat lines are used only for special effects on drawings.

The Fill and Hatch commands are similar, since KEY CAD has many patterns to employ in filling an area to show section cuts, the interior region of some body, or the surface of an object. The procedure is the essentially same for both commands. Select Fill or Hatch, the pattern, and the object that is to modified. Then clicking the LMB immediately fills the area identified with the pattern of choice.

The units to be employed are changed using the Modify/Units command. You have a choice of eight different units in both the SI and the U. S. Customary systems. You also have a choice in the number of decimals to use in stating the dimensions. We will discuss the Modify/Units command in much greater detail later in the chapter under the section on dimensioning.

OPTIONS

Click on the option item on the menu bar and a list of 12 different options are displayed. Several of these options including Fill, Hatch, Style and Units have already been discussed as choices under the Modify command. They are exactly the same options. The only difference is you select the various options before rather than after making the drawing when using the Option command. There are three selections that we will describe for the Options menu, namely Grid, Enable, and Attach.

GRID AND SNAP

On the menu bar, click on Options/Grid and a dialog box titled Grid Settings appears. Click on both the buttons for Grid and Snap so that a ✓ is superimposed on the button. The grid selection will give us an array of dots on the working area, and the snap will take the cursor to a given grid point when we get close. The snap command helps people, like the author, who are not rock steady with the mouse. Under these two buttons are boxes for dimensions. Let's use 0.300 for both the X and Y pitch on the grid dots, and 0.100 for the snap dimensions. Click on the accept button, and the screen is filled with dots that are on 0.300 inch centers on the printed page if we have selected inches as the units of measure for our drawing. With the snap settings at X = Y = 0.100, the start or end points locating a feature will be placed on a grid dot if the cross hairs are within 0.100 inches of that dot. Make sure that the icon buttons GRID and SNAP are depressed (dark), otherwise the grid and snap features are disabled.

ENABLE

When we select Options/Enable, KEY CAD displays a Global Options box. Click on the coordinate button, so that a ✓ is superimposed on the button. Click the RMB, and the X, Y coordinates of the cross hairs appear at the bottom of the screen. The coordinates are very useful in precisely locating the positions of the corners of the objects in a drawing. They are displayed with three decimal point accuracy (default setting). If the large number of decimals is bothersome, we can change the display. To show the coordinates with two decimal point accuracy, click on Options/Units and type the number 2 into the box to specify the number of decimal points. We will illustrate the value of the coordinates feature as we prepare a complex three view drawing later in the chapter.

ATTACH

The attach option is useful when you are connecting a new starting point to an existing end point on some feature such as a line. Precise control of the cross hairs with the mouse is sometimes difficult. With the attach command, getting the cross hairs close to the prescribed point is sufficient. Attach is similar to the Snap command, but with Snap we lock onto a grid dot. With Attach, we lock onto a start/end point or alternately a midpoint of some line.

Select Option/Attach, and a Select Active Attach Box is displayed. You can choose to attach at either the end points of a line segment or at some mid point on the line. Make your selection and a ✓ appears on the button. Click on the Accept button and you have programmed the strategy for the attach option. Depress the ATCH icon button to enable this feature.

To try the Attach command, draw a line, select the END button, and check to make certain that the ATCH icon button is dark (enabled). Next, draw two more lines connected to both ends of the original line. Did you Notice that the cross hairs did not need to be precisely located on the start/end points of the original line? Now try to draw another line that connects with the mid point of the original line. Can't make it happen! Why not?

AUTO

The AUTO item on the menu provides several choices to help you dimension your drawing, although it has other neat features. When you select Auto, a list of eight options appears including:

- Dimensions
- Coordinates
- Radius
- Diameter
- Angle
- Leader
- Boundary
- Query

The options, Dimensions, Radius, Diameter, Angle, and Boundary are for automatically dimensioning the objects on your drawing. The automatic dimensioning in KEY CAD is a very important time-saving feature of the program. Dimensioning, which is a tedious task in manual drawing, is very easy in CAD drawing. There is no need to measure, no need to draw leader lines bounding the dimension, no need to draw the dimension line, no need to draw arrowheads, and no need to print the number indicating the measurement. All that is required is for you to indicate the start and end points for a linear dimension. For a radius, you locate the center of the arc/circle and a point on the circumference. For a diameter, you locate two opposing points on the circumference. For an angle, you locate the apex and the end points of the arc that is subtended. For a boundary, you only have to identify the object, and the program provides the outside dimensions in both the X and Y directions. We illustrate these five different dimensioning options in Fig. 3.

The Coordinates option labels the X and Y coordinates of any point located with the cross hairs. The leader option places a leader line from the object to a note that you add later with the Draw/Text command. Finally, the query option permits you to check linear dimensions and angles on your drawing. Query also permits you to determine the area of closed regions on your drawings, which is very helpful when you need to determine the volume or weight of the part that you are designing.

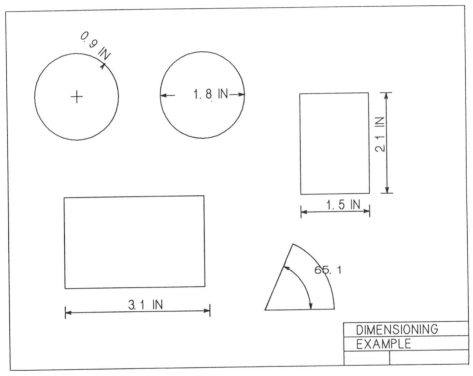

Fig. 3 Examples of five different dimensioning options available in KEY CAD.

PRINT

Printing the drawing is relatively simple. Select File/Plot and a list is displayed with four options. Click on the print option and another display reminds you of the size of the drawing, and asks you to either print or cancel. Click on the print button and the printer will produce the drawing. You get what you see except for the ✘ marks.

STARTING A DRAWING

Click on File/New and note that a dialog box titled Drawing Set Up appears on the screen. The purpose of this box is to assist you in scaling the drawing, select the units that you will use, and the size of the paper upon which the drawing will be printed. Click on the ▼ button, and observe the that both the SI and U. S. Customary units are available. Let's keep this initial experience as simple as possible, and select 1.000 In. for both the real dimensions and the paper dimensions. This selection will give us a scale factor of 1/1 for our drawing. One inch on the paper is the same as one inch on the object that we are drawing. Also pick the paper size as 8 ½ by 11 inches because that is the size of paper used in the laser printers available to the class. The border is already drawn on the screen to give you a working area of 7 ½ by 10 inches on the paper. Click on the OK button, and the dialog box disappears. You have selected the units, the scale for the drawing, and the size of paper. Before we actually start to draw objects, let's put a drawing block in the lower right corner of the paper.

Wait! Before we try to place the drawing block on the paper we need some sense of dimensions. The dimensions on the screen depend on the size of the monitor and are different than those that are printed on the paper. On the menu bar, click on Options/Grid, and a dialog box titled Grid Settings appears. Click on both the buttons for Grid and Snap so that a ✔ is superimposed on the button. The grid selection will give us an array of dots on the working area, and snap will take the cursor to a given grid point when we get close. The snap command helps people, like the author, who are not rock steady with the mouse. Under these two buttons are boxes for dimensions. Let's use 0.300 for both the X and Y pitch on the grid dots and 0.100 for the snap dimensions. Click on the accept button, and the screen is filled with dots that are on 0.300 inch centers on the printed page. If the dots do not appear, click on the GRID icon button which enables the grid. Also click on the SNAP icon button to enable the snap feature.

Before placing the drawing block on our paper, let's decide beforehand something about its size. Try a block 0.9 inch high by about 2.8 inch wide, with three rows of information.

- On the top row, show the title.
- On the middle row, give the name of the team preparing the drawing.
- On the lower row, indicate the drawing number and the date.

It is an oversimplified drawing block, but it will serve our purpose in this introductory treatment.

On the menu bar, click Draw/Rectangle then position the cursor lines at the top left corner of the drawing block. When the cross hairs are at the right location (3 dots up and 10 to the left), click the LMB to set the first corner of the rectangle in place. Drag the cross hairs to the lower right hand corner of the drawing block, and click the LBM. We finish drawing this rectangle, by clicking the RMB to return to the drawing list. From the drawing list select Line, and draw the horizontal and vertical lines needed to subdivide the rectangle into regions required for the drawing block. Remember to click LMB to start and finish the line. Click the RMB to complete the operation, and return to the draw list, so that you can select the next feature that you want to draw. An example of a drawing block is shown in Fig. 4. If you like the way your drawing block looks, save it under a file name such as DWGBLOCK. You can start all of your drawings by loading this file. You only need to draw this block once. That is a very significant advantage of any CAD program --- no need to redraw.

To add text to the drawing block select Draw/Text. A drop down list appears with three selections, --- Place, Setup, and Edit. Click Place and you are prompted to place the cursor at the position in the drawing block where you want to begin to enter the title of the drawing. Click the LMB at this location, and a box appears on the screen with a line to receive the text that you type. Click LMB again, and the text is transferred to the drawing block. Click the RMB to complete the operation.

Fig. 4 An example of a drawing block that can be used in ENES 100.

If you don't like the size of the font that is used, click on Draw/Text/Setup and you can change the size of the letters. If you notice an error in the text on your drawing, click on Edit, mark the text that you want to change, and make the corrections in the typing box.

We hope you have recognized the second huge advantage of CAD. You don't need to print. We can place text at any location on our drawings. For those of us that don't print well, breathe a sigh of relief.

THREE VIEW DRAWINGS

To illustrate the use of KEY CAD in the preparation of three view drawings, let's consider the notched block that was introduced in the chapter on three view drawings (Figs. 1 and 2). This block is three inches wide, two inches high, one inch deep, with a one by one inch notch cut from the top. Load the file DWGBLOCK, and you are ready to start the drawing. The grid spacing that we established for the drawing block, 0.3 by 0.3 inch, is too small for this drawing since all dimensions are integer multiples of an inch. Change the grid pitch, by clicking on Options/Grid, and make the X and Y pitch equal to 1.000.

Start the drawing with the front view that is positioned in the lower left corner of the paper. Select Draw/Line, and position the cursor at the lower left corner of the front view. Activate the ORTHO icon button, since all lines to be drawn are either horizontal or vertical. We suggest that you locate this corner on the second grid dot up from the bottom and the first dot from the right border, to position the three views properly on the paper. Click the LMB at the left corner, and then at each corner of the notched block as you move around the view from one corner to the next. On the ninth click of the LMB, you have closed the line on itself, and have completed the drawing of the front view. Click the RMB, to discontinue the line drawing sequence. Sap! The front view is finished. If you notice the ✗ symbols at the corners, don't fret. The ✗ indicates that you have define either a start pointing or a finishing point for some feature such as a line. They do not show when the drawing is printed. They are displayed on the screen to help you check your drawing and to aid in corrections to the drawing if required.

The biggest problem that many folks encounter, in making a drawing like this one, is to hold the mouse absolutely still after positioning the cross hairs on the correct dot. Wiggle the mouse and you miss the dot, and your drawing is distorted. You can avoid this problem, if the SNAP feature is enabled, with snap dimensions of say $X = Y = 0.25$ inch.

Let's draw the top view next. Select Draw/Rectangle and position the cross hairs at the lower left corner of the top view. This corner should be one inch above the front view for adequate separation of the two views. There is no difficulty in locating this corner because of the presence of the grid dots and the fact that the vertical cross hair can be aligned with the left edge of the front view. Click the LMB, drag the rectangle to the upper right corner and click the LMB again when the rectangle is the correct size and shape. Click the RMB to return to the Draw list. From this list select line, and draw the remain two lines necessary to show the location of the notch in the top view. Check the drawing of the notched block, shown in Fig. 5, to see if you have positioned the lines correctly in these two views.

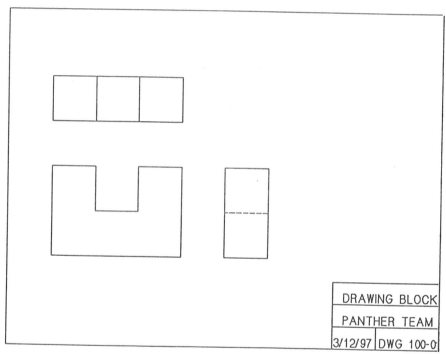

Fig. 5 A three view drawing of the notched block prepared with KEY CAD.

Next use the Draw/Rectangle selection to draw the outline of the side view. We need to add a line to this rectangle, to show the location of the bottom of the notch. However, this line must be dashed to indicate that it is hidden from our view. Before drawing the line, select Option/Style. A dialog box appears that provides 11 different line styles. Select the dashed style, draw the hidden line, and then change the line style back to the solid line. When you have completed the side view, check your drawing with the illustration shown in Fig. 5.

If you want to change the style of a line, rectangle, or some other feature after it has been drawn, it is not necessary to erase. Click on Modify/ Style and position the small box (cursor) on the feature that you intend to modify. Click the LMB to select this feature, and then click the RMB to discontinue the feature selection process. A style box is displayed on the screen and you can choose from 11 different line styles. Many skilled CAD operators complete a drawing (except for dimensions) with solid lines. Then they modify the drawing by changing select lines to the proper line styles for centerlines, hidden lines, etc.

DIMENSIONING WITH KEY CAD

The drawing shown in Fig. 5 looks good, except it does not have dimensions. Let's add them, using the automatic dimensioning capabilities KEY CAD. Select Auto/Dimensions and a small box with two choices (Place and Setup) is displayed. If you choose Setup, you can adjust the appearance of the arrows at the ends of the dimension line. We think the default settings for the arrow (i. e. parallel and notch) give nice looking arrows on the dimension lines. If you are happy with the orientation of the arrow, select Place to begin the dimensioning operation. Move the cross hairs to the start of the dimension line, click the LMB, move the cross hairs to the end of the dimension line, and click the LMB again. The leader lines, the dimension lines, and the length measurement is automatically inserted for you. No need to measure to establish any dimension, because KEY CAD has maintained the dimensional base for the drawing. If you clicked the LMB when the cursor was on the grid dots, the dimension shown on the drawing will be correct. If you were careless, and were off the mark when clicking the LMB, then the dimensions will be incorrect. Continue to use the Auto/Dimension/Place selection, until you have completely dimensioned the notched block. We show an example of the notched block with dimensions in Fig. 6. Your dimensioning can be different from that shown here, but you must locate all of the corners and you should not over dimension.

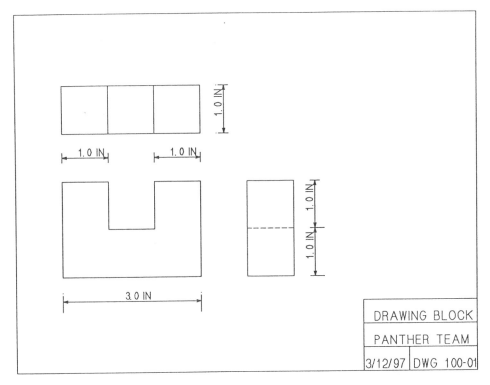

Fig. 6 Example of dimensioning a three view drawing with KEY CAD.

The default setting for the number of decimals shown in the number printed above the dimension line is 3. This fact implies that you will show a dimension of 3.000 IN for the width of the block. That is OK, if you want to fabricate the block with three decimal precision; however, be aware that the cost of manufacturing a part with three decimal precision is significant. If you need this degree of precision, use three decimals in writing the dimensions; however, if you are satisfied with one or two decimal accuracy, change the default settings. Click on Option/Units, select Inch, and type in the actual number of decimals that you wish to use in dimensioning the drawing. We have employed one decimal in expressing the dimensions in Fig. 6.

When using Auto/Dimension, KEY CAD places the units selected on each dimension. For example, the width of the block in Fig. 6 is given as 3.0 IN. This is unfortunate because the units for the dimensions used in the drawing should be stated once, and only once, in either the drawing block, or a note placed near the drawing block. We can avoid this problem by manually drawing the leader and dimension lines, and then placing the dimensions on the drawing with the Text command. However, this approach is very time consuming. We will accept the placement of units on the dimensions in this course, but recognize that it is not an accepted drafting practice.

A THREE VIEW DRAWING WITH A HOLE AND ARC

Our first illustration to show some of the neat features in KEY CAD was a simple three view line drawing. Let's move on to a slightly more complex drawing involving features such as rectangles, circles, and an arc as shown in Fig. 7.

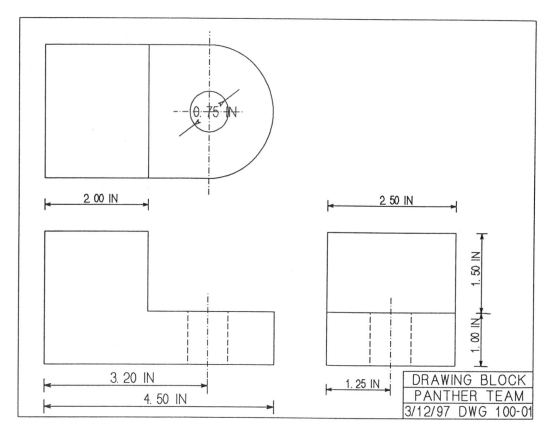

Fig. 7 A three view drawing made with lines, rectangles, circles and an arc.

Before beginning the drawing, we click on Options/Grid and decide to show the grid dots with a pitch of 0.5 inches because most of the dimensions in the drawing are multiples of ½ inch. While in the Options list, we enable the coordinates. After clicking the RMB, the X and Y coordinates of the cross hairs in the working area are displayed at the bottom of the screen. The coordinates are very useful in precisely locating the positions of the corners in the drawing. Suppose that we want to display the coordinates with two decimal point accuracy. Click on Options/Units and type 2 in the box specifying the number of decimals to be used in displaying the coordinates.

We begin drawing the front view by clicking on Draw/Line, and position the lower left corner of this view at coordinates X=0.50, Y= 1.00. Note that this location coincides with a grid dot. We have two choices to follow in drawing any view. We can either point with the mouse and click at the start and end of each line. Or we can enter the coordinates of the beginning and end of the lines. Try to draw the front view using the coordinates to position the lines. Select Draw/Line and follow the prompt at the top of the screen, and enter the following coordinates:

- X = 0.50, Y =1.00 to start.
- X = 5.00, Y =1.00 for the lower right corner.
- X = 5.00, Y =2.00 for the 1st upper right corner.
- X = 2.50, Y =2.00 for the reentrant corner.
- X = 2.50, Y =3.50 for the 2nd upper right corner.
- X = 0.50, Y =3.50 for the upper left corner.
- X = 0.50, Y =1.00 to finish.

After each coordinate entry, strike the enter key and a new line will be drawn on the screen. With the aid of the coordinates and the grid dots, it is easy to produce an accurate drawing of any object. Remember the lower left corner of the border for the drawing is the origin for the X-Y coordinate system.

Next draw the top view. Locate the left edge of this view using orthographic projection. Draw the left edge with the Draw/Line command with a length of 2 ½ inches. Locate the position of the centerlines of hole in both the top and front views, and initially draw them with solid lines. Then use the Modify/Style command, and change the centerlines to dash dot, which is the appropriate style. To draw the small hole, click on Draw/Circle and you will be prompted to locate the center of the circle. Place the cross hairs at the center, click the LMB, and then move the cross hairs outward. An expanding circle is displayed. When this circle is the correct diameter, click the LMB and you have drawn the hole that is to be drilled into the block.

To draw the large circular arc, click on Draw/Arc and use the same center location that you employed to locate the hole. After positioning the cursor on the center, you will be prompted to locate the starting point for the arc. Draw the arc with the starting point at top of the view. Move the cursor to the end point at the bottom of the arc. The arc, which is shown with a colored line on the screen, is drawn clockwise through 180° to arrive at the end point. Click the LMB, to locate this end point and then the RMB to complete the operation. The arc appears suspended on your screen. Next use the attach option to draw the two horizontal lines, which connect with the ends of the vertical line segment on the left side of the top view and the ends of the arc. These lines are tangent to the arc, and orthogonal to the vertical line. Except for dimensioning, the top view is complete.

Start the side view by drawing a rectangle (square) that is 2 ½ by 2 ½ inch in size. Next, draw a horizontal line to show the height of the step. Finally draw lines for the center line, and the sides of the hole. These lines have unique line styles. Use the Modify/Style command to change the centerline to a dash-dot line and the two lines identifying the sides of the holes to dash lines.

When you have completed the three views, dimension the drawing. Use the Auto/Dimension for the linear measurements, and the Auto/Circle/Diameter to dimension the hole. Do you need to dimension the arc? If not, why not?

ISOMETRIC DRAWINGS

KEY CAD can also be employed effectively to prepare isometric drawings. The CAD procedure is almost identical to that used in previous sections to prepare three view drawing. The only difference is that we construct lines in the three isometric directions instead of the X and Y directions. To provide the three directions required for isometric drawings, enable the ISO icon button. The cross hair cursor changes into a three line cursor, with a line oriented in each of the isometric directions. All of the other features of KEY CAD remain the same. We have drawn the isometric, shown in Fig. 8 using the Draw/Line command. Precise location of the start and end points of a line is a bit more difficult because alignment with two axes requires patience with the mouse. The alignment problem is alleviated, to some degree, by the program which changes the color of the line being drawn when the cursor is perfectly aligned.

Try drawing an isometric with KEY CAD. We show an example in Fig. 8 for your guidance. If you prefer, prepare an isometric drawing of your choice.

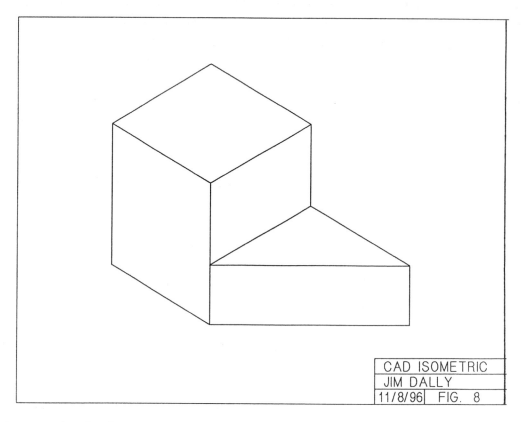

Fig. 8 An example of an isometric drawing prepared with Key CAD.

SUMMARY

KEY CAD Complete is a computer aided drawing program that has been selected for your use in the course ENES 100. It is a low cost program that is available to the student at a modest price. The program is also relatively easy to learn to use, and a beginning student can produce quickly high quality, three view and isometric drawings.

We have introduced the KEY CAD screen, defining the menu bar, the icon key pad, and the working areas for the drawing. For most applications, we recommend that you use the mouse instead of the keyboard to move the cursor because it is faster.

Many, but not all, of the operations possible in KEY CAD have been described. We emphasized the more basic menu items in this coverage. If you become familiar with the choices under Draw, Edit, Options, Auto, and File, you will be able to produce excellent engineering drawings. We suggest that you use the descriptions of the operations presented here as a reference source. Try to master the commands by attempting to duplicate the drawings shown in the chapter.

We first describe how to prepare a drawing block. It is a simple drawing block, but it will suffice for this class. We then lead you through a three view drawing of a simple notched block. Try to draw this block, and learn about the advantages of the various features offered by KEY CAD.

Dimensioning is very easy and fast in KEY CAD. The menu item Auto provides a painless process for dimensioning lengths, radii, diameters, and angles. No measurements are necessary and the dimensioning is accomplished with a few clicks on the LMB.

We introduced drawing of circles and arcs with a more complex three view drawing. The description of the approach used to make the drawing is reasonably complete. We trust that you have mastered the KEY CAD commands by this time, and that you are concentrating on a neat drawing layout, and the completeness of the drawing and dimensioning.

Finally, we give a brief treatment on isometric drawing. The treatment is brief only because it is a trivial matter to draw isometrics with KEY CAD after you have mastered three view (X-Y) drawings. The three isometric directions are defined with a three line cursor on the screen. The cursor lines are a constant reminder of the orientation of every line on each isometric plane.

REFERENCES

1. Anon, Key CAD Complete, SoftKey Software Products of Florida, Boca Raton, FL.

EXERCISES

1. Using the CAD program to prepare a drawing block. Save the drawing block to a file with the name DWGBLOCK. Print the drawing block on an 8 ½ by 11 inch sheet of paper and check the size of the drawing area inside the border on the printed sheet.
2. Prepare a CAD drawing of a notched block like that shown in Fig. 6, except for the dimensions. Make the block 4" wide by 3" high by 2" deep. Retain the same dimensions shown in Fig. 6 for the notch.
3. Prepare a CAD drawing of a support pad made of steel. The pad is a rectangle block one inch thick, by six inches wide, and four inches deep. The block has ½ inch diameter holes, that are

located a distance of one inch from each edge near all four of the corners the block. Sharp corners are taboo, so either chamfer or round them. Your pick.

4. Dimension the drawing prepared for Exercise 2.
5. Dimension the drawing prepared for Exercise 3.
6. Prepare an isometric drawing of the J. M. Patterson Building. Show the view from the intersection of the two streets fronting the building.

CHAPTER 9

MICROSOFT EXCEL

INTRODUCTION

Microsoft® EXCEL is a spreadsheet program that is an extremely important tool in engineering, because it is useful in so many different applications. We will cover three of these applications including, preparation of a parts list, performing calculations, and drawing graphs. There are several different spreadsheet programs on the market, namely EXCEL by Microsoft, QUATTRO PRO by Borland, and LOTUS 1 • 2 • 3 by Lotus. All of these programs have a similar format, and they all have essentially the same capabilities. If you learn to use one program, it is relatively easy to switch to a different program, with a modest investment in time. We have selected EXCEL because it has been adopted by the University of Maryland, and you will have access to it on the computer net during your tenure here.

The purpose of this chapter is to show you how to navigate on the EXCEL spreadsheet, to make tables, perform calculations, plot several types of graphs, print the output, and save a file. You should recognize that these objectives are limited. We are concentrating on developing your entry level skills. Hopefully you will find the spreadsheet tool important enough to develop a higher skill level with independent study. More complete and detailed treatments are given in references [1, 2].

THE SCREEN

You load EXCEL from WINDOWS by clicking on the EXCEL icon, and the program opens by displaying a spreadsheet as shown in Fig. 1. Let's explore this display. At the top you will note five rows, then below in the center is a big table that is the spreadsheet proper, and finally at the bottom two more rows.

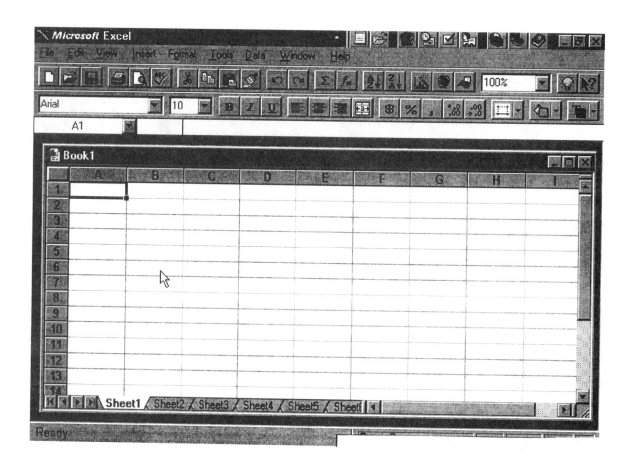

Fig. 1 The screen display in Microsoft Excel.

THE FIVE TOP ROWS

The top most row, called the title bar, tells you that you are working in the program EXCEL, and the name of the file that is open (Book 1 until you save and name the file). The three buttons to the far right side of the title row are common to all Microsoft® programs. The left hand button with the dash symbol places the program aside, so that you can work in a different program. The middle button permits you to either expand your view of the screen or to shrink it. The right button with the X closes both EXCEL, and the file upon which you are working. Do not use this button if you intend to use EXCEL again during your current session. Try clicking on these three buttons until you understand their function.

The second row from the top is the called the menu bar, which lists nine different features included in the program beginning with File and ending with Help. The menu bar is also common to all of the Microsoft® programs. Use your mouse, select one of the menu items, and click. A pull down menu is displayed. We will not list the items on each of these pull down menus, because you will learn faster by clicking than reading. The purpose of each of the menu entries is listed below:

1. File is to open or close, save, or print a file or exit EXCEL.
2. Edit is to change entries that you have already made.
3. View is to change the appearance of the screen.
4. Insert is to add material into the document often from other files.
5. Format is to change the font, paragraphs, tabs, style, etc..
6. Tools are to check spelling, grammar, language, etc.
7. Table is to provide a format that allows for rapid typing of tabular data.
8. Window is to enable you to open a new window.
9. Help is to provide answers to your questions as you attempt to learn the particular program that is loaded.

The third row down exhibits a toolbar with about twenty buttons. Again this is a standard toolbar (unless someone has customized it) that is common to all of the Microsoft® applications. The icons on each button give a good clue as to the purpose of each button, but if you are in doubt, use the mouse and point to a particular button. Don't click. Wait for a second or two, and a small label appears to tell you the function of each button. Again point and click until you understand.

The fourth row is the formatting tool bar, and again it is common to all of the Microsoft® applications. Icon labels on each button give us a hint of the purpose of each button, but if we are in doubt, point to the button and a label will appear defining the function.

The last row gives information about the spreadsheet. The block to the left defines the cell location on the spreadsheet that is active (A1 shows when you begin a new book or file). The longer block on the right, called the formula bar, is activated when you make an entry into a cell. The numbers or letters that you have entered into the cell appear in this block. If you wish to edit the entry, without completely retyping it, activate the cell, place the cursor in this block, and make the necessary changes.

OK, we have briefly defined the top five rows, but it is up to you to try to develop an understanding of the menu items and the buttons by pointing and clicking. Don't be afraid to make the computer beep; that is part of the learning process.

THE SPREADSHEET

Most of the screen is taken up by the spreadsheet, which is simply a big table with lots of columns and rows. The columns are labeled across the top with letters A, B, C, etc., and the rows are labeled down the left side with numbers 1, 2, 3, etc. Each little block, called a cell, is identified with its coordinates (i. e. C7). Note that we put the letter (column location) first, and the number (row location) second. The cells are where we enter either numbers, text or formulas on the spreadsheet.

We move about on the spreadsheet with either the mouse or the key board. When the pointer is on the spreadsheet the location, is identified with a large plus sign. We can use the mouse to point to any cell on the screen, but if the cell of interest is off screen, the scroll buttons located to left or below the spreadsheet are used to bring the cells of interest into the field of view. When the big plus sign (see Fig. 1) is pointed at the correct cell --- click, that cell becomes active, and is ready to receive the data that we enter. We can also move the active cell by using the arrow keys, the tab key, the shift-tab keys, and the control-arrow keys. Try them and watch how the active cell moves about the spreadsheet.

The spreadsheet is much larger than it looks on the screen, which shows only columns A through I and rows 1 through 16. Explore down on the spreadsheet by holding the control and the arrow-down keys, and note that the number of the last row is 16,384. Depressing the control and the arrow-right keys moves the active cell to the far right of the spreadsheet, and indicates a column heading of IV which is the 256th column. We have a total of (256)(16,384) = 4,194,304 cells on the spreadsheet. Let's hope we never have to use all of them!

At the bottom of the spreadsheet, we have tabs that give the sheet numbers. When opening EXCEL and starting a file, we begin with a workbook for a given project. The program automatically establishes 16 sheets (pages) in our workbook, although only six are visible to us. We can develop several spreadsheets in this file by clicking on the tabs to move from one sheet to another. The buttons to the left of these tabs change the sheet numbers on the tabs, permitting us to gain access to sheets 7 though 16.

The row at the bottom is called the status bar. It provides a brief statement about the function of any button that is being activated, and other information about the status of the program.

PREPARING A PARTS LIST

Let's begin to learn how to use EXCEL by preparing a parts list for the solar still. Load the program from WINDOWS by clicking the start button, select Programs, and then Microsoft Excel. The screen display should look like Fig. 1, indicating that we are ready to start. We recommend that you title the file even before beginning to develop the parts list. Click on File and select Save As. When the Save As page is displayed, you enter a suitable file name for the project, and click the save button. The file name is now displayed on the top row of the spreadsheet.

We start the parts list by typing its title in cell A1. Since the title should be obvious, we use bold font and increase the font size to 16 point. We skip a row and position the cursor on cell A3 to begin organizing the section headings as shown below:

PARTS LIST FOR SOLAR STILL				
NUMBER	NAME OF ITEM	DESCRIPTION OR DRAWING NUMBER	QUANTITY	PRICE
1	BASIN	ALUMINUM PAN, DWG NO. ENES 100- 01	1	$ 1.45
2	FELT PAD	1/8 THICK BLACK FELT, CUT TO FIT PAN	1 SQ. YD	$ 4.50
3	BASE INSULATION	FOAM INSULATION, CUT TO FIT PAN	1 SQ. YD	$ 1.25
4	COLLECTING TROUGH	ALUMINUM TROUGH, DWG NO. ENES 100-2	2	$ 1.75
5	PLASTIC FILM	TRANSPARENT MYLAR, 0.003 THICK	3 SQ. YDS	$ 1.50
6	ALUMINIZED FILM	ALUMINIZED MYLAR, 0.003 THICK	1 SQ. YD	$ 2.50
7	FRAMING	1/4 x 17 DOWEL ROD	17	$ 0.75
8	FRAMING	1/4 x 12 DOWEL ROD	8	$ 0.45
9	CONNECTOR TYPE 1	CONNECTOR 1 DWG NO. ENES 100-02	12	$ 0.25
10	CONNECTOR TYPE 2	CONNECTOR 2 DWG NO. ENES 100-03	4	$ 0.40
11	CONNECTOR TYPE 3	CONNECTOR 3 DWG NO. ENES 100-04	4	$ 0.65

We have five section headings (columns) in our parts list:

A. A number which refers to the part number. Remember that every unique part has a number.
B. The name of the item.
C. A description of the item or a drawing number defining the part.
D. The quantity of parts that will be needed to build a single prototype.
E. The unit price for the item.

When we type these column headings in cells A3, B3, C3, D3, and E3, it is clear that the columns are not the correct width to accommodate the text. The column widths are adjusted by pointing to the line between A and B on the column headings. When the pointer is positioned correctly, you will see a short vertical line with arrows to the left and right. Depress the left mouse button, and drag the column boundary either to the left or the right to adjust the width of column A. Move to the position on the column headings between column B and C, and repeat the process to size the width of column B. Continue to adjust all of the column widths.

In our example parts list, we have shown 11 part numbers. You may have more part numbers, because we have not made a serious attempt to be complete in this listing. We type the necessary information for the parts list in the table that is provided by the spread sheet. Our only concern in this process is that we have activated the correct cell before making an entry. If one of our entries is too long, we can change the column width at any time to accommodate it. However, keep the descriptions short because we want the parts list to fit the page.

When you have completed the entries, work on the spreadsheet to improve its appearance. We have centered the part numbers, the quantities and the prices. We center by marking all of the entries in a given column (point, drag with the mouse, and watch a black background color fill the column). When the black covers the column entries, that you wish to center, move the pointer to the formatting bar, and click on the centering button. On the column for price, we initially made the entries with the default format; however, prices are in terms of dollars. We changed the format of the column by marking it, and then click on the $ button on the formatting toolbar to show the prices in a currency format.

We are ready to print the parts list, but we want to check to see if it fits the page, has the correct margins, and is readable. We click on File then Print Preview, to review the appearance of the spreadsheet that we will see when it is printed. To change its appearance click on the setup button and then choose the sheet tab. From this page, point and click on gridlines, so that all of the cell boundaries are visible when the spreadsheet is printed. Printing the cell gridlines make the parts list much easier to read. Next click on the page tab, and select either the portrait or landscape mode. The default setting is the portrait mode because it is more common, but if the spreadsheet is much wider than it is long, the landscape mode is preferred. You can also adjust the size and the quality (dots per inch) of the printing on this page. Finally, click on the margin tab, and change the margins so that the spreadsheet is positioned where you want it to be on the page.

When you have made all of the modifications needed, and the spreadsheet looks professional (that means very good), click on the print button, select the number of copies, and print the spreadsheet.

PERFORMING CALCULATIONS

One of the most important advantages of any spreadsheet program is its capability of performing calculations. EXCEL performs not just one calculation, but a whole sheet full of calculations, almost instantaneously. The results can be displayed in two different ways; as an accurate table, or they can be converted into a suitable graph. In this section, we will show you two simple examples illustrating the computing power of EXCEL, and illustrate the results as spreadsheet tables.

THE RICH UNCLE EXAMPLE

For the first example, consider your rich uncle that we introduced in a previous chapter on Tables and Graphs. Recall that we discussed the compound interest which you earned from his initial investment of $5000. We now describe the results of the spreadsheet, present on the next page, that is an analysis of the growth of the investment. Let's recall the accumulation relation and the input data from the previous chapter on Tables and Graphs where:

$$S = P(1 + i)^n = PM \qquad (1)$$

Uncle contributed P = $5,000.00, and the interest rate (i) for the six month compounding period was 5%. We want to track the sum accumulated S for a total of 80 compounding periods (40years). Recall that n is the number of compounding period, and M is a multiplier dependent on n.

Load EXCEL, and Save As --- compound interest --- to establish the file name. In the results shown above, we titled the spreadsheet and entered the parameters controlling the results in the first five rows (A1 to A5). We skip a row, and define the headings for periods, multiplier and sum in row 7. Initially, we define only three columns (A, B and C). We place the active cell at location A8, and begin to enter the number of the period starting with zero. We could type all 40 entries into the A column, but it is easier to fill in the entries automatically. To let EXCEL do the work, make sure the active cell is on the zero entry in cell A8, click on Edit, select fill, and then series. A series page is displayed, and you select column to indicate that you are filling entries into column A. You also select linear, because the series that you are using to fill in column A is a linear series (i. e. 1, 2, 3, etc.). At the bottom of the page note two small boxes; one for step and the other for stop. We enter 1 for step and 40 for stop, then click on the OK button. The program fills all of the cells from A8 to A48 with numbers, starting with 0 increasing in steps of 1 until it stops at the number 40. The fill command listed in the Edit menu item saves a lot of time.

Let's go next to column B, and activate cell B8. We want to calculate the multiplier in this column. The multiplier M is a number that increases with the number of the compounding periods, and is given by $M = (1 + i)^n = (1.05)^n$. With cell B8 active, click in the formula bar in the 5th row. We begin by notifying EXCEL that we intend to feed it a formula by typing =, then we type the formula. In this case our entry would look like =(1.05)^A8. We use the cell address A8 because it contains the value of n for the row of calculations being considered. We use the ^ symbol to indicate that we are raising (1.05) to a power. Just to the left of the formula bar, note the buttons labeled X, ✔ , and f$_x$.

DETERMINING THE RUNNING SUM
FOR AN INITIAL INVESTMENT OF $5000.00
ANNUAL INTEREST RATE OF 10%
COMPOUND INTEREST SEMI-ANNUALLY
NO TAXES PAID

period	multiplier	sum		period	multiplier	sum
0	1	$ 5,000.00		40	7.0400	$ 35,199.94
1	1.0500	$ 5,250.00		41	7.3920	$ 36,959.94
2	1.1025	$ 5,512.50		42	7.7616	$ 38,807.94
3	1.1576	$ 5,788.13		43	8.1497	$ 40,748.33
4	1.2155	$ 6,077.53		44	8.5572	$ 42,785.75
5	1.2763	$ 6,381.41		45	8.9850	$ 44,925.04
6	1.3401	$ 6,700.48		46	9.4343	$ 47,171.29
7	1.4071	$ 7,035.50		47	9.9060	$ 49,529.86
8	1.4775	$ 7,387.28		48	10.4013	$ 52,006.35
9	1.5513	$ 7,756.64		49	10.9213	$ 54,606.67
10	1.6289	$ 8,144.47		50	11.4674	$ 57,337.00
11	1.7103	$ 8,551.70		51	12.0408	$ 60,203.85
12	1.7959	$ 8,979.28		52	12.6428	$ 63,214.04
13	1.8856	$ 9,428.25		53	13.2749	$ 66,374.74
14	1.9799	$ 9,899.66		54	13.9387	$ 69,693.48
15	2.0789	$ 10,394.64		55	14.6356	$ 73,178.15
16	2.1829	$ 10,914.37		56	15.3674	$ 76,837.06
17	2.2920	$ 11,460.09		57	16.1358	$ 80,678.92
18	2.4066	$ 12,033.10		58	16.9426	$ 84,712.86
19	2.5270	$ 12,634.75		59	17.7897	$ 88,948.50
20	2.6533	$ 13,266.49		60	18.6792	$ 93,395.93
21	2.7860	$ 13,929.81		61	19.6131	$ 98,065.73
22	2.9253	$ 14,626.30		62	20.5938	$ 102,969.01
23	3.0715	$ 15,357.62		63	21.6235	$ 108,117.46
24	3.2251	$ 16,125.50		64	22.7047	$ 113,523.34
25	3.3864	$ 16,931.77		65	23.8399	$ 119,199.50
26	3.5557	$ 17,778.36		66	25.0319	$ 125,159.48
27	3.7335	$ 18,667.28		67	26.2835	$ 131,417.45
28	3.9201	$ 19,600.65		68	27.5977	$ 137,988.32
29	4.1161	$ 20,580.68		69	28.9775	$ 144,887.74
30	4.3219	$ 21,609.71		70	30.4264	$ 152,132.13
31	4.5380	$ 22,690.20		71	31.9477	$ 159,738.73
32	4.7649	$ 23,824.71		72	33.5451	$ 167,725.67
33	5.0032	$ 25,015.94		73	35.2224	$ 176,111.95
34	5.2533	$ 26,266.74		74	36.9835	$ 184,917.55
35	5.5160	$ 27,580.08		75	38.8327	$ 194,163.43
36	5.7918	$ 28,959.08		76	40.7743	$ 203,871.60
37	6.0814	$ 30,407.03		77	42.8130	$ 214,065.18
38	6.3855	$ 31,927.39		78	44.9537	$ 224,768.44
39	6.7048	$ 33,523.76		79	47.2014	$ 236,006.86
40	7.0400	$ 35,199.94		80	49.5614	$ 247,807.21

After you have entered the formula, click the ✔ button, and look at cell B8. It should read 1, because your entry $=(1.05)\char94 A8 = (1.05)^n = (1.05)^0 = 1$. OK, you have used EXCEL to compute the first multiplier M; let's determine the other 40 multipliers by copying the first one. Activate B8, and then click the copy button on the toolbar. You have just stored the formula $=(1.05)\char94 A8$ in temporary memory, and it will be stored there until it is replaced the next time you use the copy command. Next mark the B column starting with B9 to B48, by dragging the mouse pointer down the column. Check that the region is black where you want to copy the multiplier term, then click on the Paste button. The cells B8 to B48 show the multiplier M superimposed on the black background color of the column. The black background is eliminated by clicking on any cell outside this region. In performing the calculations down the B column from the copy, then paste commands, EXCEL modified the formula $=(1.05)\char94 A8$. Activate cell B9, and note the formula has changed to $=(1.05)\char94 A9$. EXCEL modifies the formula to accommodate the changes in n, as we move down the column of calculations. In this instance we needed EXCEL to make this modification. However, in the next example, this type of modification leads to errors, and we will show the technique needed to control the way EXCEL modifies the formulas in the copy and paste commands.

Looking at the results for M in column B, we note that the number of decimals is not consistent from row to row. Select any cell in column B, click on either one of the two decimal buttons on the formatting toolbar, and watch the number of decimals change. Click on one or the other of these buttons until you display the multiplier with four digits after the decimal point.

To determine the sum S that is accumulated with time, we need multiply the multiplier M by the initial investment of $P = 5000$. We select cell C8, and type $=5000*B8$. The symbol $*$ is used to indicate multiplication. When we click on the check button, the entry in cell C8 changes from $=5000*B8$ to 5000. EXCEL noted that cell B8 contained the number 1, provided the calculation of $(5000)(1)$, and displayed the results in cell C8. When we need to incorporate a cell address into a formula, we can type it, or we can point to the cell with the proper address, and click the left mouse button to enter it into the formula. In the point and click approach, the math symbol, $+$, $-$, $*$ or $/$ must precede the pointing.

Look again at cell C8 and note that the result 5000 is not in the correct format. We need to show the results in a currency format, to indicate that the sum accumulated from Uncle's investment is in terms of dollars. To change the format:

1. Mark the entire column from C8 to C48, by dragging with the mouse.
2. Check that the black background covers only this region.
3. Point and click on the $ button on the formatting bar.
4. Clear the black background by clicking on any cell not in the black region.

When we converted the cell C8 into a currency format, another problem occurred. The result of 5000 changed into #######. This symbol indicates that the column is not wide enough to display the result. To widen column C, we point to the column heading row at a location between C and D. When the line with the double arrows shows in place of the pointer, depress the left mouse button, and drag to the right to widen column C. With a wider column the result in cell C8 reads $ 5000.00.

We have one result for the sum S; let's arrange for EXCEL to complete the calculations. Activate cell C8 because it has the formula, and click on the copy button on the toolbar. Next mark the cells C9 through C48 where we want the formula to apply. The black background verifies that the region is marked correctly. Next, we click on the paste button, and EXCEL applies the formula to all of the marked cells in the C column, and calculates the results in each cell. Scroll down the column and check to see that all of the results are displayed. If you encounter ####### the column needs to be widened. The result in cell C48 should read $35,199.94.

We have computed the accumulated sum S for 40 periods, but we indicated we wanted to make this determination for 80 periods. Why did we stop at n = 40? We divided the calculation into two parts so that the output, when printed, would fit better on one page. It is easy to extend the calculation to n = 80 by using the copy command.

To complete our work mark the block with corners at A7 and C8, and click on the copy button. We now have our headings and the initial formula in temporary storage (memory). Move the cursor and activate cell E7. We skip column D to provide space between the two lists of results in our table. After activating cell E7, click on the Paste button, and the results from the A7 to C8 block are copied (with modifications for the shift in columns) into the E7 to G8 block. Look at cell E8 and note that the period shown is n = 0. Let's change that value to 40 by editing the numbers displayed on the formula bar. When cell E8 is changed to 40, the results in E9 and G9 check with previous results for the period n = 40. This fact implies that the program in EXCEL has adjusted the formulas to account for the fact that we have changed the columns in which the calculations are made. Activate cells F8 and G8 and compare the formulas in them with those in cells B8 and C8. Do you see the changes automatically made by EXCEL, as we copied formulas from one column to another.

To complete the table, activate cell E8 and fill in the entries for n = 40 to 80. We again use the automatic number generator in EXCEL. Click on edit, select fill, and then series. On the pull-down series page, click on column, linear, and indicate a step of 1 with a stop at 80. Click on the OK button, and then scroll down the spreadsheet to check that you have filled in the correct entries in column E. Next, mark cells F8 and G8, and copy them. Mark the F8 - G48 block, and paste the formulas from F8 and G8 into this block. Clear the black background, and then scroll down the G column. You will probably note the symbol ####### for some of the results. Widen column G until all of the results are shown in the currency format. As a check you should have the result $ 247,807.21 in cell G48.

We are now ready to print the table showing all of the results. Click on File, then click on print review. The screen shows the spreadsheet as it will appear when printed. We note that it could be improved with gridlines and a larger left hand margin. To show the gridlines, click the set-up button. From the pull-down book which appears on the screen, select the sheet tab. Click on the gridlines square, and note that a check appears to indicate that the gridlines will be printed. Next click on the OK button to return to the preview of the spreadsheet. To adjust the margins, simply point, click and drag a margin line until the table is centered in the sheet that is displayed in the print review display. Now click on the print button to print the spreadsheet.

We will return to this spreadsheet later when we graph the results.

SOLAR STILL OUTPUT

In the chapter on Analysis of a Solar Still, we introduced an approximate relation for determining the quantity of water produced in a still that is operated in a steady state condition over some interval of time. The relationship is given below:

$$m/A = (0.01875 \ F - 0.002063)t \qquad (2)$$

where:

        F is the solar flux into the still (kW/m^2).

        m is the quantity of water produced (kg).

        A is the area of the still (m^2).

        t is the time (minutes).

Let's program this relation in EXCEL to determine the quantity of the water produced. As we examine Eq. (2), note that the output m depends on two variables, namely the solar flux F, and the time t, for a fixed area A. The quantity of water produced by the still increases linearly with both of these variables. To determine m, we fix the area A = 1 m^2, and arrange the spread sheet with one variable t displayed in column A, and the other variable, the solar flux, arranged along the 7th row. This arrangement of the spreadsheet is shown below:

DETERMINE SOLAR STILL OUTPUT						
FOR A STILL AREA OF 1 SQ METER						
SOLAR FLUX AND TIME ARE VARIABLES						
m/A = (0.01875 F - 0.002063)t						
FLUX	0.2	0.5	1	2	5	10
Time(min)	kW/m^2	kW/m^2	kW/m^2	kW/m^2	kW/m^2	kW/m^2
0	0	0	0	0	0	0
10	0.017	0.073	0.167	0.354	0.917	1.854
20	0.034	0.146	0.334	0.709	1.834	3.709
30	0.051	0.219	0.501	1.063	2.751	5.563
40	0.067	0.292	0.667	1.417	3.667	7.417
50	0.084	0.366	0.834	1.772	4.584	9.272
60	0.101	0.439	1.001	2.126	5.501	11.126
70	0.118	0.512	1.168	2.481	6.418	12.981
80	0.135	0.585	1.335	2.835	7.335	14.835
90	0.152	0.658	1.502	3.189	8.252	16.689
100	0.169	0.731	1.669	3.544	9.169	18.544
110	0.186	0.804	1.836	3.898	10.086	20.398
120	0.202	0.877	2.002	4.252	11.002	22.252

We need to determine the range for the time t, and the flux F in evaluating the quantity m of water produced in the still. Considering that the prototype still will be operated for relatively short periods of time in testing the prototypes developed in this class, let the time t range from 0 to 120 minutes in steps of 10 minutes. Also take a range in the solar flux from 0.2 to 10.0 kW/m^2, with m evaluated for F equal to 0.2, 0.5, 1.0, 2.0 5.0 and 10.0 kW/m^2. These values for F cover conditions that vary from low levels of solar radiation to stills with concentrators that provide very high flux intensities.

In the spreadsheet illustrated above, we have entered the flux data in row 7, columns B to G. In rows 1 to 3, we provide the title of the spreadsheet, and information related to the calculation of the results. On row 5, we have shown the relation that has been evaluated in the spreadsheet. In row 8, we have entered the time heading, its units, and the units for the solar flux. The spreadsheet is now organized with an arrangement that displays the two variables, and gives their units of measure.

To begin the programming of the equation for m, let's fill column A with information about time. Type 0 in cell A9, and keep this cell active. Then click edit on the menu bar, select fill, and series. On the series pull down page, select column, linear, and enter step = 10 and stop = 120. Finally click the OK button, and check to determine if the numbers filling the A column are correct.

Activate cell B9 and type the formula for m, namely =(0.01875*B7 - 0.002063)*A9. (Note that this entry is correct for cell B9, but it will give us problems later when we try to use the copy and paste commands to complete the spreadsheet). Let's proceed by copying the formula in cell B9 into cells B10 to B21. When we examine our results, they are clearly in error. To trouble shoot the problem activate cell B10, and examine the formula displayed in the formula bar. You will see =(0.01875*B8 - 0.002063)*A10. Unfortunately this relation is not correct. In the copy-paste operation, EXCEL modified our formula indexing the row locations on both the A and B column entries by 1. This indexing was OK for the column A entries, but we do not want to index the column B entries. Instead we want to use the data in cell B7 for all the calculations in column B. To accomplish this, we modify the formula in cell B9 to read =(0.01875*B$7 - 0.002063)*A9. The $ symbol before 7 locks in the value in row 7, as we paste and EXCEL indexes down the B column in modifying the formula. We now copy cell B9, and paste down the B column to generate the correct results for this column.

The copy and paste operation worked well on column B after we fixed the B$7 entry. Let's try to copy the modified formula in cell B9 into the row of cells C9 to G-9. If you copy, paste, and then examine the formulas in these cells, you will note that EXCEL has not given you the formulas that you need. Again you must modify the entry in cell B9. It reads =(0.01875*B$7 - 0.002063)*A9. As we copy along a row to the right, the cell address A9 changes to B9, C9, D9 etc. We need to multiply by the time, and do not want the A column designation to change in the copy-paste operation. To modify our entry in cell B9, we type =(0.01875*B$7 - 0.002063)*$A9. The $ symbol before the A locks column A into the formula, so that it remains fixed as we change columns in the copy-paste operation.

Now that we have corrected our entry into Cell B9, we copy and paste the formula to cells C9 to G9 along row 9. Then copy this row (C9 to G9) and paste to the block C10 to G21. The program executes these calculations and displays the results as shown in the previous spreadsheet. The quantity of water produced varies from low of 0.01687 kg for 10 minutes of operation at a flux of 0.2 kW over an area of one square meter, to a high of 22.25244 kg when the still is operated for 120 minutes at a flux of 10 kW. We have not indicated the units on the spreadsheet, although you may wish to do so in the caption for the table.

You may also want to change the number of decimals used in reporting the results. Five decimal place accuracy is misleading in this example, since the controlling equation is an approximation that involves many assumptions. You may change the number of decimals, by marking the block containing the results (B9 to G21). Then click on the decreasing decimal key in the formatting toolbar until the number of decimals shown is more realistic (two or three).

Try these examples and learn the power of EXCEL in performing not one, but a whole sheet full of calculations. Use EXCEL to solve the homework problems assigned in Physics and Math courses. You can determine the single answer usually sought in an assigned problem, and then go on to explore solution space in EXCEL. Try exploring solution space; you will like the results.

GRAPHS WITH EXCEL

EXCEL can be employed to produce several types of graphs easily and quickly after you have learned the procedure. To show the method for producing graphs, we will use examples demonstrate the capabilities of EXCEL in preparing pie, bar, and X-Y graphs. We will begin by discussing the pie graph.

PIE GRAPHS

In a previous chapter on Tables and Graphs, we demonstrated the manual technique for preparing a pie chart. Remember that this chart is used primarily to show the distribution of some quantity. The larger the piece of pie the larger the share of the distribution. To illustrate how to make a pie chart in EXCEL, we open a new book and title it --- pie chart --- using the As Save selection under the File menu item. We use the top rows to title the spreadsheet, and enter the tabular data, that describes the distribution of time in various assignments for Mechanical Engineers in their initial positions in industry in cells B9 to B17, as shown in the spread sheet presented on the next page.

This pie chart looks very good. How did we generate it? After the numerical data on the distribution has been entered in cells B9 to B17, we mark them. Then click on the chart wizard button on the toolbar. When we depress the chart wizard button, the pointer becomes active. We move the active pointer to an area below the tabular data to create a box in which the pie chart will be located. We make the box large enough to permit us to view the chart when it is generated. Don't worry about the size of the box, since we can change its size later to improve the appearance of our visual display.

The chart wizard presents five pull down pages, that lead us through the steps necessary to convert the data displayed on the spreadsheet into a graph of one type or another. The first page (Step 1) identifies the range of data. In our example, we have already marked the data in cells B9 to B17, so we confirm that these cells are correct in the dialog box. Clicking the Next button moves us to the next page (Step 2), where we find that EXCEL offers 15 options for our chart. Two of these options are for pie charts. Let's select the three dimension pie chart by clicking on its button, and then the Next button. The next page (Step 3), shows seven different options for displaying our three dimensional pie chart, and we select option seven.

The page for Step 4 previews our pie chart. Since it looks perfect, we do not alter the default settings in the row and column dialog boxes. Finally, the last page (Step5) is to assist us in titling the graph, and providing legends to identify the different slices of the pie. We click on the legend dot, and add our title. Except for sizing the chart and locating it on the spreadsheet, we have completed the pie chart. We click the finish button on the Step 5 page, and examine the results. If the chart is too small or too large, click on a corner of the chart and drag the corner to adjust the size.

When you are satisfied with the appearance on the screen, click on File and select Print Review. You can add gridlines and adjust margins if you wish on the Print Review display. Print the spreadsheet, and the pie chart and observe its professional appearance.

PIE CHART

RESPONSIBILITIES OF MECHANICAL ENGINEERS
FIRST ASSIGNMENT IN PERCENT TIME

ASSIGNMENT	PERCENT
1. DESIGN ENGINEERING	40
2. PLANT ENGINEERING, OPERATIONS, MAINTENANC	13
3. QUALITY CONTROL, RELIABILITY, STANDARDS	12
4. PRODUCTION ENGINEERING	12
5. SALES ENGINEERING	5
6. MANAGEMENT	4
7. COMPUTER APPLICATIONS, SYSTEMS ANALYSIS	4
8. BASIC RESEARCH AND DEVELOPMENT	3
9. OTHER ACTIVITIES	7
TOTAL	100

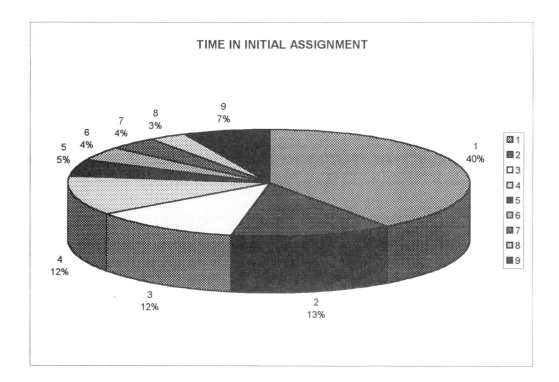

BAR CHARTS

Bar charts are most suited for showing comparisons. In the chapter on Tables and Graphs, we introduced an example of a bar chart that compared the percentage of high school students graduating with three or more years of secondary mathematics and science in 1982 and 1994. It is a very simple comparison, but it indicates the power of visual graphics to carry a message.

We begin by loading EXCEL, which opens to a new book. Again we title this book by clicking on File, Save As, and then we name the file ---bar chart. We enter the title of the new spreadsheet in the first five rows, and then enter the data for the graduating high school students in the block A7 to C9, as illustrated below:

BAR CHART						
COMPARISON OF GRADUATING HIGH SCHOOL STUDENTS COMPLETING THREE OR MORE YEARS OF MATH AND SCIEN FROM 1982 TO 1994						
YEAR	MATH	SCIENCE				
1982	38	33				
1994	60	52				

MATH AND SCIENCE PREPARATION

Legend: SCIENCE, MATH

YEAR OF GRADUATION: 1994, 1982

PERCENT: 0 10 20 30 40 50 60

In the spreadsheet we note that the column headings are in row 7, which is the first row of the data entries. Note also that years involved in the comparison are given in column A. We begin to create our bar chart by marking the region on the spreadsheet where the data exists, namely A7 to C9. We then click on the Chart Wizard button, move the cursor to cell B10, to mark a box for the approximate location of our bar chart.

Step 1 from the Chart Wizard shows the range for the data, that we have already marked. Moving to the next page (Step 2) shows illustrations for 15 different graph options. Of these 15 options, four have the appearance of bar charts. Two options are labeled bar charts, and two others are labeled column charts. They are nearly the same. The bar charts display comparison categories along the Y axis and numerical values along the X axis. The column charts display comparison categories along the X axis and values along the Y axis. We consider both the column and the bar chart representations in EXCEL to be suitable for preparing bar charts. Take your pick; we have selected the three dimensional bar chart option in this example. The next page (Step 3), gives five options for the format of our bar chart. We selected option 4 which shows gridlines in the background of the chart.

The next page (Step 4) is most important in arranging the appearance of our bar chart. It shows a preview of the chart that changes as we modify the entries in the dialog boxes. We click on the column dot because the numerical data showing the comparisons is arranged in columns B and C. In the top dialog box for columns we select 1 which corresponds to the 1st column in the marked data block. The numbers in column A (1982 and 1994) are used for the label along the vertical axis. In the lower dialog box, we select row 1 the 1st row in the marked data block, which is actually row 7 on the spreadsheet. The entries in this row are used for the legend text. This may be somewhat confusing, so we suggest that you change the column and row settings, and observe the changes to the bar chart. You will soon understand that EXCEL can quickly image the data, and you can easily correct your selections to give the correct display.

The final page (Step 5) is to assist you in adding titles to the chart. You have already provided the data for the legends in Step 4, but you need to add a title in the appropriate dialog box. The title must be short and to the point; we have used MATH AND SCIENCE PREPARATION for this example. We have also used the dialog boxes to caption the vertical axis as the year of graduation and the horizontal axis as percent. When you click on finish, the bar chart is displayed on the spread sheet. The appearance of the chart depends on the size of the box that was marked just after clicking on the Chart Wizard button. If the box is too small, click on the suitable corner and drag to enlarge the view.

When you are satisfied with the appearance of the spreadsheet, click on File and Print Preview. Add gridlines, adjust the margins as you wish, and then print the output. Try to duplicate the spreadsheet and chart shown above.

X-Y GRAPHS

The graph most frequently employed by engineers is the X-Y graph which is very effective in visually conveying trends indicated by numerical data. Is the trend increasing, decreasing, level, or is it oscillating? The X-Y graph quickly and dramatically shows the trends. To demonstrate the method for producing X-Y graphs in EXCEL, we will consider the quantity of water produced in the solar still as predicted by Eq. (2).

We have previously used Eq. (2) to demonstrate how to perform calculations using EXCEL. Let's save some work by recalling the spreadsheet showing the results of evaluating Eq. (2). These calculations provide the numerical data necessary for preparing our X-Y graph. In examining this spreadsheet, we note that the units for the solar flux listed in row 8 (cells B8 to G8) will cause difficulty in Step 4 of the Chart Wizard. The legends for our graph are supposed to be located in the first row of the data block used for the X-Y graph, and not the units for the solar flux. To correct this difficulty with our spreadsheet, we mark cells B8 to G8 and delete the contents. Then we copy the flux values from cells B7 to G7 into cells B8 to G8. Finally, we edit the entries of these cells as shown in the spreadsheet below:

DETERMINE SOLAR STILL OUTPUT							
FOR A STILL AREA OF 1 SQ METER							
SOLAR FLUX AND TIME ARE VARIABLES							
m/A = (0.01875 F - 0.002063)t							
FLUX	0.2	0.5	1	2	5	10	
Time(min)	F=0.2kW/m^2	F=0.5kW/m^2	F=1kW/m^2	F=2kW/m^2	F=5kW/m^2	F=10kW/m^2	
0	0	0	0	0	0	0	
10	0.017	0.073	0.167	0.354	0.917	1.854	
20	0.034	0.146	0.334	0.709	1.834	3.709	
30	0.051	0.219	0.501	1.063	2.751	5.563	
40	0.067	0.292	0.667	1.417	3.667	7.417	
50	0.084	0.366	0.834	1.772	4.584	9.272	
60	0.101	0.439	1.001	2.126	5.501	11.126	
70	0.118	0.512	1.168	2.481	6.418	12.981	
80	0.135	0.585	1.335	2.835	7.335	14.835	
90	0.152	0.658	1.502	3.189	8.252	16.689	
100	0.169	0.731	1.669	3.544	9.169	18.544	
110	0.186	0.804	1.836	3.898	10.086	20.398	
120	0.202	0.877	2.002	4.252	11.002	22.252	

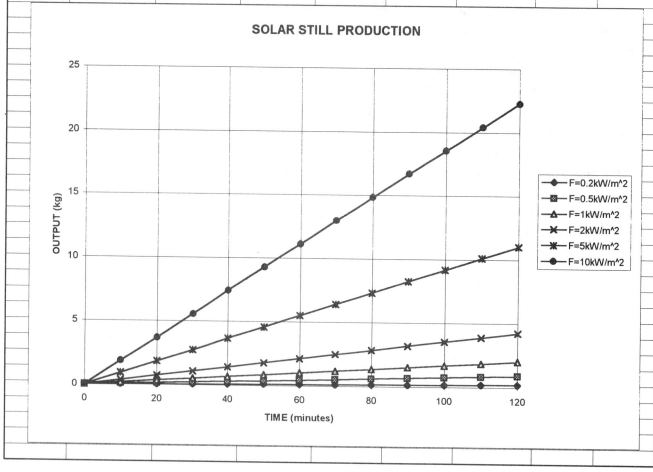

Note that the entry in cell B8 reads F = 0.2 kW/m^2. This and the other entries in cells B8 to G8 will be the legends for the six curves that we will superimpose on the X-Y graph. OK, the modification of our previous spreadsheet is complete, and we are ready to begin to prepare the X-Y graph.

Start by marking the data block, namely A8 to G21. Observe that we have included the headings for the six columns of Y data that are given columns B to G of the data block. Remember that the X data is listed in column A. After the data block is marked, click the Chart Wizard button, and position the top left corner of the area reserved for the graph in cell A22. The page for Step 1 confirms that we have already marked the correct data. If there is an error you have the opportunity to correct it in the dialog box. The next page (Step 2) offers you the options for the type of graphs. Do not select the line graph, because it often distorts the data along the X axis. Instead you select the X-Y scatter graph type.

Step 3 provides several options for scaling the axes and the appearance of the plot. We selected option 2, because it provides both lines and data points on the graph. This option does not provide for the major grid lines, but we can add them later as we modify the appearance of the graph. Note also that the 4th and 5th options provide scales for semi-log and log-log X-Y graphs. We will not demonstrate the use of these options, but you should know that they exist.

Step 4 is the important part, where we define the axes and the legends. We have made our task easier by the modifications made to the spreadsheet that properly arranged the data block used in the X-Y graph. We select the column dot, since the numerical data for Y (the solar still output) is arranged in columns B to G. We select row 1 in the top dialog box, because the scale on the X axis is listed in column A which is the 1st column in our data block. Finally, we select row 1 (row 8 on the spreadsheet) which is the 1st row in the data block because it contains the legends. In making these selections, we preview the appearance of our X-Y graph. It looks good to me.

The final page (Step5) is to add the title, and to caption the X and Y axes. We added the title SOLAR STILL PRODUCTION, and captioned the X and Y axes as TIME (minutes) and OUTPUT (kg). The draft of the graph is completed when we click the Finish button. We click on the graph to activate it, and then drag the corner of the graph to enlarge it. With the graph still active, we click on the menu item Insert, Gridlines, and add major gridlines for the X and Y axes. Before printing the graph, click on File then Print Preview and check to see that you have arranged the display so that it conveys the numerical data as well as the X-Y graph.

The combination of the spreadsheet and the graph displayed either below the tabular data or beside it is an effective technique for presenting the results of theoretical or experimental data. However, in some instances we want to show the graph without including the spreadsheet. We can show the graph alone by copying it. Click on the graph to activate it, then click on copy. Next click on the sheet 2 Tab to bring a new spreadsheet onto the screen. Position the cursor on cell A1, and click on the Paste button. The graph from Sheet 1 is copied onto Sheet2. Click on the graph to activate it, then drag its corners or sides to position and size it on the sheet. Examine the appearance of the graph with Print Review prior to printing. The result is shown below:

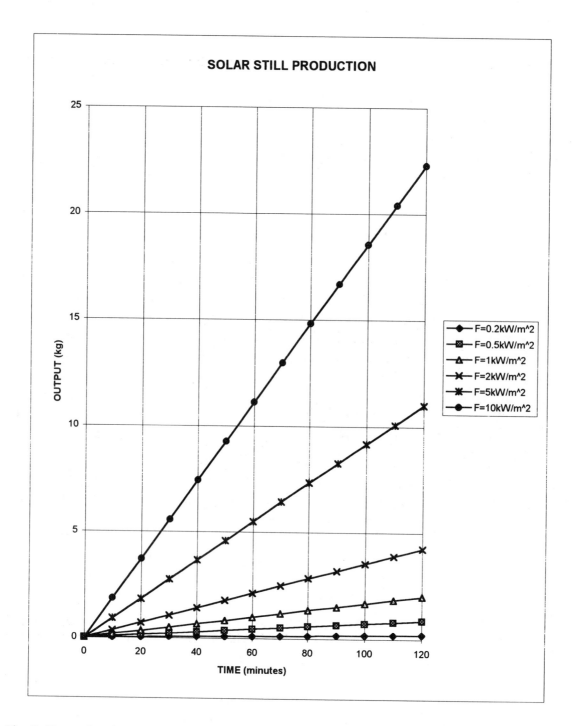

Fig. 2 Example of an X-Y graph printed without showing the spreadsheet.

SUMMARY

We have introduced you to EXCEL one of the popular spreadsheet programs in use in the United States. The introduction was limited because our purpose was to develop only entry level skills. You should know how to interpret the screen, the menu and the toolbars. You should also know how to navigate on the spreadsheet with the keyboard or the mouse, and to mark cells or blocks of cells by dragging with the mouse.

We showed three examples related to the solar still being developed in this course. The first illustrated the technique for preparing a parts list. In this instance, the spreadsheet was used to organize a table containing both descriptive and numerical data. The second example showed how to perform calculations using EXCEL to operate on simple formulas. We first illustrated how to perform a single calculation in a cell, then a line of calculations down a column, and finally a sheet full of calculations when we considered two variables. The third example was related to preparing graphs. We demonstrated the techniques involved in preparing a pie chart, a bar or column chart, and a X-Y graph. We made extensive use of the Chart Wizard in EXCEL, that leads you through the technique in a five step process.

EXCEL is a tool, somewhat like a hammer. With time and practice as you learn to use a hammer, and you hit the nail more squarely and with more force. The same is true for any spreadsheet program. You will grow more proficient with time. The results that you can produce with a spreadsheet make the effort well worthwhile.

REFERENCES

1. Gottfried, B. S., Spreadsheet Tools for Engineers, Mc Graw Hill, New York, NY, 1996.
2. O'Leary, T. J. and L. I. O'Leary, Microsoft Excel 7.0a for Windows® 95, Mc Graw Hill, New York, NY, 1996.

EXERCISES

1. Explore the Excel screen and learn the purpose of the icon buttons.
2. Explore the Excel menu and learn the options available to you as you employ this spreadsheet program.
3. Prepare a parts list for the solar still that your team is developing.
4. Suppose that you have a rich grandmother, who has provided an inheritance for you. Unfortunately it is in trust, and you can not get your hands on the loot until you are a mature 50 years of age. If the amount of the inheritance was $ 7,000.00, and the trust yields 7 % per annum, determine the value of the trust each year until your fiftieth birthday. Also prepare a X-Y graph showing the value of the trust with time.
5. Duplicate the work involved in producing the spreadsheet shown on page 10 of this chapter.
6. Prepare a pie chart using the data shown on page 13, except select a two dimensional option.
7. Prepare a bar chart comparing the percentage of men and women in your high school graduating class with the percentage in the freshman engineering class in 1996.
8. Suppose that you decide that the chart on page 18 of this chapter covers too large a range of solar flux. Prepare a new chart covering the range in solar flux from 0.2 to 2 kW/m^2.

CHAPTER 10

MICROSOFT PowerPoint

INTRODUCTION

During this course your team will be responsible for two design reviews, and you will have to make a presentation before the class and your instructor. In the presentation, you will describe the product specification, the important features that your team is incorporating in the design, and illustrate your concepts with suitable drawings. If you want to make a very good presentation, it is important that the audience follow your descriptions of the activities of the team. To help in this regard, use graphics which enable you to transmit information through two senses, --- audio and visual. This chapter provides instruction for a graphics presentation program, (GPP) that facilitates the preparation of the visuals needed for your presentations.

Microsoft PowerPoint is a graphics presentation program, that markedly reduces the time needed for you to prepare professional quality aids. It has a wide range of capabilities from simple overhead transparencies to sophisticated on-screen electronic displays. GPPs assist you in producing either black and white or colored transparencies, 35 mm slides, full screen projected electronic slides, and valuable support materials such as hard copy printouts, notes and outlines.

Before beginning to learn about PowerPoint, you need to understand that preparing a presentation is a five step process. First, plan the presentation to provide the information necessary for a design review. In planning, determine the amount of time that you have to speak, the size and layout of the room, and the type of equipment available for visual aids. Second, formulate the presentation by preparing an outline that identifies all of the topics, that you need to cover. Third prepare the slides needed in your presentation, using a GPP such as PowerPoint to guide you. As you compose the slides, edit them in the process, making certain that there are no misspellings.

After you have completed the slides, review them, and make modifications for their enhancement. Can you add graphics or bullets, to better capture the attention of the audience? Is the font size correct, and have used the bold, underline or shadow options to the best advantage. If you are using electronic displays, you have significant latitude for enhancing the visuals, and controlling the pace of the presentation. Finally, you must rehearse the presentation. It is necessary that you know the material on your slides. Nothing is more deadly than a speaker reading his or her material from the slide to the audience. Rehearse until the presentation is smooth and polished, and you feel confident about the message to be conveyed, and your ability to handle the slides and the projector.

THE PowerPoint WINDOW

Let's begin by loading PowerPoint. If the Tip of the Day dialog box shows on the screen, read and then close it, to reveal the PowerPoint window as shown in Fig. 1. There are four rows of controls located above the body of the window. The top row, called the title bar, displays the file name that you assign when you first save your work. At the right side of the title bar, you will find the three buttons to minimize, restore/maximize, and close the file. The second row contains Microsoft's standard menu items. Click on one of the items, and a pull down menu is displayed. Click an explore the menu items, until you are comfortable with the menu, and have an understanding of their purpose.

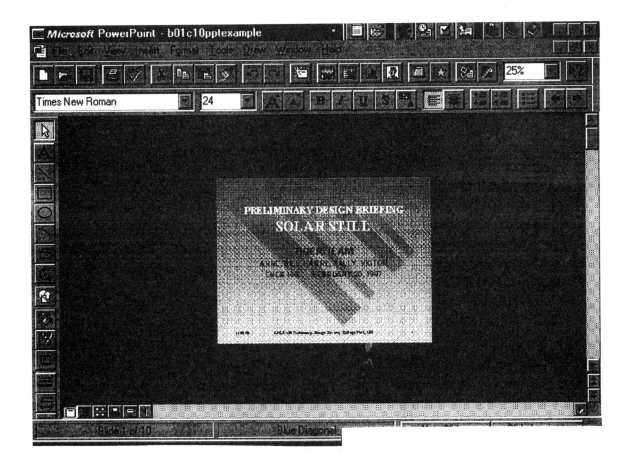

Fig. 1 PowerPoint display showing toolbars and working window.

The third row is the standard toolbar that displays 21 buttons, and a zoom control arrow to change the size of the display. Point to any button, and its purpose is shown in a small box attached to the pointer. The buttons on the left side of the toolbar are common to all of the Microsoft applications; however, the buttons that are unique to PowerPoint are on the right side of the bar. We will introduce them later, as we prepare an example presentation for a design review. The fourth row down from the top is the formatting bar. Again most of the buttons are common with other Microsoft applications.

The center area of the window is the workspace, where you will prepare the slides. On the left side of the window, you will find a vertical drawing toolbar. We can prepare drawings in PowerPoint, to enhance the visual impact of the slides. The vertical scroll bar is located on the right side of the window. The two buttons at the bottom of the scroll bar permit us to move from one slide to the next, either forward or backward.

At the bottom of the window, we have two more rows. The top one is for the horizontal scroll controls. To the left of the scroll bar, you will find five buttons that control the presentation views. These buttons are very helpful, as we work to develop a multi-slide presentation, because they:

1. Present the slides individually.
2. Present the outline of all the slides, showing all of the titles and text.
3. A slide sorter to permit you to rearrange the slides.
4. A note page to permit you to add notes to the speakers copy.
5. A slide show to enable a review of the complete presentation.

These buttons will be described in more detail later, when we edit a presentation prepared as an example of a design review. The bottom row contains the usual the status bar, where helpful messages are displayed. To the right of the status bar are shortcut buttons, that enable you to introduce a new slide into the presentation, and to select a specific slide layout.

PLANNING AND ORGANIZING WITH PowerPoint

The PowerPoint program has built-in features to assist you in planning, organizing and timing your presentation. To show these features, let's load PowerPoint, and click on File then New. A folder is displayed, as shown in Fig. 2, with three tabs named General, Presentation Design, and Presentations. Select presentations, and then note that you have 20 choices for different types of presentations. Select the first one offered, namely Auto Content Wizard. The Auto Content Wizard page, which appears on your screen, indicates that wizard provides ideas and organization for your presentation. Click on the Next button, and the first of five dialog boxes associated with the wizard is displayed. This first dialog box prompts you for information pertaining to the title slide. After providing this title information, click Next, and the second dialog box provides you with a many choices for the type of presentation that you are creating. Let's hope that you do not need to Communicate Bad News, and that you select Reporting Progress. The next dialog box gives you choices on style and timing. We suggest that you select the professional style, and decide that your presentation will require 30 minutes or less. The fourth dialog box gives you four choices for the type of output, and a choice of preparing materials to hand out to the audience. For this first example, select Black and White Overheads, and indicate that you will print handouts. Click on

Finish, and PowerPoint provides you with nine slides organized in sequence to provide the necessary information for your design review.

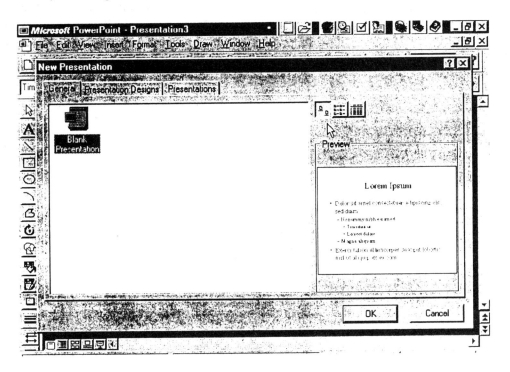

Fig. 2 New presentation page where selection of the Auto Content Wizard is made.

We will use these nine slides, and prepare part of a preliminary (first) design review for the solar still. Begin with the title slide. Note that you have already provided the title in responding to the questions raised by the Auto Content Wizard. You may want to edit the title, or provide additional information in the subtitle. To edit the title double click on the upper box to activate it, and then make the changes needed to improve its appearance. Keep the title and the subtitle information very brief. You will have the opportunity to expound later in the presentation. Typing information onto the slides is the same as typing in a word processing program. An example title slide is shown in Fig. 3-1.

Click on the lower button on the vertical scroll bar, to advance to slide 2. In the organization provided by PowerPoint, the purpose of slide 2 is to define the subject. The slide prompts us to divide the subject into the areas that we plan to discuss, and then to list these areas. In other words, we tell the audience in the beginning what we intend to tell them later in the presentation. It is a good idea, because no one likes surprises. We show an example of this slide in Fig. 3-2. The information contained in slide 2 was entered on the presentation outline, as shown in Fig. 4. You can convert from the slide format to the outline format, by clicking on the outline button that is located to the left of the horizontal scroll bar. Under slide 2 on the outline, you can respond to the prompts provided by wizard, and add bullet items to define the topics that you intend to discuss. When you have completed the outline for slide 2, click the single slide button on the horizontal scroll bar, and review the appearance of the slide. You may want to edit the slide, by changing the font size to better use the space available.

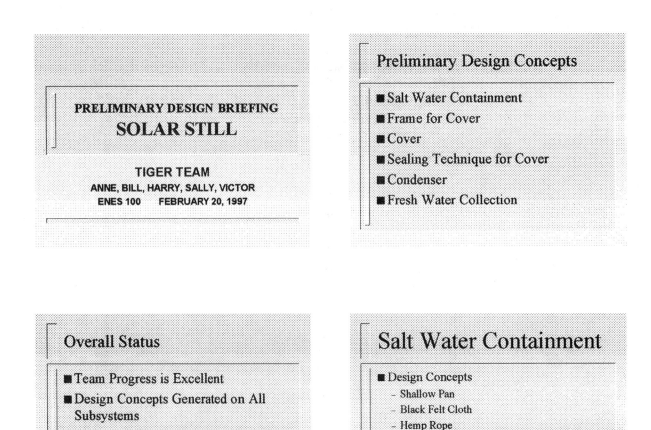

Fig. 3 Example showing content of four slides for a design briefing (before enhancement).

Click on the next slide button, and edit the entries that the wizard provides for slide 3. The title of this slide is overall status, which we believe is appropriate for a design review. You should report on the current status of the team. Describe the tasks that have been completed, report if you are behind schedule on any task, and raise any issues that concern the team. The example slide, presented in Fig. 3-3, describes uncertainties regarding the condenser, and the fresh water collector.

Wizard has titled slide 4 as Component One: Background. This title lead us to think about reporting on the first subsystem, and so we double click on the title to activate it. We then edit the title, changing it to Salt Water Containment. In the large area below the title block, we describe our progress in generating design concepts, and show two key criteria for the selection of the concept. You will note that we have made use of bullets and sub-bullets in the descriptions. We change from one bullet to the other by clicking the arrow button, that is located on the right side of the formatting toolbar. Try clicking on the arrow buttons, and observe the changes to the position and style of the bullets.

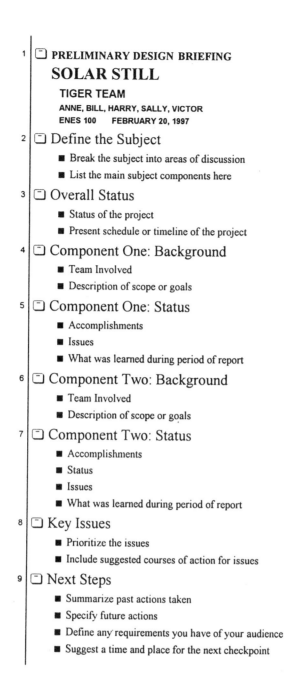

1 ☐ **PRELIMINARY DESIGN BRIEFING**
   SOLAR STILL
   TIGER TEAM
   ANNE, BILL, HARRY, SALLY, VICTOR
   ENES 100   FEBRUARY 20, 1997

2 ☐ Define the Subject
   ■ Break the subject into areas of discussion
   ■ List the main subject components here

3 ☐ Overall Status
   ■ Status of the project
   ■ Present schedule or timeline of the project

4 ☐ Component One: Background
   ■ Team Involved
   ■ Description of scope or goals

5 ☐ Component One: Status
   ■ Accomplishments
   ■ Issues
   ■ What was learned during period of report

6 ☐ Component Two: Background
   ■ Team Involved
   ■ Description of scope or goals

7 ☐ Component Two: Status
   ■ Accomplishments
   ■ Status
   ■ Issues
   ■ What was learned during period of report

8 ☐ Key Issues
   ■ Prioritize the issues
   ■ Include suggested courses of action for issues

9 ☐ Next Steps
   ■ Summarize past actions taken
   ■ Specify future actions
   ■ Define any requirements you have of your audience
   ■ Suggest a time and place for the next checkpoint

Fig. 4 Example of the outline page which can be used in preparing entries for the slides.

Slide 5, in the sequence suggested by wizard, is to report our status on the design of Component One.   We modify the title to indicate that we are reporting on the Salt Water Containment, and then click on the lower block of the slide, and respond to the prompts provided by wizard. You should provide information describing accomplishments, issues, and lessons learned. These are all excellent topics to include at this point in the design review. We show an example of this status slide in Fig. 3-4.

In preparing a complete design review, you will cover each subsystem using two slides similar to Slide 4 and 5. The wizard has only provided for two components (subsystems), so you will have to insert addition slides to cover all of the subsystems in your design. Adding new slides is easy.

With slide 5 displayed on the monitor, click on the new slide button on the right side of the status bar. A new slide page is displayed on the screen, that gives you a choice of 12 different formats. A format consistent with that of slide 5 is highlighted. Since we want to retain this format we click on OK, PowerPoint introduces the new slide, and changes the entry on the status bar to read slide 6 of 10. In the top block of your new slide, type the title, and in the lower block you provide description information pertaining to the second subsystem.

After you have briefly reviewed the subsystems in you development, you will want to conclude the presentation. The last two slides in the wizard sequence provide a template for preparing your concluding remarks. We show suggestions for these two slides in Fig. 5. The next to last slide in your presentation is titled "Key Issues". This is your opportunity to raise any issues (questions), that your team has discovered to date. Do not hide uncertainties; come forward, and seek help. The design review is a formal venue for this purpose. The example shown in Fig. 5-1 indicates that we are concerned with the flow of air over the cover, and the surface tension between the cover and the water droplets.

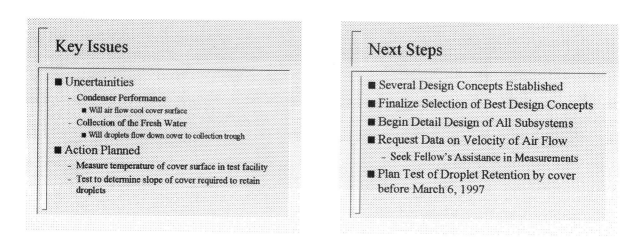

Fig. 5 Example of the two slides used to conclude the design review.

The final slide, illustrated in Fig. 5-2, describes your plans for action in the near future. Wizard titles this slide as Next Steps, which is appropriate. Wizard then prompts you to:
- Summarize past actions taken by the team.
- Specify future actions that are planned.
- Define any requirements that you have of the audience.
- Suggest a time and place for the next design review.

These are excellent suggestions for the final slide concluding your design review.

You are now ready to print the output. Click on File, and select print. The print page that is displayed is adapted for PowerPoint. It contains a selection box labeled Print What. You have several choices including: slides, handouts with 2, 3 or 6 slides per page, note pages, and an outline view. You can prepare the overheads for your presentation, and the handout that you intend for the audience. Print your presentation using these options, and examine the output to decide which style is the most suitable for the handout that you intend for the audience. The black and white paper versions of the slides can be copied to give the transparencies necessary for the presentation. If you have your own laser or ink jet printer, the transparencies can be printed directly. Be sure that you save the file before exiting the program.

ENHANCING THE SLIDES

Suppose you decide to use color slides, instead of black and white. It will cost a lot to use color if you take the job to a commercial copy center, but you may decide that it is worth it. How can you change the black and white slides to color slides? It is easy, and you do not have to retype all of the information into a new version of wizard. To change the color, and the design of the slides, click on the Apply Design Template button on the right side of the PowerPoint toolbar. The design template page, that is displayed on your screen, has a menu listing of 30 templates, which start with Azure and end with Wet Sand. With the mouse, select one of the templates, and note that it is displayed for your review in a small preview box. Try several templates, before selecting the one that you like the most.

If you would like to change the color of the background, go to the menu bar and click on Format, and select Custom Background. The Color page that is displayed gives you several options for the style of the background, and the colors. Click on the options, and review the results until you get the style, and the colors that you wish to use. Be careful and stay with relatively light colors, because they are more visible to the audience. Dark slides do not project, well unless the room is very dark. And dark rooms are an invitation for your audience to fall asleep.

Suppose that you like the background style and color, but are unhappy with the color of the text and the bullets. Change them by clicking on Format, and select Slide Color Scheme. The Color Scheme page has two tabs, namely standard and custom. The standard tab illustrates four choices of color for the titles and bullets. If they are not to your liking, click on the custom tab, and prepare to become a painter. You have the opportunity to select the colors, that you want to use in the background, shadows, fill, text and title and bullets. The colors are changed by selecting a feature on your slide, such as the title text. Click the Change Color button, and a multicolored hexagon appears with many choices of different shades of the basic colors. Select the color that you wish to employ, for each of the features on the slide. You can have a single design for all of your slides (recommended), or you can have a different color scheme for each slide. Have fun, because you have the means to make great slides.

Some folks like to use either a header or footer on their slides. A footer is helpful, if you give many presentations, and want to retain the slides for your files. The information in the footer can include date, occasion for the presentation, and location. For example you may decide to use a footer stating February 20, 1997 --- ENES 100 --- Preliminary Design Review --- College Park, MD. How do we incorporate this footer on our PowerPoint slides? Click on View on the Menu bar, and select Header and Footer. The Header and Footer page is displayed with two tabs; one for the slide, and the other for the notes and handouts. Let's select the slide tab, and add a footer to our slides. We click on the Date and time square and select automatic. We mark the slide number, because it will help us time the delivery of our presentation. We click on the footer, and type in a short message to appear in the center region of the footer. We also click on the box to indicate that we do not want the footer to appear on the title slide. We delete the footer from the title slide, because we want the audience to remain focused on our subject in the very beginning of the presentation. The Header and

Footer page has a small preview window, that permits us to review the input prior to printing. We illustrate the footer developed with this procedure in Fig. 6. The slide was in beautiful color on the monitor, but the figure is in black and white. Our apologies, but the use of color in printing in a low volume, low cost textbook is prohibitive.

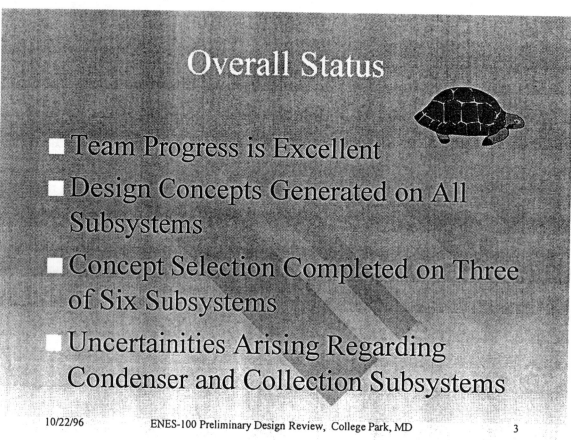

Fig. 6 Example of an enhance slide showing modified background, footnote and clip art.

Still not happy, with the impact that your slides will make. What about adding some clip art? Select a slide that you want to enhance with the addition of some photo or sketch, which is available in the Microsoft clip art files. You don't know what's available. Not to worry; click on the Insert Clip Art button that is located on the right side of the toolbar. (The button with the funny face on it.) There is a pause while the clip art files are loaded into the active PowerPoint program. A page entitled Microsoft Clip Art Gallery 2.0 appears on the screen. On the left side of this page, you will find a listing of clip art categories. Select the Animal category, and illustrations of the selections of clip art available under this category appear in the large preview window. Click on the turtle, and then click the insert button.

Now look at the slide that you had previously selected for enhancement. We have a large picture of a turtle, smack in the middle of the slide. To move the picture and change its size, we drag it by the one of the little squares, to position it appropriately on the slide. We show the turtle in the upper right hand area of the slide in Fig. 6. Note, if you push while dragging the object gets smaller, but if you pull it gets larger. Try it, and you will soon manage to move and size the turtle.

REHEARSING

Rehearsing is an essential part of preparing for a design review. Fortunately PowerPoint has a neat feature, that will help you handle the visuals as you rehearse. Go to the first (title) slide, and then click on the Slide Show button, to the left of the horizontal scroll bar. The screen changes with all of the toolbars disappearing. The slide occupies the entire screen, and the PowerPoint presentation simulates the screen in the class room. You can practice your presentation moving from one slide to the next, by using the arrow buttons on the keyboard to forward or reverse the slides.

COMPUTER PROJECTED SLIDES

The ability to project your slides directly from the computer, gives you several significant advantages, which are available in PowerPoint. First, you can store a large number of slides in memory. If questions arise during your presentation, you can call on these back-up materials to improve your response. Second, you do not need a color copier to make the slides. Third, you can use special effects incorporated in PowerPoint to give your presentations some real class.

Let's first explore the special effect know as transitions, where PowerPoint controls the manner in which we switch from one slide to the next. Go to the title slide in your presentation, click on Tools in the menu bar, and select Slide Transition. The Slide Transition page appears with an Effect box that states No Transition. Click on the arrow located beside this message, and a list of about 50 different types of transitions is given. Select one of them, and watch the slide switch from one view to another in the small preview window. Select the type of transition that you like the best. We think the dissolve transition is an excellent choice. Next, select the speed of the transition. Again you can review your choice in the preview window. Finally, select the advance method. Until your a real pro at delivery of design briefings, we suggest you advance the slides on the click of the mouse. Click the OK button, and you have set up the transition of the title slide.

Click on the Slide Sorter View button near the horizontal scroll bar, and the first six slides of your presentation are displayed. The first slide has a small slide transition icon visible near its lower left corner. A new toolbar also appears at the top of the window, replacing the formatting toolbar. You are now ready to select the type of transition for the remaining slides. Select slide 2, and click on the transition arrow button on the new tool bar. You can select the type of transition from the long list for slide 2. Proceed to mark any slide that you wish to transition in the Slide Sorter View, and to select the type of transition that you want for that slide. After you have made your choice, it is confirmed by the presence of a small transition icon just below the slide. If you employ the same transition for all of your slides, mark them all (Edit/Select All), and then select the type of transition of your choice.

PowerPoint also permits you to build your slides progressively for your audience. It is a bit like watching the construction of a building from the foundation to the roof. For slides, we start with the title, and add one line at a time to the text in the block below the title. To modify your slide to incorporate this feature, repeat the slide transition procedure described in the preceding paragraph. The new tool bar that is evident just above the window has a box that is titled No Built Effect. Click on the arrow beside that box, to reveal a wide choice of techniques for building you slides. Pick an option; fly from the left is very common. When you select an option for building the slide, a second small icon shows under the view of the slide in the slide sorter view. You can proceed to build your slides, one by one, or you can use the same style on all of them. Select all of the slides on the slide sorter view, and depress the Control + A keys.

When you have completed the transitions and the building effects, you are ready to review the dynamic nature of your electronic presentation. Real high tech. Go to slide 1, and click on the Slide Show button. As you advance from slide to slide, with arrow keys on the keyboard, you will see the transitions, and the lines of text for each bullet item being moved onto the screen.

If you have computer facilities available in the classroom, electronic presentations should be mandatory. Creating electronic slides, and using them in a professional presentation are skills that are important for you to master. The transitions keep the audience on their toes, and the building effects permits you to pace the flow of information. It takes less than an hour to learn how to prepare a very professional, dynamic presentation using PowerPoint. Take this opportunity in ENES-100 to develop your computer graphic presentation skills.

SUMMARY

We have introduced you to PowerPoint, a graphics presentation program that is an extremely useful tool in preparing for design reviews, or any other type of presentation. We strongly suggest that you take an hour or two to acquire PowerPoint skills. The results will be your capability to produce professional quality overheads at the least, and, if the equipment is available in the class room, the ability to produce computer projected slides.

The screen for PowerPoint has been briefly described. As with all Windows® based programs produced by Microsoft, many of the buttons on the toolbars have common uses. The coverage is brief, because learning is more rapid if you click, study, and understand. Hopefully, our coverage, and the examples will be helpful.

We suggest that you start to learn how to use PowerPoint by preparing your preliminary design review, using the Auto Content Wizard. The wizard organizes your presentation, arranges the sequencing of your slides, and provides excellent suggestions for the content in each slide.

After you have completed the standard presentation with the Auto Content Wizard, you should enhance the slides to improve their appearance. Procedures have been described, for changing the design template, the colors of the background and the text, adding a footer, and clip art. Clip art is particularly impressive, and easy to implement.

Finally, we introduced techniques for preparing electronic presentations. These presentations depend upon the availability of a computer controlled projector for the classroom. If this equipment is available, the use of a computer in your presentation has very real advantages. The use of transitions, as you move from one slide to the other, maintains the audience interest. Employing the build effects, where the text is presented one line at a time, has the significant advantage of controlling the flow of information to the audience. The procedures for preparing, and rehearsing a computer aided presentation are described in this chapter.

EXERCISES

1. Prepare a title slide suitable for a final design briefing using PowerPoint.
2. Prepare a subject slide that provides an overview of a final design briefing using PowerPoint.
3. Prepare a status slide using the slide outline format in PowerPoint. After completing the slide in the outline format, edit the slide, and print a paper copy of it.
4. Prepare a pair of slides describing your progress in the development of one of the subsystems for the solar still.
5. Prepare a slide that describes the key issues facing your team as you design the solar still.
6. Prepare a slide showing your plans for action in the near future.
7. Using clip art enhance a slide by inserting an animal in the lower right hand corner of the slide.
8. Prepare a transition from the title slide to the second slide. What type of a transition did you select?
9. Prepare a slide using the building effect, where single lines of text are added to the slide one by one as you click the mouse button.

PART IV

PRODUCT

DEVELOPMENT

CHAPTER 11

DEVELOPMENT TEAMS

INTRODUCTION

The development of quality, leading-edge, high performance products requires the coordinated efforts of many skillful individuals from different disciplines over an extended period of time. This group of individuals is organized within a corporation to act in an integrated manner to successfully complete the product development. The organizational structure that is employed varies from one corporation to another, and it also depends to a large degree on the size of the company that is involved. For relatively new firms in the entrepreneurial stage, team structure is usually not an issue. These firms are small with a single product, and usually only a small number of individuals are involved. Everyone that is on the payroll is deeply committed to this product, and communication is frequently accomplished around the lunch table. On the other hand, for very large corporations with thousands of employees, the company is organized into divisions or operating groups. These large companies have many products or services that are offered by each division, and many new products are introduced each year. Communication is often very difficult because personnel involved in the development of a given product are sometimes separated by hundreds or even thousands of miles. In a large corporation, organization of the product development team and the physical location of the team members becomes extremely important.

You might be wondering if this introductory material about organization and communication of a development team in a corporation is important in this course. After all you are just beginning your studies of design in ENES 100. The answer is a resounding **YES**! In this class we attempt to simulate in so far as possible an industrial design experience. Accordingly, we have assigned you to a small group of five students. This group is a development team, and the product that you will design will be a solar still. We discussed the problems of a large corporation in organizing their development teams and insuring effective communications. You will also encounter problems of organization and problems of communication even though your group is small and all of you are located on the College Park campus.

In a corporation cross disciplinary teams are necessary in staffing a product development team. Usually, at least five disciplines are represented on the team including, marketing, finance, design engineering, operations or manufacturing, and quality control. When we assigned you to a team, it was not possible to follow the corporate procedures for staffing. You have yet to establish your disciplines; however, you do have interests and talents. In so far as possible, we have used the information that you provided on your application for team membership in the team assignments. We trust that you will find a diversity of interests, talents, and skills in the members assigned to your team. It is suggested that you organize the team and assign work to individuals according to these skills.

TEAM LEADERSHIP

Experience and leadership skills are required of the product manager (team leader) in industry. The product manager is a seasoned staff member well known for his or her expertise and respected for performing at a level that exceeds expectations. The appointment as a product manager often represents a promotion for the individual involved and a first experience in managing a technical group. But what about you? You are not "seasoned," and you do not yet understand our level of expectation for your performance or that of your team. Nevertheless, your team must have a leader. We usually encourage you to meet for a few hours as a team, to exchange information about yourselves. From this interchange some bonding between team members should occur, and the team should eventually develop a consensus regarding the team leader. We will expect that the team will announce its leader before the end of the second week of class. The selection of the team leader is entirely up to the team members. The class instructor will not be a part of this decision. The class instructor will serve as a consultant to the team, but he or she will never attempt to provide leadership.

In industry, the responsibility and authority given the product manager is significant. His or her career depends strongly on the success of the product in the market and the productivity of the development team. We recognize that you and your team leader does not have the experience needed to insure a successful development. For this reason, we do not expect every team to develop a solar still that meets every requirement listed in the product specification. However, we do expect that the team leader will guide the development team by:
1. Providing a development schedule.
2. Assigning tasks to the most qualified team member.
3. Insuring that every team member is working productively.
4. Chairing and organizing team meetings.
5. Maintaining "good" behavior at each team meeting.
6. Insuring that each team member is treated with respect.

We also expect that each team member will work diligently with the team leader, cooperate completely at team meetings, and commit to holding the development schedule.

TEAM MEMBER RESPONSIBILITIES

Members of a product development team in industry have two different sets of responsibilities-- one to his or her disciplinary function, and the other to the team. A team member, from a specific engineering department, provides the technical expertise in his or her specialty and ensures that the product is correctly designed with leading edge state of the art technology. The team member acts to bring all of the important functional issues that affect the product performance to the attention of the team. As a beginning student in engineering, you have not yet established an expertise in some discipline. However, you do have natural talents, skills, and interests. We want you to represent these skills on your development team, and discuss issues in your area of interest at your team meetings.

The most important team activity for any individual member is to share responsibility. The team member shares responsibilities with other members to increase the team's effectiveness and to insure its success. Next, the team member must recognize and understand all of the product features and fully participate in the methods and techniques that are employed to meet the design objectives. Individual team members must assess team progress and participate in improving team performance. The team member must cooperate in establishing all of the relationships that are required to maintain communication between the team and the instructor. Flexibility and cooperation on the part of the individual team members are required for the team to be effective. Finally, the team members must be able to communicate in a clear concise manner in all three modes: **writing, speaking, and graphics**.

TEAM MEMBER TRAITS

When a group of individuals work together on a team to achieve a common goal, they can be extremely effective. The team interaction promotes productivity for several different reasons. First, meeting together is synergistic. One's ideas freely expressed stimulates additional ideas by other members on the team. The net result is many more original ideas than would have been possible by the same group of individuals working independently. Another advantage is in the breadth of knowledge available in the team. The team is cross disciplinary with different interests, talents and skills. The very wide range of skills necessary for the product development process are inherent within the team. Each member of the team is different with some combination of strengths and weaknesses. Acting together, the team can build on the strengths of each individual and eliminate the weaknesses. The grouping of individuals provides social benefits that are important to the individuals and to the corporation. There is a bonding that takes place over time, and a support system develops that is appreciated by the team members. Feelings of trust and mutual understanding, so important to everyone involved, develop over the course of the project. The team with its strength in numbers develops a sense of autonomy that is valued by the individual members. The team develops solutions, implements them, and then monitors the results with little or no direction from management (the instructors). Empowered teams assume ownership of the project, and they commit to the product development process. Successful teams consistently perform beyond expectations.

While cross disciplinary teams have been employed in industry for a decade or more, little has been done by our secondary educational system to develop team skills. On the contrary, the secondary schools and even the college systems encourage competitive attitudes and independence. Students compete for the few A grades that might be given in the course and are discouraged from cooperating on the assignments. The system trains the students to work independently, and team building skills are not addressed. The work place in industry is much different. Team members compete, but not within the team. They compete with a similar development team from a rival corporation. Team members bond together, cooperate and consistently help each other. In a team, we cooperate as much as possible and work together by sharing assignments. Competition between its members is discouraged. Recognition and rewards go to the team much more often than to select individuals.

There is a set of characteristics that describe a good team member and another set that depicts an individual that can destroy the efforts of a team. The characteristics of a good team member are:

- Respects other team members without question.
- Listens carefully to the other team members.
- Participates but does not dominate.
- Displays self-confidence but is not dogmatic.
- Is comfortable with his or her disciplinary skill level.
- Communicates effectively by speaking, and writing and with graphics.
- Disagrees, if it is important, but with good reason and in good taste.

You should think about your behavior as you work with fellow team members. Evaluate how well you follow the guidelines for "good" team member behavior. Are you helping or hindering the progress of your team?

The characteristics of a destructive team member are:

- Shows lack of respect for others.
- Tends to intimidate.
- Stimulates confrontation.
- Dominates discussion.
- Talks all the time, but does not listen.
- Criticizes unnecessarily.
- Does not communicate effectively.

As you compare your traits with those listed above, you will note characteristics from both of the lists of good and bad traits. To be effective an team members, you must work to enhance the favorable traits and to suppress those that are destructive to the efforts of the team.

EFFECTIVE TEAM MEETINGS

Teams are effective because they meet together to focus their wide range of disciplinary and individual skills toward the solution of well formulated problems. The team meeting is the format for the synergistic efforts of the team. Unfortunately, not all teams are effective because some members are disruptive and they destroy the cohesiveness of the team. Bonding of the team is vital if it is to successfully solve the multitude of problems that arise in the product development process.

Teams fail for three main reasons which are:

1. They deviate from the goals and objectives of the development and cannot meet the milestones on the development schedule.
2. The team members become alienated and the bonding, trust, and understanding, critical to the success of a team, never develops.
3. When things begin to go wrong, adversity almost always occurs, and "finger pointing" starts. Fixing blame replaces creative actions, and the team is destroyed.

Leadership ensures that the team remains focused on the overall goals and objectives of the project and on the agenda of each meeting. Creating the correct team environment or atmosphere is essential so that the team members cooperate, share ideas and support each other to achieve the many solutions. It is important for the team leader to assess the performance of the team as a whole at each meeting. When the team fails to make progress, it is critical for the team leader or possibly an individual member to make the changes necessary to enhance the teams effectiveness. There are several measures of team effectiveness that can be observed by everyone on the team during the course of a typical team meeting, and corrective measures to improve team performance are not difficult to implement. We will identify some of the difficulties encountered during team meetings in subsequent paragraphs.

When the goals and objective of the meeting are not clear or they appear to be changing, progress is impeded. While in many cases team meetings are planned well in advance and are suppose to follow an agenda, sometimes new topics are introduced and the meeting drifts from one item to another. This team behavior indicates that either some of the team members do not understand the goals; or worse --- they do not accept them. Instead, they are marching to their own drummer and trying to take the team with them. Unless corrective actions are taken to focus the team on the original goals, this team meeting will fail and time and effort will be lost. A team that is focused stays on the task. The team members accept the goals and their discussions deal with all of the issues important in considering a wide set of solutions to the problem being considered. The discussion continues until the team members reach a consensus and all of the members accept the solution. This type of a meeting is successful because a problem has been solved, and all of the team members accept the solution. The team can then move forward and focus its talents to address the next problem.

Team leadership is an essential element for success. The most effective teams are usually democratic with a large amount of shared leadership. While there is a recognized leader, with a considerable degree of responsibility and authority, he or she is supported by each member of the team. The team member with the appropriate expertise (relative to the problem being considered) will usually lead the discussion and effectively act as leader of the team during this period. However, in some instances, the team leader maintains strict control of the meeting and does not share the leadership role with any member of the team. Some team members resent this style of leadership and may not participate as fully as possible. The result is that complete utilization of the resources of the team does not occur. The "tightly controlled" team leader will almost always insist on sitting at the head of the table.

Attitude of the team members is an important element in the success of the team. Are the team members committed? Commitment is evidenced by attitude. If team members come to the meeting exhibiting interest and willingness to participate, they are committed and will make a positive contribution. However, if they are bored and indifferent, they will not become involved in a meaningful way. In fact, if they are sufficiently disinterested, side conversations or arguments may develop and actually destroy the atmosphere necessary for an effective meeting. Every team member should evaluate each person on the team and assess his or her commitment to the goals and objectives of the project, and to the meeting's agenda.

As the meeting progresses it is important to assess the discussions that are occurring. For a meeting to be successful, the interactions should involve everyone on the team. Discussion should focus on the agenda items with few if any deviations to unrelated topics. Team members must listen carefully to one another. All of the ideas presented are given a serious hearing. No one should be intimidated or made to feel foolish for making suggestions that appear to be too radical. An informal and relaxed attitude exhibited by the participants is the key to free flow of ideas. Teams tend to accomplish less when the discussion is dominated by only a few of the participants. Some team members speak well but do not bother to listen to others. They may introduce discussion that is off the topic and ignore suggestions for getting back to the agenda. These members tend to intimidate others in their efforts to control and dominate the team. The result is disastrous because they essentially eliminate the contributions of the other team members. Teams do not operate with total agreement on every issue. There must be accommodation for disagreements and for criticism. All of the ideas or suggestions made by every team member at any meeting will not be outstanding. In fact, some of them may be ridiculous, and criticism of these ideas must occur. Criticism should be frank, but without hostility. Personal attacks must not be a part of the critique of an idea. If the criticism is to improve an idea, or to eliminate a false concept, then it is of benefit to the progress of the team. The criticism should be phrased so that the team member advancing the flawed idea is not embarrassed. When disagreements occur, they should not be suppressed. Suppressed disagreements breed hostility and distrust. It is much better for the team to deal with the disagreements when they arise. When the root cause of the disagreement is ascertained, the team can take the actions necessary to resolve it.

On some occasions voting is a mechanism used to resolve open issues. This procedure must be used with care, particularly if the vote indicates that the team is split almost evenly in their opinions. A better practice is to discuss the issues involved and to try to reach a consensus. More time is required to reach a consensus than is necessary for a simple vote, but the results are worth the effort. Consensus implies that all members of the team are in general agreement and willing to accept the decision of the team. When the team votes, a simple majority is sufficient to resolve an issue. However, the minority members may become resentful if they are always on the short end of the voting. In a very short time they will not accept the outcome and will not commit to the actions necessary to implement the decision.

The team meetings must be open to all of the members. The agenda should be available in advance of the meetings and subject to change during the "new business" agenda item. Team members should believe that they are important, and have the authority to bring new issues before the team. They should feel free to discuss procedures used in the team's operation. Hidden agenda items detract from the harmony and trust developed through open and fair operation of the team. Secret meetings of an inside group should be carefully avoided. When the fact leaks that secret meetings are being held and that issues are prejudged by a select few, the effectiveness of the team is destroyed.

At least once during a meeting it is useful to evaluate the progress of the team. Are we still following the agenda? Is someone dominating the meeting? Is the discussion to the point and free of hostility? Is everyone properly prepared to address their agenda items? Is the team attentive or are they bored and indifferent? Is the team leader leading or is he or she pushing? If a problem in the operation of the team is identified during the pause for self appraisal, it should be resolved immediately through open discussion.

Finally, the team must act on the issues that are resolved and the problems that are solved. To discuss an issue and to reach a consensus is part of the process, but not the closure. Implementation is the closure, and implementation requires a plan for action. When decisions are made, team members are assigned action items. These action items are tasks to be performed by the responsible individual, and only when the tasks are completed can the problem be considered solved. It is important that the action items be clearly defined, and that the role of each team member in completing their respective tasks be evident. A realistic date should be set for the completion of each action item. The individual responsible should be clearly identified and accept the assignment without objection. A checking system must be employed to follow up on each action item to insure timely completion. If there is a delay, the schedule for the entire product development cycle may be at risk. Delays should be dealt with immediately, and the entire team should participate in the development of modified plans to correct the situation.

PREPARING FOR MEETINGS

Effective team meetings do not just happen. To insure success, it is necessary to prepare for the meeting and to execute post meeting activities. The preparation usually involves selecting, arranging and equipping the meeting room, scheduling the meeting so that the necessary personnel are in attendance, and conducting the meeting following some set of rules accepted by the team. Also critically important are actions taken by the team members following the meeting to implement the decisions.

The meeting room and its equipment are essential to the progress made by the team. The room should be sized to accommodate the team and any of the visitors that have been invited. Rooms that are too large permit the members to scatter, and the distance between some members becomes too long for effective and easy communication. The chairs should be comfortable but not so soft as to promote napping. The seating arrangement should be around a table so that everyone involved can see each others face. It is very difficult to engage anyone in a meaningful conversation if they have their back to you. In industry, water, coffee, tea or soft drinks are often available if the meeting duration exceeds and hour. (Sorry, but we cannot manage this nicety in the typical college classroom). Smoking is strictly prohibited. The equipment that will be needed for presentations must be available, and its operation should be checked prior to the start of the meeting. Flip charts and white boards are useful for recording the key ideas generated during the meeting. Tape, pens, markers, and other supplies necessary for making and mounting charts and lists should be available. A computer with projection capability is of growing importance in a well-equipped meeting room. The availability of a computer during the meeting permits one to draw from a large data base, and to modify any solution in real time. Also the results can be displayed in a graphical format for the entire team to review. Finally, make sure that the room temperature is comfortable, and that the light intensity can be controlled from low for projecting overheads to high for round table discussions.

Prior to the scheduled meeting, it is important to make careful preparations. Minutes from the previous meeting and the agenda should be distributed with sufficient time for review before the next meeting. The detailed agenda includes the topics and/or problems that will be addressed in the next meeting. Individual team members responsible for specific agenda items are identified. The details are clear to all, and the responsibility that is shared by the individual members is defined. In some instances information will be needed from corporate members or visitors that are not members of the team. These people should be invited to the meeting so that they can provide the necessary expertise, and respond to questions from all of the disciplines represented on the team.

In conducting the meeting it is important to start on time. It is very annoying to the majority of the members to wait five or ten minutes for a straggler or two. The team leader must make certain that everyone involved understands that 8:00 am means 8:00 am, and not 8:08 or 8:12 am. The objectives of the meeting should be displayed, and the time scheduled for each item should be estimated. A team member should be assigned as the timekeeper, and another should act as a secretary to record notes and to prepare the minutes of the meeting. If team meetings are frequent and are held over a long period of time (several months), the duties of the timekeeper and the secretary should be shared with others on the team. The meeting should follow a set of rules that govern the behavior of the individual members. We have assigned, in Exercise 11, the preparation of a list of rules which should be followed in conducting an effective meeting. As the meeting draws to an end, the team leader should take a few minutes to summarize the outcome of the discussions. The summary is the ideal place to insure that assignments are understood, responsibility accepted and that completion dates are set. The meeting must be completed on time and every ones schedule should be respected. If the meeting is not periodic (i. e. every Tuesday at 8:00 am), then it is important that the time and place for the next meeting be scheduled.

After the meeting, the team leader checks to make certain the minutes have been prepared, that they are complete, and that they have been distributed. If any member was not able to attend the meeting, the team leader briefs that person on the important happenings. Finally, the team leader checks on each action item to make certain that progress is being made and that new or unanticipated problems have not developed. It is clear that effective meetings do not happen by accident. Many members of the team work intelligently before, during and after the meeting to make certain that the goals and objectives are clearly defined, that the issues and problems are thoroughly discussed, and that the solutions developed result in assignments that are executed with dispatch.

POSITIVE AND NEGATIVE TEAM BEHAVIOR

All the members on a team and particularly the team leader must behave in a positive manner for the team to function effectively. Frequent negative behavior is detrimental and inhibits the progress that can be made by the team and delays the product development cycle.

Positive mannerisms for the team leader, and team members are:

1. Treat every team member with respect, trust their judgment and value their friendship.
2. Maintain an inquiring attitude free of predetermined bias so that team members will all participate and share knowledge and opinions in a free and creative manner.
3. Pose questions to those team members who are hesitant to encourage them to share their knowledge and experience more fully. Share your experiences and opinions in a casual easy going manner. Help other members to relax and enjoy the interactive process involved in team cooperation.
4. Observe the body language of the individuals to determine lack of interest, defensive attitudes, hostility, etc.. The team leader should act to defuse hostility and to stimulate interest.
5. Emotional responses will occur when issues are elevated to a personal level. It is important to accept an emotional response even when you are opposed. It is also important to control you emotions and to think and speak objectively.
6. Seating arrangements once established tend to become permanent. It is productive to break these patterns changing the seating arrangements to mix the team members. The result, with time, is to enhance bonding, and to stimulate new ideas generated by different combinations of members.
7. Allocate time for self-assessment, so that the team can determine if it is performing up to expectations. The team leader may make suggestions during these assessment periods to build team skills.

Negative behavior:

1. The team leader must be extremely careful about intervention. If the team is moving and working effectively the leader should be quiet, because intervention in this instance is counter productive. If the team is having difficulty, intervention may be necessary depending on the problem. If an individual becomes hostile, intervention should be quick and the disagreement producing the hostility dealt with immediately. If the team is seeking consensus, the process may require time and the leader should wait 10 to 15 minutes before intervening. Under no circumstances should the leader intervene if he or she can not make a positive contribution.
2. The leader should never argue with a team member. The leader can introduce a different opinion and participate in a discussion with a different viewpoint. However, the discussion should never deteriorate into an argument. It is the leaders responsibility to quickly resolve arguments that arise among the team members.
3. The team leader cannot be opinionated. The leader is not a judge determining the right solution. The leader facilitates, so that the team can reach a consensus on the correct solution. It is only when the team accepts the solution that implementation can begin.
4. No member of the team should ever participate in a conversation that is derogatory about a person on the team or in the corporation. If you can not make

complimentary remarks about a person, keep your thoughts to yourself. Remember respect, trust, and friendship are vital elements in the founding of a product development team.

5. The leader is responsible for the attendance and punctuality at the meeting. If a member is absent, the leader should know the reason beforehand and explain it to the team to avoid resentment among members present. Every effort should be made to prevent erosion of mutual respect among team members.

REFERENCES

1. Smith, P. G., D. G. Reinertsen, Developing Products in Half the Time, Van Nostrand Reinhold, New York, NY, 1991.
2. Barra, R. Putting Quality Circles to Work, Mc Graw Hill, New York, NY, 1983.
3. Barczak, G. and Wilemon, D., "Leadership Differences in New Product Development Teams," Journal of Product Innovation Management, Vol. 6, 1989, pp259-267.
4. Clark, K. and Fujimoto, T., Product Development Performance, Harvard Business School Press, Boston, MA, 1991.
5. Wheelwright, S. C. and Clark, K. B., Revolutionizing Product Development, Free Press, New York, NY, 1992.

EXERCISES

1 Write a paragraph describing why team structure is so important in the product realization process that takes place in a large corporation. Add a second paragraph indicating why it is much less important in a very small company.

2 Write a letter to a prospective employer explaining why you are a good team member.

3 Write a letter, with the best of intentions, to a friend explaining why you think he or she is not an effective team member.

4 You have been a member of a functional team for two months. The team is not doing well, and it is beginning to miss milestones in the schedule of the development plan. You are to meet with your instructor for a formal performance review. Write a script for a two person play with your instructor. Questions and comments, and your answers and comments covering what you expect to occur during your review should be included in the script.

5 You (a male/female figure) are attending weekly team meetings and are always seated next to Sally/Bill who is young and very attractive. Sally/Bill is apparently interested in you, because she/he frequently involves you in side conversations that are not related to the ongoing team discussions. Write a plan describing all of the actions you will take to handle this situation.

6 Brad, the team leader, is a great guy who believes in leading his team in a very democratic manner. He encourages open discussion of the issue under consideration for a defined time period, usually 5 to 10 minutes. At the end of the time period, he intervenes and calls on the team to vote to resolve the issue. Write a critique of this style of leadership.

7 You together with Harry and Mary are senior members on a development team with 14 other members. The three of you are really very knowledgeable and experienced. You get along

very well, and have developed a habit of gathering together at the local watering hole the evening before the schedule team meeting. During the evening you discuss the issues on the agenda and reach some decisions between the three of you. Write a brief describing the consequences of continuing this behavior.

8 Sue has a wonderful personality and as a team leader is skillful in promoting free and open discussion by all of the team members. After the team reaches a consensus she calls for volunteers to implement the required action. When two or more people volunteer, she assigns them as a group to handle the action item. When no one volunteers she assigns the least active person on the team to the action items and moves promptly to the next item on the agenda. Write a critique of this leadership style.

9 Efficient Edie prepares a meeting agenda that includes 16 major items. She schedules each item on the agenda with a 15 minute discussion period without indicating that she will lead the discussion on each topic. The meeting is scheduled to begin at 8:00 am and to adjourn at 11:59 am. Write a description of what you imagine happened during the meeting. If you were the team leader how would you handle the 16 issues that had to be resolved in a short time?

10 You are the leader of a team of eight members that is meeting to develop a new hair dryer. During the first meeting the following events occur:
   - The temperature the meeting room is 88 °F.
   - The room is set up for a seminar speaker.
   - The meeting is scheduled to begin at 9:30 am and at 9:35 am only five of the eight members have arrived.
   - During the meeting Horrible Harry begins to verbally abuse Shy Sue.
   - At 9:50 am Talkative Tom begins to describe his detailed positions on the world situation and is still going at 10:10 am.
   - The team breaks for coffee at 10:15 am and has not returned at 10:30 am.
   - Sleepy Steve begins to snore.
   - Procrastinating Peter refuses to accept an action item after leading the discussion on the issue.

11 Prepare a list of ground rules that should be followed by all the members of a team in conducting an effective meeting.

12 You are a member of a team with an ineffective leader. What can you do to improve the productivity of the team? In responding to this question consider the irresponsible actions on the part of the team that are listed in Exercise 10. Remember in your response that you are not the leader and the most that you can do is to share the leadership role from time to time.

CHAPTER 12

A PRODUCT DEVELOPMENT PROCESS

INTRODUCTION

The design and development of new products and services are essential for the welfare of most industries operating in the world. The only industries that can operate today, disregarding the marketplace and continuing to ignore to the consumers' needs, are those protected by government regulations (i. e. the U. S. Post Office). For private enterprise to be successful, their product line must be competitive in every category. The products must be attractive, functional, efficient, durable, reliable, affordable, and most importantly they must satisfy the needs of the customer. How do we systematically design products that will be a success in the marketplace and generate profits for the company? Over the years companies have evolved a product development process that has evolved over the years, that is intended to provide a steady stream of new successful products. During the past decade there have been many changes, and new approaches to product development have been advanced by many of the more successful companies. A general framework for a product development process, that is followed with some modifications by many companies in the U. S. today, is described below:

1. Identify the customer needs.
2. Establish the product specification.
3. Define alternative concepts for the design.
4. Select the most suitable concept.
5. Design the subsystems and integrate them.
6. Build and modify the prototype.
7. Design and build the tooling.
8. Produce and distribute the product.

The listing is shown in sequence, but we emphasize that we must attempt to conduct many of these phases concurrently. The phrase "concurrent engineering" has been defined to indicate that the eight phases are conducted in parallel, in so far as possible and not in series.

In this one semester course, we do not have enough time to simulate all eight phases of the product development process. We essentially give you the product specification, and you begin the product development process with Step 3 and continue through Step 6. The final two phases of the product development process have not been included, because we are not stressing mass production at this early stage of your studies. While the course does not cover the complete development process, it is a good start for so early in your program. You will get a broader exposure in several course scheduled later in the curriculum.

THE CUSTOMER

We develop a product so that it may be sold at a profit. If a product is to be sold, someone must like it well enough to spend his or her money to purchase it. How do we design a product that the customer will like? The answer is to talk to the customer. Yes, design engineers do go into the field and talk with the customers one on one. These talks (interviews) are conducted at the customer's location, and usually last 30 minutes to an hour. Another approach is to quietly watch the customer use the product over an extended period (several hours). By observation, we determine all of the ways the product is used and record the customer's reactions in each application. Individual interviews and observation periods with the customer represent very cost effective methods of establishing what improvements the customer prefers in a new product.

Focus groups similar to those used in the news programs on TV are also effective in determining the customer's needs. The focus group (eight to ten customers) is assembled in an off-site location to discuss the product. A moderator with group dynamics skills leads the discussion. The focus session, which lasts for about two hours, is video taped. The development team reviews and analyzes the tape. They gain insight regarding the needs of the customer, and the value that customers place on features that may be included in the development of a new product. Focus groups have the advantage that they encourage cross communication among the customers, and this sometimes reveals information that is not discovered in the individual interviews. However, the disadvantage of this approach is higher costs, because of the need to hire a moderator, tape the session, and rent the meeting room in a hotel that is convenient for the members of the focus group.

Who is the customer? Clearly the person buying the product in the marketplace is a customer, but usually there are others involved with the product that we need to consider as customers. To illustrate this point, let's consider Black & Decker (B&D), a company that designs, manufactures, and sells moderately priced power tools. Clearly, Harry the happy home owner is a customer because he goes to the store and buys power tools. B&D will certainly interview Harry to get his input, but they will also interview the store managers at retail outlets like Home Depot, Walmart, Lowes, etc. These store mangers are stakeholders, and they share in the success of the product. They are concerned with attractive packaging, the size of the package, the lead time for the delivery, the market introduction date, price, etc. The retail store managers needs are at least as important as the needs of the individuals buying the product.

THE PRODUCT SPECIFICATION

Once the customer and stakeholders' needs are established and prioritized, we must convert the vague statements gleaned from the customer interviews into meaningful engineering terms. If the customer states that the tool vibrates too much, we must conduct experiments and measure the vibration level. Only then can we set a realistic vibration level in the product specification that will satisfy the customer. We need metrics (measurable quantities) describing each product feature that can be employed as targets to include in the product specification. We establish these metrics by testing not only our own products, but those of the competitors. In this extensive testing program (called benchmarking in industry), we establish the market norms for the product. If our new product is to be successful, we must improve on these norms.

The benchmark testing provides the basis for writing the product specification. In preparing the product specification, we attempt to provide metrics associated with each feature or subsystem in the product. We establish a target for the individual specification, with a lower limit that is marginally acceptable and a higher limit that is essentially the best that we can achieve. Design is a compromise particularly when several metrics are to be satisfied simultaneously. We design to meet all of the specification targets, but, on some features, it may not be possible to achieve the highest level of performance while maintaining cost and development time targets.

There is a systematic procedure for generating a product specification, where the vague statements made by the customer are converted to well defined metrics included as design targets in the product specification. This procedure called the "house of quality" is outside the scope of this course, but the interested reader is referred to the excellent book by Dr. D. Clausing [1] for a complete description.

DEFINING ALTERNATIVE DESIGN CONCEPTS

Let's suppose that we begin an assignment on a development team the day after the product specification has just been completed. Our next task is to develop design concepts. A design concept (idea) determines the approach taken to develop a specific feature or subsystem in the product. For example, in the development of a power tool for sanding flat wooden surfaces, we must attach the sandpaper to a sanding pad. Do we attach the paper by clamping, gluing, with vacuum, snaps, zipper or Velcro? We have presented six different design approaches (concepts) for attaching the sand paper to the sanding pad. Some of these ideas may be well known, others may be new, but wild, and hopefully one will be new and feasible. In the initial stages of generating design alternatives all ideas are acceptable (the good and the bad). We will evaluate all of them and select the better ideas later in the concept development process.

Let's consider an example pertaining to the design of a solar still. We clearly need a supply of brackish water within the still. How will we contain this water? Try to think of some ideas for accomplishing this task. Should we use a shallow pan to hold the water, or a piece of saturated cloth, or a saturated piece of string, or a plastic tube? There are many ways of holding a small quantity of water. In this phase of the product development process, it is important to generate as many design ideas as possible to consider in designing each product feature or subsystem.

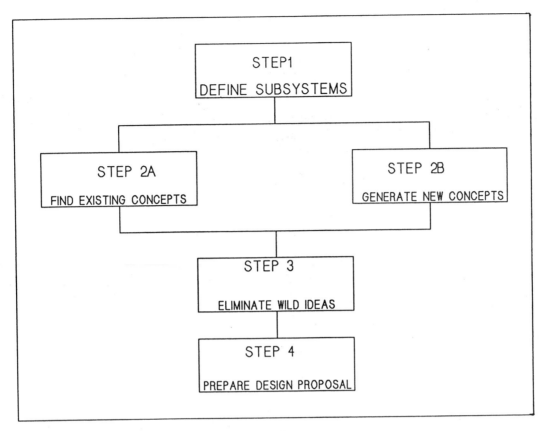

Fig. 1 A systematic approach to the concept generation process.

A systematic approach to the concept generation phase of the development process, is shown in Fig. 1. The first step in this approach is to define the subsystems involved in the operation of the product. In our case, the solar still, we may have several subsystems including:

1. The salt water container.
2. The cover.
3. The frame for the cover.
4. The solar concentrator if used.
5. The vapor transport scheme.
6. The condenser.
7. The seals to retain the water vapor.
8. The fresh water collectors.
9. The insulation for the base.

We have examined the solar still, and have subdivided it into nine different subsystems. This is not a unique list. In fact, your team may decide to divide the many functions of the solar still differently. The exact list is not important as long as it is complete. We divide the product into its major parts to simplify the design problem. It is easier to think about several smaller design tasks involving a limited number of concepts, than it is to handle a giant task involving a very large number of concepts.

The second step is to generate design concepts for each of the subsystems identified above. We approach the concept generation in two different ways. First, look to others for ideas. You are not the first design team in the world to design a solar still or any other product. Someone else was first. If you go to the library and search the literature, you will find scores of papers or books describing solar stills that have been built over the past century. A careful review of this literature and a search of the patents should permit you to develop a listing of design concepts that already exist for each of the nine subsystems listed above. Don't worry about using someone else's idea. We do it all the time. We call it by a special name --- "reverse engineering". We examine the competitors product, test it, and then adopt the good features and reject those that are poor. We also try to improve on the good features by making them better. As long as we do not violate a patent, there is no requirement that the design be original. However, the new product must be superior to the competing products when compared feature by feature.

OK, we have a complete listing of the existing design concepts used in previous designs of solar stills. Let's next generate some new ideas from within the design team. There are two approaches to follow. First, we suggest that each team member think about the subsystems and understand their purpose, function, and the way that they work. Then after developing a thorough understanding, the individual team members should list as many design ideas as possible for each subsystem. The independent thinking by team members is important early in our attempts to generate alternative design concepts. Write your ideas on index cards, with one idea on each card, and then give the cards to the team leader. Keep a copy of the card for yourself, because you will use it in the next part of the new concept generation task.

The second step in generating alternative design concepts involves a collective effort of the team. One of most widely used methods for generating ideas is brainstorming. The development team, five or six people, is a good number of participants in a brainstorming group. The team leader moderates the group, keeping it on task and avoiding any tendency to begin a round table discussion of any idea. The team leader must formulate the questions posed to the team that initiates its response. A typical question might be: present ideas that improve the pan used for the water basin. The questions should be focused on a subsystem, but it should not be so narrow as to limit the response from the team.

The team spends the next few minutes quietly thinking about the question, and if ideas occur to you, write them on an index card. You may also use the index cards that you prepared when you considered the design concepts independently. The team leader goes around the table in sequence, and each team member briefly presents one idea to the team, and hands that card to the team leader. The brainstorming method is very effective when a few simple rules are followed:

1. No criticism is allowed during the session. The critique comes later.
2. The team responses should be short and to the point. Detail is deferred until later.
3. Wild ideas are OK because our goal is to generate many ideas.
4. Improvements and combinations of ideas are sought.

Brainstorming should be fun, with everyone participating. Begin with prepared ideas from your index cards and then add spontaneous ideas as they occur to you from the synergism of the group. You should, if possible, try to embellish the ideas of other team members with improvements. Humor helps during the brainstorming process, because it breaks down barriers and improves the bonding of the team members. As the session moves from discussion based on the index cards to the generation of spontaneous ideas, the team needs a recorder to write the ideas on the blackboard or a flip chart (a very large pad of paper). The visual display of the emerging ideas keeps the team on track and facilitates continued improvement of the ideas.

The session should run for 20 to 30 minutes, or it should be concluded when the team has exhausted all of their ideas. The team leader takes the index cards, and recorders notes, and is responsible for sorting and classifying the teams contributions. These team generated ideas are added to the list of concepts that were determined from our literature and patent searches. Together they give us relatively complete lists of design ideas for each subsystem. At this point in the process the lists, one for each function or subsystem, are composed of many ideas with very brief descriptions.

A follow-up meeting of the team is conducted to consolidate the lists. The wild ideas were encouraged in the brainstorming session to create a fun-like, open and creative environment. The following session is a return to realism, and its purpose is to remove the crazy ideas from our list. The team reduces the list so that it includes only three or four of the most feasible ideas for each subsystem. Reducing the lists means that someone's idea must be eliminated. It is important that the team reach consensus in rejecting ideas. The procedure to cull ideas should not generate ill feelings. Good reasons for excluding an idea should be given in good humor. Considerable time is needed for thorough discussion. No one should feel belittled by the idea elimination process.

When the lists of the design concepts have been reduced so that they include only feasible ideas, we expand on the ideas. The ideas are represented by short written statements on index cards or notes without significant detail. Discussion of the concepts occurred in the meeting to reduce the number of alternatives, but we have not prepared detailed written descriptions of the concepts. To proceed with the evaluation of the remaining concepts, we need design proposals which include much more detailed information, and drawings or sketches showing the key features of each idea. Individual team members should develop a design proposal for his or her concept. The proposal should describe the idea in a few paragraphs, present a sketch if needed, a list of advantages and disadvantages, and a design analysis if possible. The proposal contains much of the information necessary for the team to select from among the few remaining design concepts.

SELECTING THE BEST CONCEPT

We have reduced the number of design concepts originally generated by a preliminary meeting that weeded out the obviously weak and deficient design ideas. We have also expanded the ideas, providing the team with drawings, descriptions and perhaps even analyses. But we still have too many good ideas. We must now select the best from the good, and that is not always easy to do. Fortunately we have the technique developed by Stuart Pugh [2] to help us in the selection of the best concept. The Pugh selection technique is a team activity that involves the preparation of an evaluation matrix. Keep calm its not a math matrix, and it is very easy to evaluate. Let's consider the nine steps in the Pugh selection technique that are:

1. Select the alternative design concepts to be evaluated.
2. Define a criteria upon which the evaluation is based.
3. Form the Pugh matrix.
4. Choose a datum or a reference for concept comparisons.
5. Score the concepts.
6. Evaluate the ratings.

7. Discuss the good and bad elements of each concept.
8. Select a new datum and repeat the Pugh matrix.
9. Revise select concepts as needed and evolve a superior concept.

Step 1 concerns the selection of the design concepts to be evaluated; however, we have already selected the most feasible three or four concepts based on previous team discussion. What is essential in this step is that all of the team members understand each concept in considerable detail. If all of the team members are to participate effectively in the Pugh selection process, then every one must understand each concept in great detail. For example, consider that we have generated four concepts for holding the salt water in the solar still, which include:

    A. A shallow pan
    B. A piece of felt
    C. A coil of hemp twine or rope
    D. A piece of braided rug

Do you understand how each of these four concepts can be implemented in the design so that they can be used to hold the salt water that is necessary to test the solar still in the limited time allotted for prototype evaluation in this course?

Step 2 defines the criteria that will be used in the selection process. This criteria may change in evaluating concepts for different features or subsystems, but it is fixed for any one feature. All of the concepts being considered must be judged against the same scale. What are the criteria that should be used to evaluate the four concepts listed above for holding the salt water? In the instruction provided to you for the design of the solar still, we specified the performance expected in terms of the quantity of water produced, and we listed some constraints on the size of the still, the time available for testing, and the cost. Clearly the criteria used to judge the concepts must take into account all of the requirements imposed by the course instructors as well as any additional criteria that your team imposes. Let's list some items that you may wish to include in the criteria:

    1. Cost of materials
    2. Availability of materials or components
    3. Simplicity
    4. Ease of manufacturing
    5. Ease of assembly
    6. Ease of disassembly
    7. Impact on the environment
    8. Weight
    9. Heat capacity
    10. Water capacity

Your team may want to add addition items to include in this list of criteria. For instance, do you believe that a thermal property known as emissivity should be included as a criterion?

Step 3 forms the Pugh matrix as shown in Fig. 2. The matrix is a simple table with rows and cells. You could use a spreadsheet program to prepare the matrix, or a sheet of engineering paper as illustrated in Fig. 2. The concepts A, B, C are placed in the column headings, and the criteria 1, 2, 3,....10 are placed in the row headings.

Fig. 2 Format for the Pugh chart used for concept selection.

Step 4 chooses the datum or reference against which your comparisons will be made. The datum is simply one of the concepts that you are evaluating. We initially select what is believed to be one of the better concepts, which serves as our reference. Suppose that we consider Concept A (the shallow pan) to be the datum. We then compare the remaining three concepts B, C and D to the shallow pan concept.

Step 5 scores the concepts and enter the results in the Pugh matrix. The scoring is simple. We consider each criterion separately and compare a selected concept (say B) against the datum concept (say A). The evaluation is a team activity. If the team reaches a consensus and decides that concept B is superior to concept A for criterion 1, then we score the intersecting cell in the Pugh matrix with a plus sign (+). On the other hand the team may decide that concept A is superior to B, and mark the cell with a minus sign (-). If the team decides that there is not a significant advantage of one concept over the other, the cell is marked with the letter S, indicating that the concepts are the same. It is important to recognize that the team discussion leading to the scoring is of great benefit. The team members interchange information in reaching a consensus. This heightens everyone's awareness and understanding of the design issues involved in implementing the concept. The scoring continues with each concept compared to the datum for every criterion. An example of a completed Pugh matrix is shown in Fig. 3.

Let's use the matrix presented in Fig. 3 as an example to illustrate the scoring technique. Note that this scoring was performed by the author without the very significant benefit of a team discussion. In your team's evaluation you may score the items differently, because you are considering different information or you may modify the concept slightly during your discussion. The matrix is not unique, since it is totally dependent on the information available to the team at the time of the evaluation.

CRITERIA	CONCEPTS			
	B	C	D	A
1	-	+	-	
2	S	S	-	
3	+	-	+	DATUM
4	+	+	+	
5	S	-	S	
6	S	S	S	
7	+	+	+	
8	+	S	-	
9	+	+	+	
10	S	S	-	

Fig. 3 Example of a completed Pugh chart where four concepts have been compared.

Let's consider the author's scoring for the 1st criteria in Fig. 3. I was comparing concepts B, C and D against concept A on the basis of cost. First, I estimated that the cost of the datum (shallow pan). The pan has to be relatively large in area to capture the incident radiation, and that fact lead me to consider a cookie sheet available at the local supermarket for about $2. The piece of felt (concept B) is available at a local fabric shop for about $3 a square yard, and so we place (-) in the cell B1. Hemp twine is available in the local hardware store for about $1.50 for a small roll, and so we give the cost advantage to concept C by marking (+) in cell C1. Finally, a small braided rug is available at Walmart or a similar discount retail outlet for about $5. Accordingly we score the D1 cell with a (-) showing the cost advantage with the shallow pan concept. Now, your teams' score could be different if you consider different purchasing alternatives. If you can buy the braided rug at a garage sale for $0.50, you have information different than mine and you score cell D1 with a (+) instead of a (-).

We repeat the scoring for each criterion, and mark each cell in the matrix with +, -, or S. Each score represents a consensus, and the discussion leading to that consensus gives the team an opportunity to share information in depth about every concept as it is judged against every criterion. The matrix should not be considered fixed. If a criterion is not effective in the selection process, it can be eliminated from then matrix. Concepts can be modified during the rating process, or elements from one concept can be incorporated in another. The Pugh matrix is not a strict scoring device. Instead, it is a technique that leads to the interchange of information between team members, which gives additional opportunities to modify and improve the design concepts.

Step 6 evaluates the ratings, by examining the scores for concepts B, C and D when compared to concept A. In Fig. 3 for concept B, we have 5 + signs, 1 negative sign and 4 Ss. Do not cancel the negative with one of the positives, because the negatives will be examined later in the Pugh process. For concept C, we have 4 positives, 2 negatives and 4 Ss, and for concept D, we have 4 positives, 4 negatives and 2 Ss. Concepts B and C seem to have the edge over concept A, but concept D is about the same as concept A. We have evaluated the ratings and summarized the pluses and minuses, but we defer the selection.

Step 7 is inserted in the Pugh selection process to formalize the discussion of the advantages and disadvantages of each concept. Let's examine concept B and focus on the minus sign in cell B1. That minus score indicates that the felt used to contain the water in the solar still costs too much. Can we retain the same concept but reduce the cost? Think about replacing the felt with a thick fabric or even two layers of a thick fabric. Does the fabric have to be new for it to be effective in your prototype? No, it has to hold a few ounces of water for about one hour. What about 100% cotton, heavy, denim fabric from a worn out pair of jeans? The modification of concept B substituting scrap cotton fabric for new felt improves the concept, because it lowers the cost of implementing it in the final design. The minus sign in the Pugh matrix, permits the team to focus its attention on a weakness in a concept.

Sometimes minus signs lead us to abandon a concept. Let's consider cell C5, which contains a minus indicating that the assembly of the twine in the solar still is more difficult than the placement of a shallow pan. Can we do anything to change the concept and make it easier to use saturated twine to hold the salt water? We know that the water must be spread over a large area to be warmed by the solar flux. This means that we must arrange the twine in a coil or some other configuration one layer thick over the large area in the still that is illuminated by the sun. You will have one hour to assemble, test, and disassemble your prototype still. Do you want to spend 20 minutes arranging the twine, or do you abandon the concept?

Step 8 selects a new datum and repeats the Pugh procedure. We recommend this additional step if there are many concepts that remain after the first evaluation which represent uniquely different approaches. For the example given here, we would not gain much from a reevaluation. Concept C has been eliminated, and concepts B and D have many similarities. We need to decide between containing the water in a pan versus holding it by capillary action in some type of a sheet of fabric or felt.

Step 9 revises the selected concept to evolve to a superior concept. Suppose we have selected concept B with a sheet of 100% cotton heavy denim fabric saturated with salt water. How can we improve on this idea? Presume you want to place 3 ounces of water in the still. Will the size of the piece of fabric be sufficient or will you need a double layer? What is the emissivity of the fabric? Dark colors have a high emissivity and absorb radiation, while white colors reflect the sun light. Can you find a sheet of heavy dark fabric? Why have we suggested 100% cotton? Will a blend of polyester and cotton serve as well when we attempt to saturate it with salt water? Do we need to worry about the interface between the saturated fabric and the insulation at the base of the still? If the insulation is an open cell foam plastic, it could absorb the water from the fabric depleting your supply of salt water. Will a layer of plastic film between the fabric and the insulation inhibit water migration to the insulation? Improving design concepts involves asking a lot of questions. The answers to those questions often result in design modifications that lead to the superior concept.

When we finally have superior concepts for every feature or subsystem, we can proceed with the detailed design.

DESIGN FOR ????

No, we have not made a typo in the section heading. When we design, we must consider so many different aspects, that we replaced the listing of them with ???? in the section title. Let's begin our discussion of design with the four Fs, namely form, fit, function and finish. The four Fs refer to detail design of piece parts involved a some system. This is the easiest part of the design, and that is reason for considering it first. Form refers to shape. Is the part shaped correctly to perform its function? If it is too thin it may fail by breaking or by deforming excessively. If it is too large or too thick, it will weigh too much and cost too much.

Fit is involved when we assemble two or more pieces to form a subsystem. Will the pieces fit together without gaps or discontinuities. If holes are drilled in the part for bolts, are they in alignment so that bolts fit without interference? Fit becomes critical when we deal with rotating shafts that require bearings. Tolerances required for several of the diameters in a housing containing the bearing are very tight and require precise machining of the component parts, if the bearing is to fit properly.

Function refers to the ability of the system to perform satisfactorily with its components. If a part fails in service, then the system cannot function. Suppose you design a crankshaft for an auto that resonates at an engine speed of 3800 RPM. Your crankshaft is great. It has the right form, it fits and it has the correct surface finishes on the bearing journals. But the crankshaft vibrates at or near highway cruising speed. The design fails because the performance of the auto has been severely compromised by the vibrations induced in the engine by the crankshaft. The crankshaft has not functioned correctly.

Finish refers to the surface finish of the part. Is the surface rough, smooth or polished, or does it matter? Some surfaces are important because of appearance. The sheet metal on our auto is very smooth so that the paint that is applied will produce a high gloss finish. Other surfaces are not important. The block on an auto engine is die cast, and its outside surface reflects the finish of the die. We rarely look at the engine so this surface roughness is acceptable. Some surfaces are polished or ground to enhance their performance in bearing applications. When we design a part, we must know how it will be used and specify the appropriate surface finishes on the detail drawing of that part.

DESIGN FOR MANUFACTURING

In designing a piece part or a subsystem, it is essential that we consider how the parts are to be fabricated. Manufacturing methods are probably as important as function in the design of parts that are to be produced in large quantities. For a component that is mass produced, we must carefully consider manufacturing methods such as die casting, injection molding, forging, casting, drawing, machining, stamping etc. in the detail design of the parts. We have good and bad design rules to follow depending on the production methods to be employed in manufacturing [3].

In the development of the prototype, manufacturing methods remain important, but they are less critical. For the design of the prototype solar still that we are developing in this course, we are much more limited in our manufacturing capabilities. We have a model shop with power saws with safety qualified operators that cut wood and plastic according to your drawing. You will also be able to use hand tools such as hammers, saws, chisels, wrenches, etc. Small power tools such as the drill, bayonet saw and belt sander, illustrated in Fig. 4, are also available in the student workshop. Any component that you design must be fabricated with these tools unless the components are procured from a retail outlet in finished form.

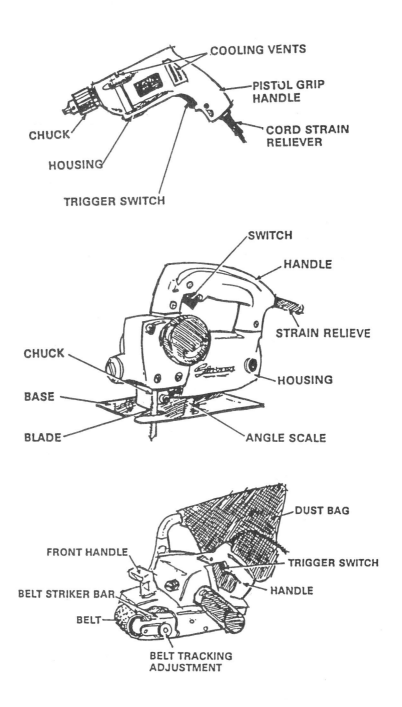

Fig. 4 Power hand tools available in the student workshop.

As an example, let's consider the frame of your still that serves to support the cover. We will assume that your cover resembles a shallow tent with a projected horizontal area of 17 by 30 in., as shown in Fig. 5. Each member of the frame is limited to a length of 17 inches, so that they can easily be packed for storage in the copy paper box. We can make the members of the frame from thin lengths of wood and cut the appropriate lengths with a saw. Alternatively, we can make the members from aluminum angle which can also be cut with a hack-saw. It appears that we will not encounter any problems manufacturing the pieces needed for the frame. Will we encounter any problems when we try to assemble all of these pieces in short period of time?

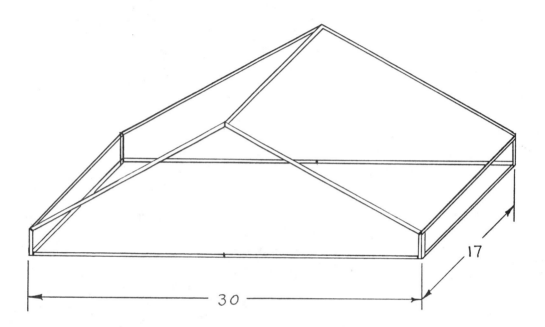

Fig. 5 Illustration of the frame for the solar still showing the joints that must be fastened in assembly.

DESIGN FOR ASSEMBLY

Products are systems containing subsystems, and the subsystems in turn contain several components. In the design of each of the components, we must consider the assembly of all these components to construct the subsystem and then the assembly of the various subsystems. There are several levels of consideration in design for assembly. The first and most important is whether or not the components can be assembled. Don't laugh. The author has seen designs which were impossible to assemble and had to be scrapped. Second, the assembly operation should be easy and not require special operator skills. Finally, the time required for the assembly should be minimized. The assembly time is very critical to the success of very complex products that are mass produced. For example, Ford Motor Company has announced savings in billions of dollars, because they used design for assembly in the development of the first model of the Ford Taurus.

One approach to design for assembly is to minimize the number of parts used in the product. As designers we tend to use many more parts than are needed based on assembly theory. Boothroyd et al [3] has developed three criteria that are used to justify the use of a part in the design of a product.

1. The part must move relative to other parts in the operation of the product.
2. The part is fabricated from a different material or must for some other reason be separated from adjacent parts.
3. The part must be separate from adjacent parts to permit assembly or disassembly of the product.

Using these three criteria, we can develop a theoretical part count for any given product. With very rare exceptions, we exceed the theoretical minimum part count when we design. Nevertheless these rules are valuable, because they stimulate the development team to consider combining parts, and designing unique parts to serve dual functions. Part counts are often reduced by 50% by applying the design for assembly criteria.

How does this affect you in the design of the solar still? After all you are designing a one of a kind prototype to learn about the product development process. Well, you are stuck with an assembly problem, because you have a very limited time to assemble, test and disassemble your solar still. If you need more than 45 minutes to assemble and 15 minutes to disassemble, then you will have to use test time for assembly, and you may not have enough time to produce the ounce of fresh water required in the product specification.

Let's return to the example of the frame for the solar still as illustrated in Fig. 5. Suppose we cut the various pieces of the frame from lengths of wood with a cross section of ½ by ¾ in. A close inspection of Fig. 5 reveals that we have 22 joints to make in the assembly of the frame from 17 separate pieces of wood. The author appears to have been a little careless about minimizing the part count in the design of the frame. How can we assemble that many parts quickly? What about nailing the pieces together? Will the nails split the wood? Will the nails pull the joints tight? What are the alternatives to nails? We can use wood screws, because they will not split the wood, and they will pull the two pieces of wood together to form a tight joint. But we must drill small pilot holes for each screw to avoid splitting the wood. Drilling at least 22 holes will take a huge amount of time. Is there a faster method to produce tight and strong joints? What about adhesives? Epoxies are very strong, but they require several hours of cure time to solidify and gain strength. My dentist uses adhesives in fixing teeth that cure almost instantly, but they are too expensive for this application. My friend has a hot glue gun which heats a stick of adhesive and melts it within a few seconds. The hot adhesive is applied to the joint and is strong as soon as it cools and solidifies. If we use the hot adhesive we can align the 17 pieces of wood and make the 22 joints in about 10 or 15 minutes. Sounds good, but you need to think about disassembly if you glue the joints together.

There is still a lot of work involved in the assembly of the prototype. Can we shorten the time by conducting several tasks at the same time. After all we have five team members, and they should all be involved in the assembly operation. The team should divide the assembly operation into several assembly tasks that can be conducted in parallel. For example, the cover can be assembled from individual sheets of plastic while the frame is being assembled. The other subsystems can be assembled simultaneously, and the overall time required to complete the assembly can be shortened by working tasks in parallel rather than series. You are not expected to work like a pit crew at the Indianapolis raceway, but every one should stay productively busy.

There are many aspects to design for assembly, and this treatment is only a brief introduction to a very important topic. For a much more complete coverage see the excellent book identified in reference [3].

DESIGN FOR MAINTENANCE

Have you ever changed the oil filter on your auto? On some cars you have to raise the body, crawl under it, and reach up to unscrew a horizontally oriented filter. When the filter is loosened, it leaks, oil runs down the side of the engine, and the oil spill is difficult to contain. Clearly, the design of this engine, and the placement and orientation of the oil filter did not accommodate the need for periodic and scheduled maintenance. Other cars have the oil filter on the other (front) side of the engine. The filter is replaced from the front without going under the car. The designers have also oriented the filter nearly vertically so that the oil does not spill when the filter is loosened and the seal is broken. This second filter is an example of design for maintenance. The designer recognized the need for periodic maintenance and developed the product to allow easy access, and rapid, inexpensive replacement of the required parts.

In the design of the solar still, you should not have to perform any maintenance. However, you should recognize that many commercial products do require some periodic maintenance, and that maintenance is a very real design criterion..

PROTOTYPE BUILD AND EVALUATION

There are several important reasons for building a prototype. The first is to determine if all of the component parts fit together. Frequently we find errors and some of the parts do not fit properly. It is much easier to change the drawings and to fix the fit problems occurring in building the first unit. Imagine trying to assemble 10,000 units of product using parts that are in error. The prototype, often called the first article build, is vital to insuring perfect fit. The assembly of the first article also reveals difficulties that may arise at a later date on the production line when the product is mass produced. The idea is to find the problems and fix them in the prototype stage. Finding problems later is much more expensive. Also problems discovered after the product has been introduced to the market requires a recall and harms the reputation of the company for producing a high quality product.

The prototype also enables engineers to test the product. These tests permit us to measure the performance parameters and verify the analysis used in the design phase to predict performance. If any deficiencies in performance are revealed in the test program, design modifications are made to the prototype, and the tests are repeated. The prototype is a vehicle for design change. It is instrumental in enhancing the performance of the product. In some instances prototype development is nearly a continuous process, with one prototype following another. At select times in this process the company will freeze a design, and introduce a new product based on a select prototype.

You are building a prototype of a solar still. As you build the first article, you will probably find some mistakes. Do not be depressed. Drawing errors and other analytical mistakes are common. Find the errors and fix them. Make the prototype work as early as possible in the semester. When you fix a mistake, make sure that you revise the drawing to reflect the revision. An early test of your prototype, prior to the last week of class is to be encouraged. The workshops and testing facilities will be ready for you.

TOOLING AND PRODUCTION

In many instances we design and develop products for a very large market with sales of 100,000 units or more each year. Also, the life cycle of the product may range from five to ten years, so that the total production over the product life is huge. The production of large quantities requires extra care in the design phase. It is widely accepted that 70 % of the final product costs are determined by the design [4]. Decisions made in the design affect the cost of producing the product over its entire life. Selecting a fastener that has a premium in cost of only 2 cents adds $20,000.00 to the cost of producing a product if the lifetime volume is one million units. Designing a component that requires an extra machining operation could easily add more than several hundred thousand dollars to the life cycle costs for high volume products. Clearly, when designing components intended for use in high volume products, we need an excellent understanding of costs, manufacturing process design rules, and assembly theory.

We trust that the procurement of the materials and the components for the solar still will provide a small lesson in cost control. For lessons in manufacturing processes, and assembly theory we defer to later courses in the curriculum, or independent study on your part. The references at the end of the chapter will get you started.

MANAGING THE PROJECT

When a development team works on a project, they are charged with the responsibility for completing the project according to a schedule and a budget. The team leader should manage time and costs. Development costs can be extremely large. Chrysler spent about one billion dollars to develop the Concorde auto. The project took 3.5 years and involved a total of about 2250 people [5]. As you move up in a corporation, your position will likely involve some degree of management. You will need to learn about scheduling and project costs relatively early in your career. Let's start now with scheduling.

You know something about scheduling already, because the University imposes a schedule on you from day one. Classes start on January xx and end on May yy. The final exam schedule is fixed before the semester starts. You have a schedule of classes --- M, W and F at 9, etc. The instructor has imposed some deadlines for design reviews that you must meet in this course. You will need to incorporate these deadline dates into the Gantt schedule, that we will develop later in this section.

Scheduling starts with listing the tasks that you need to formulate in order to develop the prototype solar still. The list of tasks should be in reasonable detail to enable you to realistically assess the time that you can allocate to each task. Let's begin by setting up a scheduling table that shows all of the tasks that must be completed during the development of the solar still. Note that the listing is in sequence according to time except for the design reviews.

TABLE 1
Task List for Developing a Solar Still

TASKS	TIME (weeks)
CONCEPT DEVELOPMENT	
Receive and understand specification	1
Concept generation	2
Concept evaluation and selection	2
DETAIL DESIGN	
Salt water containment	1/3
Frame	1/3
Cover	1/3
Base	1/3
Fresh water collectors	1/3
Drawing reviews	1/3
DESIGN REVIEWS	
Preliminary review	1
Final review and design release	1
MANUFACTURING	
Procure materials and components	1
Manufacture piece parts	1
Inspect piece parts and rework as required	½
Prepare assembly kit	½
ASSEMBLE AND TEST	
Pre-assembly	1
Final assembly and test	1
TOTAL	14

Your team should review the list and the time estimates, and make the modifications necessary to conform with your design. The time estimates are particularly important. We have scheduled 4 weeks for the team to generate, evaluate and select design concepts. That is a lot of time (five-people weeks). Do you need that much time? Estimate the time carefully, and then check to see if your estimates are correct. Estimating the time required for team members to complete a task is very difficult. Take this opportunity to start developing your time estimating skills.

After completing the listing of tasks, we construct a Gantt chart as shown in Fig. 6. The Gantt chart shows a listing of the tasks in the rows down the left side. The time line, in this case expressed in terms of calendar months during the spring semester, is displayed along the X axis. We draw bars to represent the time required to complete a specific task. The left edge of the bar corresponds to the time when the task is scheduled to begin. The right edge of the bar indicates the completion date. Of course the length of the bar shows the number of weeks scheduled to complete the task. When the tasks are completed the bars are darkened. In the example presented in Fig. 6, the bars for the concept development tasks are darkened indicating that these tasks are complete. A vertical line is shown in Fig. 6 to indicate a current date, that is, in this example, sometime in mid February. The vertical line intersects the horizontal darkened bar for concept evaluation and selection. This configuration indicates that the team is ahead of schedule. The bar is darkened for a week ahead of the current date.

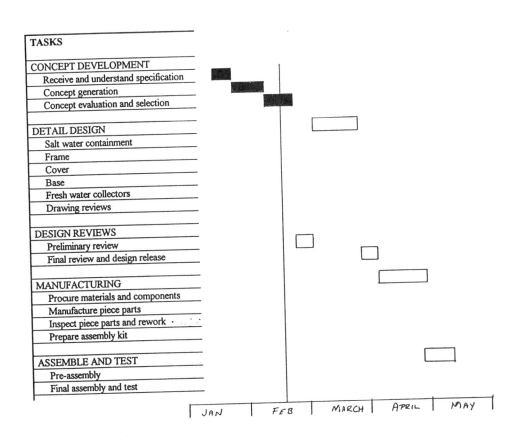

Fig. 6 Example of a Gantt chart for the solar still development during the spring semester.

The placement of the bars in Fig. 6 is typical of what is called series scheduling. We schedule one task after the completion of the previous task. However, it is possible to overlap the bars along the time scale. Overlapping the bars (parallel scheduling) implies that we will start a new task before the current task is completed. In many instances we can effectively pursue two tasks simultaneously, and important time savings can be made whenever parallel scheduling is possible. In procuring materials, we often encounter delays of weeks or even months in delivery of components necessary to build the prototype. In procuring these long lead time components, parallel scheduling is mandatory because it is necessary to place the purchase order long before the design is complete.

In Fig. 6 we have provided your team with an example Gantt chart for developing a solar still over a 14 week semester. You should consider the scheduling and change the beginning and completion dates of each task to correspond with your plan. Prepare the Gantt chart early in the semester and revise it periodically to reflect changes to the plan as the design of the still evolves. Be sure to add the deadline dates imposed by your instructor as milestones on the Gantt chart.

SUMMARY

The complete product development process has been outlined in this chapter. We very briefly described the beginning of the process, where the customers are identified, and interviewed to determine their needs and the amount that they would be willing to pay for new product features. The vague customers' comments are converted into meaningful engineering targets. The targets are incorporated into an engineering specification that defines the goals and objectives, which the designers are to meet in the development of the product.

Methods for generating alternative design concepts were covered in detail. The most essential element of this process is the synergism of the team members in generating new ideas for design. The approach is to divide the product into subsystems, and then to generate as many design ideas for each subsystem as possible. From these many concepts, we select the best one and then improve it by eliminating its disadvantages. A selection technique based on the Pugh chart has been described in considerable detail with an appropriate example.

The four Fs of design were introduced to show the importance of form, fit, function and finish. We then briefly discuss several important aspects of design for manufacturing, assembly and maintenance. These are all extremely important subjects, and the treatment here is only an introduction. Several references are cited for independent study.

Reasons are given for the importance of building the prototype. The prototype is critical to insuring the success of a development. It verifies that all of the parts fit, that they can be assembled with ease, and that the system performs in accordance with the product specification. The prototype is a vehicle for design change, and it affords the opportunity to correct the design errors prior to the introduction of the product to the market.

Finally, we introduce a method for managing the project. The method involves a listing of all of the tasks that must be accomplished to complete the prototype development, and an intelligent estimate of the time necessary to complete each task.. The data from the listing is then used to construct a Gantt chart that enables the team to track the completion of each task relative to a predefine time schedule.

REFERENCES

1. Clausing, D. Total Quality Development: A Step by Step Guide to World Class Concurrent Engineering, ASME Press, New York, NY 1994.
2. Pugh, S., "Concept Selection---A Method that Works," Proceedings of the International Conference on Engineering Design (ICED), Rome, March 1981, pp. 479-506.

3. Boothroyd, G, Dewhurst, P. and W. Knight, <u>Product Design for Manufacture and Assembly</u>, Marcel Dekker, New York, NY 1994.
4. Anon, Company Literature, Munro and Associates, Inc., 911 West Big Beaver Road, Troy, MI 48984.
5. Ulrich, K. T. and S. D. Eppinger, <u>Product Design and Development</u>, McGraw-Hill, New York, NY, 1995.
6. Cross, N., <u>Engineering Design Methods: Strategies for Product Design</u>, 2nd ed., Wiley, New York, NY, 1994.
7. Carter, D. E. and B. S. Baker, <u>Concurrent Engineering: The Product Development Environment for the 1990s</u>, Addison-Wesley, Reading MA, 1992.

EXERCISES

1. Consider a household refrigerator as a product. List the customers that you should consider in any redesign. Also give reasons for including each person or organization as a customer.
2. Interview a family member, Mom, Dad, Sister or Brother about some product that they own and use frequently. Try to list all of the favorable comments, as well as their complaints. Are they willing to pay for improvements?
3. Working together with your fellow team members prepare divide the solar still that you are designing into sub systems. Briefly describe each sub system and define any interfaces that exist between sub systems.
4. With the team conduct a brainstorming session to generate design concepts for each of the sub systems defined in exercise 3. List all of the concepts generated, the good and the bad, for each sub system.
5. Define the criteria that you plan to use to evaluate one of your subsystems in the Pugh selection process.
6. Construct a Pugh matrix and evaluation several design concepts using the criteria defined in exercise 5.
7. When the Pugh analysis of exercise 6 is complete, discuss the implications of the positive and negative scores that appear in the Pugh matrix.
8. Write an engineering brief describing design for manufacturing.
9. Write an engineering brief describing design for assembly.
10. Write an engineering brief describing design for maintenance.
11. Why do we bother to build prototypes before we release a product to the market?
12. What was your reaction when your auto or a friend auto was recalled to replace a design defect?
13. Discuss the implications of mass production on the development process.
14. Prepare a task list for your development of the prototype solar still.
15. Prepare a Gantt chart for your solar still product development.

PART V

COMMUNICATIONS

CHAPTER 13

TECHNICAL REPORTS

INTRODUCTION

We hope that you like to write, because engineers usually have to prepare several hundred pages of reports, theoretical analyses, memos, technical briefs, and letters during a typical year on the job. We trust that you will learn how to communicate in every way, ---by writing, speaking, listening, and by employing superb graphics. Communication, particularly good writing is extremely important. Advancement in your career will depend on your ability to write well. We recognize that you will be taking several courses in the English Department and other departments in Social Sciences, Arts and the Humanities. These courses will require many writing assignments, and they should help you immensely with the structure of your composition. However, most of the assignments will be essays, term papers, or studies of different works of literature. There are several differences between writing for an engineering company, and writing to satisfy the requirements of courses like English 101 or History 102.

In school you write for a single reader, namely the instructor, and he or she must read the paper to grade it, and to determine how well you are doing in class. In industry your report may be read by many people, within and outside the company, and with different backgrounds and experience. In class the teacher is the expert, and in industry you, the writer of the report, are suppose to be the one with the knowledge. Many of these folks in industry don't want to read your report. They are busy, the phone is ringing continuously, and they have lots of other things to accomplish. They read the report only because they must be aware of the information that it contains. They want to know the key issues, why these issues are important, and who is going to take the action necessary to resolve them. In writing reports in industry, we cut to the chase. There is no sense in writing a 200 word essay, when the facts can be given in a 40 to 50 word paragraph that is brief and cogent.

In the following sections, we will cover some of the key elements of technical writing including, an overall approach, report organization, audience awareness, and objective writing techniques. Then we will describe a process for technical writing that includes four phases including, composing, revising, editing and proof reading.

APPROACH AND ORGANIZATION

The first step in writing a technical report is to be humble. Realize that only a very few of the many folks, that may receive a copy of your report, will read it in its entirety. Busy managers, and even your peers read selectively. To adapt to this attitude, organize your report into short, stand-alone sections that attract the selective reader. There are three very important sections, namely the title, summary, and introduction. You locate them at the front of the report, so that they are easy to find. Up front they attract attention, and are more likely to be read. In college you call the page summarizing your essay an abstract, but in industry it is called an executive summary. After all if its prepared for an executive, perhaps a manager will consider it sufficiently important to take time to read it. Follow the executive summary with the introduction, and then the body of the report. A common outline to follow in organizing your report is:

- Title page
- Executive summary
- Table of contents, list of figures and tables
- Nomenclature only if necessary
- Introduction
- Technical issue sections
- Conclusions
- Appendices

The title page, the executive summary and the introduction are the most widely read parts of your report. Spend a lot of time polishing these three parts, as they provide you with the best opportunity to convey the important results from your investigation..

The title page should give a concise title of the report, usually in less than ten words. Keep the title short, as you have an opportunity to give detail in the body of the report. The authors give their names, affiliations, addresses, and often numbers for the phone, fax and e-mail. The reader, who may be anywhere in the world, should be able to contact the authors to ask questions. For large firms or government agencies, a report number is formally assigned, and it is listed with the date of release on the title page. An example of a title page of a report prepared for a government agency is shown in Fig. 1.

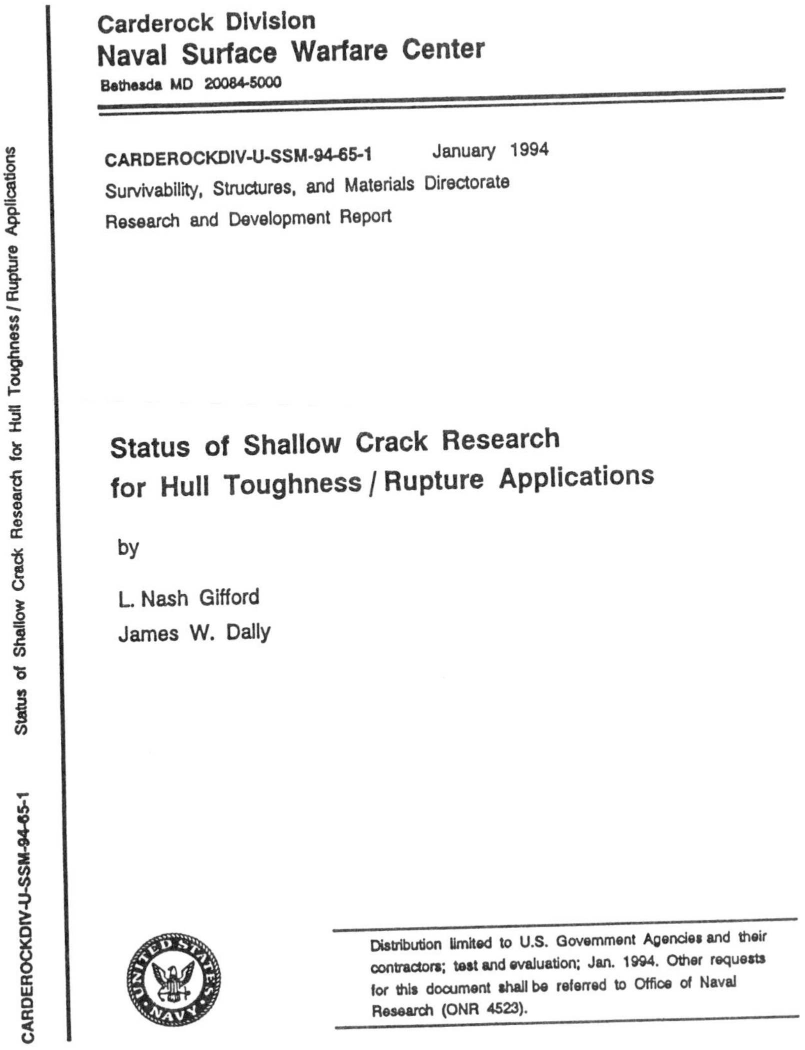

Carderock Division
Naval Surface Warfare Center
Bethesda MD 20084-5000

CARDEROCKDIV-U-SSM-94-65-1 January 1994
Survivability, Structures, and Materials Directorate
Research and Development Report

Status of Shallow Crack Research
for Hull Toughness / Rupture Applications

by

L. Nash Gifford
James W. Dally

Distribution limited to U.S. Government Agencies and their contractors; test and evaluation; Jan. 1994. Other requests for this document shall be referred to Office of Naval Research (ONR 4523).

CARDEROCKDIV-U-SSM-94-65-1 Status of Shallow Crack Research for Hull Toughness / Rupture Applications

Fig. 1 Illustration of the title page of a professional report.

The executive summary should, with rare exceptions, be less than a page in length (about 200 words). As the name implies, the executive summary gives in a concise and cogent style, all the information that the busy executive needs to know about the content of the report. What does the big boss want to know? Three paragraphs usually satisfy the chief. First briefly describe the objective of the study, and the problems or issues that it addresses. Don't include the history leading to these issues. There is always a history, but the introduction is a much more suitable section to develop history and other background facts related to the issues or problems. In the second paragraph, describe your solution to the problem, and/or the resolution of the issues. Give a very brief statement of the approach that you employed, but reserve the details of the approach for the body of the report. If actions are to be taken by others to resolve the issues, list the actions, those responsible, and the dates of implementation. The final paragraph indicates the importance of the study to the business. Cost savings can be cited, improvement in the quality of the product, gain in the market share, enhanced reliability, and etc. You want to convince the executive that your work was worthwhile to the corporation, and that you did a superb job.

In the introduction you restate the problem. But you say that the problem was already defined in the executive summary. That's OK, redundancy is permitted in technical reports. We recognize that we have many readers, so we place important information like the definition of the problem in different sections of the report. In the introduction, the problem statement can be much more complete. Expand the statement giving more information related to the problem. A paragraph or two on the history of the problem is in order. Folks reading the introduction are more interested than those reading only the executive summary, and they want to know more detail.

Following the problem statement, establish the importance of the problem to the company and to the industry. Again this is a repeat of what was included in the executive summary, but you expand your arguments for the importance of the study. You can cite statistics, briefly describe the cost analyzes that lead to the cost savings claimed, give a sketch of customer comments indicating improved quality, etc. In the executive summary, you simply stated why the study was important. In the introduction, you develop arguments to convince the reader that the investigation was important and worth the time, effort and cost.

In the next part of the introduction, you briefly describe the approach followed in addressing the problem. You began with a literature search, followed by interviews with select customers, a study of the products that failed in service, interviews with manufacturing engineers, and the design of a modification to decrease the failure rate and improve the reliability of the product. In other words, tell the reader what you did to solve the problem.

The final paragraph in the introduction outlines the remaining sections in the report. Yes, we know --- that information is in the table of contents, but again we repeat for the selective reader. Also placing the report contents in the introduction gives us the opportunity to provide a one or two sentence description about each section. Perhaps we can attract some reader interest in one or more sections, and manage to convince a few people to study the report more completely. The added description for each section in the report is not possible in the table of contents.

The organization of the report was suggested by the bullet list shown previously. However, you should recognize that there is an organization for every section, and every paragraph in the report. In writing the opening paragraph of the section, you must convey the reason for including the section in the report, and the importance of the content covered in the section. You certainly have a reason for including the section in the report, or you would not have wasted your time in writing it. Make sure you share this reason with the reader, and convince the reader that the section is important before you go into the detail of the content.

A paragraph is written to convey an idea, thought or a concept. The first sentence in the paragraph must convey that idea, clearly and concisely. The second sentence should describe the significance or importance of the idea. The following sentences in the paragraph support the idea, expand its scope, and give cogent arguments for its importance. Give the idea in the first sentence, and then add more substance in the remaining sentences. A speed reader should be able to read only the first two sentences of every paragraph, and glean 90% of the important information conveyed in the report, if it written properly.

As you add detail to a section or a paragraph develop a pattern of presentation that the reader will find easy to read and understand. First, tell the reader what you will tell him or her, then tell the story, then follow with a summary indicating the action to be taken to implement the solution. Do not try this approach in the theme that you have to write for English class, because the instructor will clean your clock for being redundant. But technical writing is not theme writing. In technical writing, we pound on the reader to get the point across, and to take corrective actions for the benefit of the company and the industry.

We often include sections in engineering reports on analysis. In these sections, we state the problem, and then give the solution. After the problem statement and the solution, we introduce the details. The reader is better prepared to follow the details (the tough part of the analysis) after they know the solution to the problem.

KNOW YOUR READERS AND YOUR OBJECTIVE

Another important aspect to technical writing is to know something about the readers of your report. The language that you use in writing the report depends on the knowledge of the audience. We are writing this book primarily for 1st year engineering students. We know your math and verbal skills from the SAT scores required for admission. We know that you have relatively good language skills, and very good math skills. You are bright and articulate. Most of the chapters in this book are in line with your current abilities. However, there are one or two chapters in the book that may stretch your technical background. These have been added as a challenge for some of the brighter or more interested readers, and as theoretical background for all of the readers.

As you write a report for this class, you know that the instructor is the only reader with which you need to communicate. You also know that he or she is knowledgeable. In that sense the report writing assignments in this class are not realistic unless they are modified. Suppose we asked you to write an assembly routing (a step by step set of instructions for the assembly of a product) for the production of you solar still in a typical factory in the U. S. What language would you use as you write this routing. Remember that a significant fraction of the factory workers in the U. S. are functional illiterates, and many other detest reading. You would use few words, and many cartoons or pictures.

Know the audience before you begin to write, and adapt your language to the audience. Consider four different categories of readers:

1. Specialists with language skills comparable to yours.
2. Technical readers with mixed disciplines.
3. Skilled readers, but not technically oriented.
4. Poorly prepared readers, who read with difficulty if at all.

Category 1 is the audience that is the easiest to address in your writings, and the audience in the last category is the most difficult. Indeed with poorly prepared readers, it is probably better to address them with visual presentations conveyed with TV monitors and video tapes.

A final topic, to be considered in planning, is the classification of the technical document that you intend to write. What is the purpose of the task? Several classifications of technical writing are listed below:

- Reports
    - Trip, progress, design, research, status, etc.
- Instructions
    - Assembly manuals, training manuals, safety procedures.
- Proposals
    - New equipment, research funding, development funding.
- Documents
    - Engineering specifications, test procedures, laboratory data.

Each classification of writing has a different objective, and requires a different writing style. If you are writing a proposal for development funding, you need persuasive arguments to justify the costs of your proposed program. On the other hand, if you are writing an instruction manual to assemble a product, arguments and reasons for funding, are not an issue. Instead, you would be trying to prepare complete and simple descriptions, that precisely explain how to accomplish a sequence of tasks involved in the assembly.

THE TECHNICAL WRITING PROCESS

Whether you are writing a report as part of your engineering responsibilities in industry, or as a student in ENES 100, you will face a dead line. In college, the deadlines are imposed well in advance and you have a reasonable time to prepare you report. In industry you will have less time, and you will have to get approvals from management before you can release the report. In both situations you have some limited period of time to write the report. The idea is to get started as soon as possible. Waiting to the day before the deadline is a recipe for disaster.

Many professionals do not like to write, and they suffer from writer's block. They sit at the keyboard hoping for some ideas to occur. Clearly, you do not want to join this group, and there is no need for you to do so. There is a technique for you to follow that helps to avoid writer's block.

Start your report by initially following the procedure described in the previous sections. Understand the task at hand, and classify the type of technical writing that you have to produce. Define your audience, so that you establish before hand the sophistication of the detail, and the language that you may employ. Prepare a skeleton outline of the report. Start with the outline presented previously, and add the section headings for the body of the report. This outline is very brief but it provides the organization of the report. That organization is important because it has divided the big task (writing the entire report) into several smaller tasks (writing the report a section at a time).

It is impossible to write a report without information. You must generate the information that goes into the report. You can use a variety of sources, interviews with peers, instructors, or other knowledgeable folks that are willing to help. Go to the library and execute a complete literature search, and then read the most suitable references. Take notes as you read, gleaning the information that you can use in your report. Be careful not to plagiarize. You can use material from published works, but you can not copy the exact wording. The statements must be in your own words. If the report has an analysis, get to work and prepare a statement of the problem, execute its solution, and make notes about the interpretation of the solution.

When you have collected most of the information that is to be covered in your report, organize your notes into different topics that correspond to the section headings, and incorporate them in your initial outline. This initial outline of the report organization will grow from a fraction of a page to several pages as you incorporate your notes in an organized format.

You are now ready to sit down and write. Writing is a tough task that requires a great deal of discipline and concentration. We suggest that you schedule several blocks of time, and reserve these exclusively for writing. The number of hours that you should schedule will depend on the rate at which you compose, revise, edit and proof read. The author can compose at about a page an hour, but most students need more time.

In scheduling a block of time for composing, you should know your productive interval. Most writers take about a half an hour to get into the swing, and then they compose well for an hour or two, before their attention and/or concentration begins to deteriorate. The quality of the composition begins to suffer at this time, and it is advisable to quit. This fact alone should convince you to start your writing assignments well before the deadline date.

While you are writing avoid distractions. Writing requires deep concentration. You must remember your message, the supporting arguments, the paragraph and sentence structure, grammar, vocabulary, and even spelling. Find a quiet, comfortable place, out of the mainstream and focus your entire concentration on the message, and the manner in which you will present it in your report.

Some sections of a report are easier to write than others. The easiest are the appendices, because they carry factual details that are nearly effortless to report. The interior sections of the body of the report that carry the technical details that are also easy to prepare. The writing describing the detail is less concise and less cogent. Don't get careless on these sections, because they are important, but each sentence does not have carry a knock-out punch.

The most difficult sections are the introduction and the executive summary. It is better to write these two sections, after the remainder of the first draft of the report is completed. We suggest that the introduction be written before the executive summary. The introduction contains much of the same information as the executive summary, although it is more expansive. The introduction can be used later as a guide in preparing the executive summary.

REVISING, EDITING AND PROOFREADING

Writing is a difficult assignment. Don't expect to be perfect in the beginning. Practice will help, but for most of us it takes a very long time to improve, because it is such a complex task. Expect to prepare several drafts of a paper or report, before it is ready to be released. In industry several drafts are essential, since you often will seek peer reviews, and manager reviews are mandatory. In college you have fewer formal requirements for multiple drafts, but they are a good idea if you want to improve the document and your grade.

The first draft is focused on composition, and the second draft is devoted to revising the initial composition. We try to get our ideas down in reasonable form, and in the correct sections of the report. In the second draft, we seek to revise the composition, and do not concern ourselves with editing. Concentrate on the ideas, and their organization. Make sure the message is in the report, and that it is clear to all of the readers. We will polish the message later.

Several hours should elapse between the first and second drafts of a given section of the report. If we read a section over and over again, we soon lose our ability to judge its quality. We need a fresh, rested brain, for a critical review. In preparing this textbook, the author composed on one day, and revised on the next day. Revising is always scheduled for the early morning block of time, when the brain is rested and concentration is at its highest level.

Let's make a clear distinction between composition, revision, editing and proofreading. Composition is the writing the first draft, where we get our ideas down, and we organize the report into sections, subsections and paragraphs. Unless you are a super person, your first draft is far from perfect. The second draft is for revisions, where you focus on improving the composition. The third draft is for editing where we correct errors in grammar, spelling style and usage. The fourth draft is for proofreading where we polish the manuscript.

As you revise your initial composition, you are concerned with the ideas and the organization of the report. Is the report organized so that the reader will quickly ascertain the principal conclusions? Are the section headings descriptive? Sections and their headings are helpful to the reader and the writer. They help the reader organize his or her thoughts. They aid the writer in subdividing the writing task, and keeping the subject of the section in focus. Are the sections the correct length? Sections that are too long tend to be ignored.

Question the premise of every paragraph. Are the key ideas presented together with their importance, before the details are included. Is enough detail given, or have we included too much trivia. Does the paragraph contain a single idea or have we tried to pass two or even three ideas in the same paragraph? It is better to use a paragraph for every idea, even if the paragraphs get short.

Have you added transition sentences or transitional phrases? The transition sentences, usually placed at the end of a paragraph, are designed to lead the reader from one idea to the next. Transitional phrases, embedded in the paragraph, are to help the reader place the supporting facts in proper perspective. You contrast one fact with another, using words like however and although. You indicate addition facts with words such as also and moreover.

When the ideas flow smoothly, and you are convinced that the reader will follow your ideas, and agree with your arguments, you can begin to edit. Run the spell checker, and eliminate the typos and most of the misspelled words. Try to find the remaining misspelled words, because the spell checker does not detect the difference between certain words like grate or great, or say like and lime. If you wanted to say that you like something, and typed the word lime instead, the spell checker doesn't help find your typo.

Look for excessively long sentences. When sentences get to be 30 to 40 words in length they are going to begin taxing the reader. It is better to use shorter sentences, where the subject and the verb are close together. Make sure that the sentences are sentences. Remember, that a sentence needs a subject and a verb, and they should have the same tense. Have you used any comma splices, which is attaching two sentences together with a comma? Examine each sentence, and eliminate unnecessary words or phrases. Find the subject and the verb, and attempt to strengthen them. Look for redundant words in a sentence, and substitute different words with similar a meaning to eliminate redundancy.

The final step is proofreading the paper to eliminate all of the errors. Start by running the spell checker for the final time. Then print out a clean, hard copy to use for proof reading. Check all the numbers and equations in the text, tables and figures for correctness. Then read the text for correctness. Most of us have real trouble reading for correctness, because we read for content. We have been trained since 1st grade to read for content, but we rarely read for correctness.

To proof read, you read each word separately. You are not trying to glean the idea from the sentence, so stop reading the sentence as a whole. Read the words as individual entities. If it is possible, arrange for some help from a friend. One person reads aloud to the other. The listener concentrates on the appearance of each word, and checks the text against the spoken word to verify it correctness.

WORD PROCESSING

The word processor is a great tool to use in preparing you technical documents. The very significant advantage of the word processor is the ability to revise, edit and make the necessary changes without excessive retyping. You can mark text, delete, copy or move it. You can insert words, phrases, sentences and/or paragraphs.

While working with a word processor, it is very difficult to revise, edit, and proof read on the screen. Much better results are obtained if you have hard copy, and can view the entire page. With the entire page, you can see several paragraphs and check that they are in the correct sequence. Use double spacing when printing the first few drafts to give space between the lines for the modifications that you make to the hard copy.

After you have completed the revisions on the hard copy, make the required modifications to the text on the word processor, and save the results on your own floppy disk. We recommend that you keep only the most recent version (draft) of the document. If you save several versions of the document, it is necessary to keep a log book to record the changes to each version. If the writing takes place over a few week period, it is very easy to lose track of what changes you made, and which version of the hard copy goes with which electronic copy. We find it easier to keep one electronic file (on your floppy disk) of the most recent draft with a hard (paper) copy to serve as a back-up.

The word processor has several features that are helpful in editing. The spell check program finds most of our typos and provides suggestions to correct many of the words that we misspell. The search command permits you to systematically examine the entire document, so that you can replace a specific word with a better substitute. The thesaurus is available on command to help you with word selection, but you must be careful when using it. Make sure you understand the meaning of the word that you select, and don't try to impress the reader by using long or unusual words. Short words that are easily understood by the reader are always to be preferred in technical writing.

Formatting the report is another significant advantage of word processing. You can easily produce a document with a very professional appearance. The formatting bar permits you to select the type of font, the point size (the height of the characters), the pitch (the number of characters per inch), and emphasis such as bold, underline or italic.

You can also format the page with four different types of line justification commonly available. We are using the word processor in preparing this textbook, to justify alignment for both the right and left margins. The word processor automatically adds the spaces in a line and aligns both margins. In designing your page use generous margins. One inch margins all around are typical. If the document is to be bound, the left margin is usually increased from 1.00 to 1.25 inch.

Tables and graphs can be inserted in the text. Take advantage of the ability to introduce clip art into the text, or to transfer spread sheets and drawings produced in other software programs into the word processing program. Position the tables, and figures as close as possible to the location in the text where they were introduced. Avoid splitting a table between two pages, even if it means leaving an unused space at the bottom of a page. Place the caption directly beneath the figure, and use it to identify the illustration and to describe its message.

SUMMARY

Writing is a difficult skill to master, and most engineers experience a number of different problems early in their careers. Unfortunately, the writing experiences in college do not correspond well with the writing requirements in industry. In school we write for a knowledgeable instructor. In industry we write for a wide range of people, with different reading abilities, that vary from assignment to assignment. In both college and industry, we write to meet deadlines imposed by others. While writing is not much fun, at least early in your career, there are many techniques that you can employ to make writing much easier and more enjoyable .

The first technique is to organize the report, and we have suggested an outline for a typical report. Gather information for the report from a wide variety of sources, and generate notes that you can use to refresh your memory as you write. Sort the notes and transpose the information on them to expand the outline for your report.

As you organize the outline, before you begin to write, determine as much as possible about the folks who will be reading your document. They can be as technically knowledgeable as you are, but they can also be functionally illiterate. The language that you use in the report will depend on the readers ability to understand. Also be clear about the objective of your document. Is it a report, an extended memo, a proposal or an instruction manual. Styles differ depending on the objective, and you must be prepared to change accordingly.

There is a process to facilitate the preparation of any document. It begins with starting early, and working systematically to produce a very professional document. Divide the report into sections and write the easy sections (appendices, and the technical detail portions) first. Defer the more difficult sections, such as the executive summary and the introduction, until the other sections have been completed.

The actual writing is divided into four different tasks, namely composing, revising, editing and proofreading. Keep these task separate, and compose before revising, revise before editing, and edit before proofreading. Multiple drafts are necessary with this approach, but the results are worth the effort.

Finally, word processors do not substitute for a clear brain, but they are extremely helpful in preparing professional documents. They save enormous amounts of time in a systematic editing process. They enable a mix of art, graphics, and text neatly integrated into a single document. Word processors have a thesaurus and word search features that are helpful in editing. They essentially turn a computer into a print shop, so that you have a wide latitude in the style and appearance of your professional documents.

REFERENCES

1. Eisenberg, A., Effective Technical Communication, 2nd ed., McGraw Hill, New York, NY, 1992.
2. Goldberg, D. E., Life Skills and Leadership for Engineers, McGraw Hill, New York, NY, 1995.
3. Elbow, P. Writing with Power, Oxford University Press, New York, NY, 1981.

EXERCISES

1. Prepare a brief outline of the organization of the final report for the solar still development.
2. Prepare an extended outline of the final report for the solar still development.
3. Write a section describing one of the subsystems in the solar still.
4. Write a section covering the analysis of the fresh water produced by the solar still during the prototype test period.
5. Write the Introduction for the final report on the solar still development.
6. Write the Executive summary for the final report on the solar still development.
7. Revise the Introduction that another team member wrote.
8. Edit the Introduction after it has been composed and revised by others.
9. Proof read the Introduction after it has been composed, revised, and edited, by others.

CHAPTER 14

DESIGN BRIEFINGS

INTRODUCTION

We communicate by writing, speaking and graphics. All three modes of communication have their place, as we try to convey our ideas and concerns to others, and all three are important. Let's focus our attention on speaking in this chapter. We use speech almost continuously in our daily life, so why do we need to study about design briefings? There are several reasons. We usually speak with our friends and family in an informal style. We know them and feel comfortable with them. They know us. They are concerned with our well being, and genuinely like us. They are usually interested in what we have to say. A professional presentation is different. It is formal event that is usually scheduled well in advance. The audience may include a few friends, but mostly they will be strangers. The time we have to convey our thoughts is very limited. The audience may not be very interested in our message. A person or two in the audience may be managers who control our advancement in the company. There are lots of reasons for tension headaches as one prepares for the professional presentation.

The design briefing is extremely important to both the product development, and to your career. Information must be effectively transmitted to your peers, the management, and to any external parties involved in the project. Clear messages, that accurately define the problems that the development team can effectively address, are imperative. On the other hand, ambiguous messages are often misunderstood, and they lead to delays in defining problems and implementing timely solutions. The design briefing is an opportunity for a healthy review. It permits your peers to share your ideas, and it affords management an open forum for assessing your work and progress. Since the professional presentation is critically important, let's learn some great techniques for accurately conveying our messages to a random group of strangers.

SPEECHES, PRESENTATIONS AND DISCUSSIONS

To begin let's distinguish between three types of formal methods of oral communication, namely the speech, the presentation, and group discussion. The speech is the most formal of the three. 1996 is a good year to refer to in describing speeches, because we have been besieged with political addresses that clearly illustrate their key features. Speeches are given to large audiences in huge rooms, stadiums or coliseums. The setting is usually not appropriate for visual aids to be used. The audience rarely has very much in common. They are of widely different ages, with different interests and persuasions. The speech is carefully scripted, and the speaker usually reads or very closely follows the script. Ad-libbing is avoided. Communication is one way, --- from the speaker to the audience. Questions are usually not appropriate. Time is strictly controlled. Fortunately engineers are rarely called upon to make speeches, so we will not dwell on this topic.

Professional presentations differ from speeches. Presentations are made to smaller audiences, in smaller rooms with electric power and light controls. We depended on visual aids, demonstrations, simulations and props to help convey our message. The audience is knowledgeable (about our topic), and usually has many common characteristics. The presentation is carefully prepared. It has order and structure, but it is not scripted. The flow of information is largely from the speaker to the audience, but questions are permitted. The speaker is considered the expert, but discussion of questions gives the audience a chance to share their knowledge of the topic. The time is carefully controlled, and it is usually insufficient from the speakers viewpoint. Professional presentation is a mode of oral communication that you must master.

Group discussions are also very important to the design engineer. The audience is smaller, with much more in common. They may be all be members of a development team. The topic being discussed will be narrowly focused. The speaker serves as a moderator, and is an expert on the topic being considered. However, members of the discussion group (audience) may be as knowledgeable as the speaker (moderator). The moderator works in two modes. He or she may act as a presenter, giving brief background information to frame an issue that leads to discussion from any member of the discussion group. The moderator may also direct questions to a member of the group know to be the expert on the issue being addressed. The speaker (moderator) controls the flow of the information, but the flow is clearly two ways, from speaker to the group, and from one group member to the other group members. In group discussions, time is difficult to control, and the content and the range of coverage is strongly dependent on the skill of the moderator. The group discussion is very important in industry because the leader of a development team will often use this method of communication to identify problems, and to initiate an effort directed toward their solution. We will not address discussion group methods in this course; however, we recommend that you watch Washington Week in Review on PBS to gain some insights. While the participants are journalists, we can adopt many of their clever techniques in engineering.

A design briefing is a type of professional presentation. It is the method of speaking that we will emphasis in this course. Indeed, you will be required to make presentations describing your development of the solar still on two occasions. The first will be the preliminary design review, and the second will be the final design review.

PREPARING FOR THE BRIEFING

A design briefing is far too important to take casually. You should prepare very carefully, and insure that you will convey the information necessary to accurately report the status of the development, and to identify problems or unresolved issues facing the team. There are three aspects that you should consider in your preparations, which includes identifying the audience, planning the organization and coverage, and preparing the visual aids.

In this class, it is too easy to identify the audience. You have your class mates, the undergraduate fellow, and the instructor. In industry the situation will be a lot different, as the audience will be much more diverse. The size and diversity of the audience depends on the magnitude of the development project. A small briefing will have 10 to 20 in attendance with most participants from within the company. A large briefing may include 50 to 100 representatives, that are both internal and external to the company. The characteristics of the audience is important, because you must adapt the content of the presentation to the audience. Classify your audience with regard to their status, interest, and knowledge before you begin to plan the style and content for your presentation.

The status of the audience refers to their position in the various organizations they represent. Are they peers, managers, or executives? If they are a mix, which is likely, who is the most important? If you are preparing a design briefing for high level management, it must be concise, cogent and void of detail. Executives are busy, stressed, and always short on time. High level managers are impatient, and rarely interested in the technical details that engineers love to discuss in their presentations. Recognize these characteristics, and adjust the content and the timing of your presentation accordingly. The executives are interested in costs, schedule, market factors, performance, and any critical issue that will delay the development or increase projected costs of either the development or the product. Usually you will have from 5 to 10 minutes to deliver convey this information at an executive briefing.

First and even second level managers are more human, more interested in you and your designs. If you prepare the presentation for this lower level of management, you can plan for more time (10 to 20 minutes). These managers are likely to be engineers, and they will share your knowledge of the subject. In fact, they probably will be more expert or more knowledgeable than you. They will want to know about the schedule and costs, because they share responsibilities with the higher level management for meeting these goals. However, they are also interested in the important details, and you can get into discussion of subsystem performance with them. The first and second level managers often control the resources for the development team. If you need help, make sure that they get the message in enough detail to provide the assistance required. Do not hide the problems that your team is encountering. Managers do not like to be surprised. If you have a problem make sure they understand it, and are able to participate in its solution. If you hide a problem from management and it causes a delay or an escalation in costs, the manager will take the heat and you will be in one very unpleasant dog house.

Design briefings for peers are less tension producing, and you will have more time (20 to 30 minutes). You will address schedule and cost issues, because everyone needs to know if you are meeting the milestones on the Gantt charts. However, the main thrust of your presentation will be on the details. If you are working on one subsystem, that interfaces with other subsystems, you will cover your subsystem in sufficient detail for all to understand its geometry, interfaces, performance, etc. It is particularly important that the interface issue be fully addressed in the presentation. If four subsystems are to be integrated in a given product, a lot of details about all four subsystems need to be addressed to ensure that the integration goes smoothly. Suppose for example, that we are developing a power tool with a motor that draws 20 amps, but we employ a 10 amp switch to turn the power on and off. The switch will function satisfactorily in the short term tests with the prototype, but it will malfunction in the field with extended usage long after the product has been released to the market. Clearly, the two folks responsible for the interface between the motor and the switch did not communicate. The integration of the two subsystems failed.

The most important purpose of design briefings with peers, is to make certain that all of the details have been addressed, and that the subsystems will be integrated without problems occurring as the prototype is assembled and tested.

Peer reviews in the absence of management are very beneficial in the development process. The knowledge of all of the members is about the same, although some team members are much more experienced than others. The topic is usually a very detailed review of one subsystem or another. The audience is fresh, and they can provide a critical assessment of the technology that you employed. They can check the accuracy of you analysis, and comment on the choice of materials, and relate their experiences with similar designs on previous products. Peer reviews afford the opportunity for the synergism that make fine products even better. They also provide a forum for passing on important lessons from the more experienced designers to the new designers in a friendly, stress-free environment.

The subject of the presentation is self evident in a design review. We are developing a product, and the subject will address one issue or another regarding the development. There is a choice of specific topics, and considerable latitude regarding the content. We have given advice in previous paragraphs about matching the content with the interests of the audience. Executive reviews serve a different purpose than peer reviews, and the content and the time allotted for the presentation is adjusted accordingly.

In all types of reviews there are two absolute rules that you must follow. First, know the material cold. It takes an audience about two seconds to understand that you are faking it. When they realize that you are not the expert, your presentation is a failure, and you have lost the opportunity to communicate. Second, be enthusiastic. It is OK to be calm and cool, but don't be dead on arrival. You must command the attention of your audience, or they will turn you off. You control the attention of the audience only if you are enthusiastic and knowledgeable in presenting your material.

PRESENTATION STRUCTURE

There is a well accepted structure for professional presentations. We discussed this in some detail in a previous chapter dealing with PowerPoint, a graphics presentation program marketed by Microsoft. We show a recommended structure or outline for the presentation in Table 1.

TABLE 1
Recommended Structure for a Professional Presentation

- Title
- Overview
- Status
- Introduction
- Technical Topics
- First Topic
- Second Topic
- Third Topic
- Summary
- Action Items

Let's examine each of these topics individually, and discuss the content that you will include on the visual aids that accompany your presentation. Recognize that the visual aids(slides), control the flow and the content of information that you will present. For this reason, we will address the topics listed above in the context of the information to be placed on the slides.

The title slide obviously carries the title of the presentation. But it also gives your affiliation, and the names of the team members that contributed to the work. Remember, you may be reporting on the work of the entire team, and it is necessary for you to acknowledge their contributions on the title slide, and in your opening remarks. The title should be brief. Ten words or less is a good rule to follow in drafting the title for your presentation. It is also a good idea to use descriptive words in the title. For example, you could use **PRELIMINARY DESIGN REVIEW OF THE PANTHER TEAM SOLAR STILL**. Nine words and you have told us the topic (a design review), the type of review (preliminary), the owners of the development (tiger team), and the product being developed (the solar still). That is a lot of information to convey in nine words. It is possible to improve the title by removing the articles and using **PRELIMINARY DESIGN REVIEW --- PANTHER TEAM SOLAR STILL**. This title conveys the same information with seven words.

Below the title, the members involved in the development are listed. It is essential that you share the ownership of the material covered in your presentation. Often the work of several people is covered by a single member of the team. It is not ethical to make the presentation without acknowledging the contributions of others.

It is also a good idea to date the title slide, and cite the occasion for the presentation (i. e. ENES 100 Introduction to Engineering Design, February 21, 1997). This information is useful if you make many presentations, want to refer to your files, and to reuse some of the slides after editing. An example of a title slide prepared with PowerPoint is shown in Fig. 1.

The second slide is an overview. The overview for a presentation is like a table of contents for a book. You list the main topics that you intend to cover in the presentation. In other words you tell the audience, what you intend to tell them in the next 10 to 20 minutes. The number of topics should be limited. In a focused presentation you can cover about a half of dozen topics, but if you try to over a lot of topics (10 to 15) you will have difficulty retaining the attention of the audience.

Constrain the tendency to tell all, and instead focus on the important issues. In a design review, the topics usually are organized to correspond with the subsystems involved in the product under development. We show such an example for a preliminary design review of a solar still in Fig. 2.

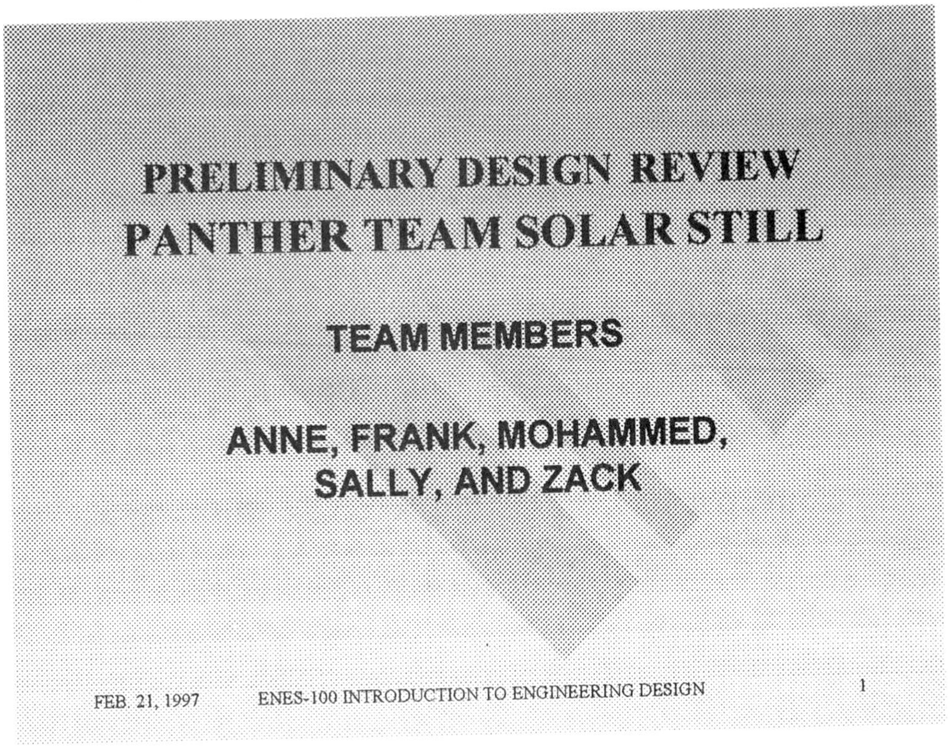

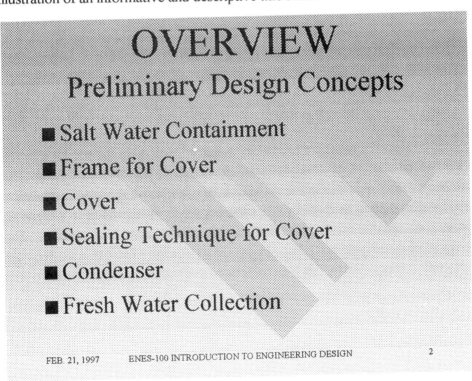

Fig. 1 Illustration of an informative and descriptive title slide.

Fig. 2 The overview slide indicates the content in your presentation.

The third slide is used to present the status of the development. You should report on the progress made by the team to date. It is a good idea to incorporate a Gantt chart on the status slide to show the schedule, and the progress of the team on each task defined on the chart. If there are problems or uncertainties, this is the time to air the difficulties that the team is encountering. An example slide, shown in Fig. 3, illustrates uncertainties that the team has with regard to the condenser and fresh water collector on the solar still development.

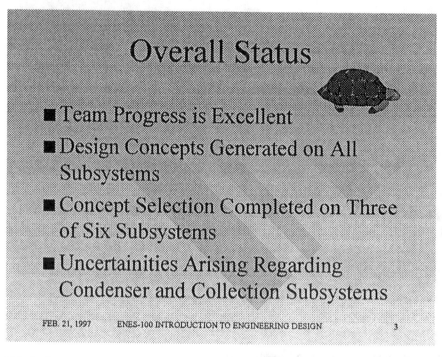

Fig. 3 Status slide indicates overall progress, some accomplishments, and signals potential problems.

The fourth slide covers the introductory material such as background, history, or previous issues. It is important that the audience understand the product, the main objectives of the development, the role the team has in that development, and the most pressing of the current issues. This introductory slide permits you to set the stage for the body of the presentation that follows.

The body of the presentation deals with five or six technical topics. Usually the topics selected correspond to several of the more critical subsystems involved in the product. Avoid trying to cover a very large number of topics. It is better to report on a limited number of topics thoroughly, than to rush through a dozen topics with incomplete coverage. We suggest two slides for each topic. The first slide is to describe the progress made by the team in generating design concepts, and to indicate the criteria that was employed in selecting the best concept. The second slide covers the status of developing the selected concept. The type of information reported on this slide includes accomplishments, outstanding issues, lessons learned, etc. An example is presented in Fig. 4.

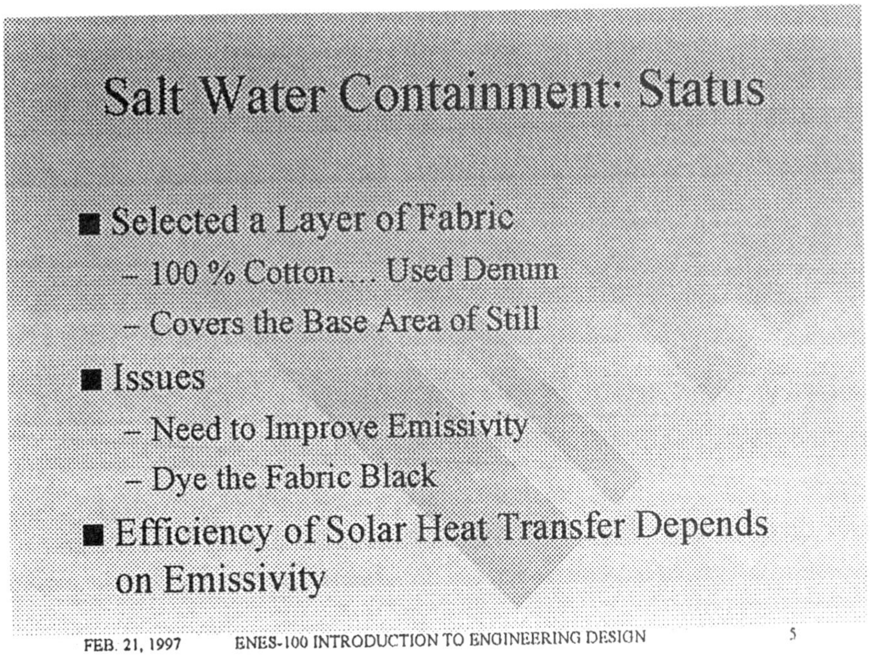

Fig. 4 Example of information presented in describing the development of a subsystem.

After the technical topics have been covered, you must conclude the presentation with a decisive pair of slides. Suggestions for your two concluding slides are given in Fig. 5. The next to the last slide is titled "Key Issues". This is your opportunity to identify very important issues (questions), that your team has discovered. Don't hesitate, as this is the time to introduce the uncertainties, and to come forward and seek help. Design reviews are not competitive. We seek to help, regardless of our status or our role as a member of the audience. Managers will arrange support for your team if it is required. Peers will make suggestions, and introduce fresh approaches that the team may find useful. The design review is a formal process for all to participate in the development. Take advantage of the review to reveal uncertainties, and to seek help whenever your team needs assistance.

The final slide is to indicate plans for the future. Management wants to know how you intend to solve some of the issues that you have revealed, and the time involved in the solutions. Your peers will be interested in the technical approaches that you intend to follow. You should also define any requirement that you have of anyone in the audience. If you need help from your peers, or more resources from the manager, make sure it is clearly indicated on this final slide. Be certain that the individuals agree to provide the support that is requested. If action items are listed, identify the responsible individual, and estimate the time to completion. The planning incorporated in the final slide is very important. It is the prescription for your team's get well program.

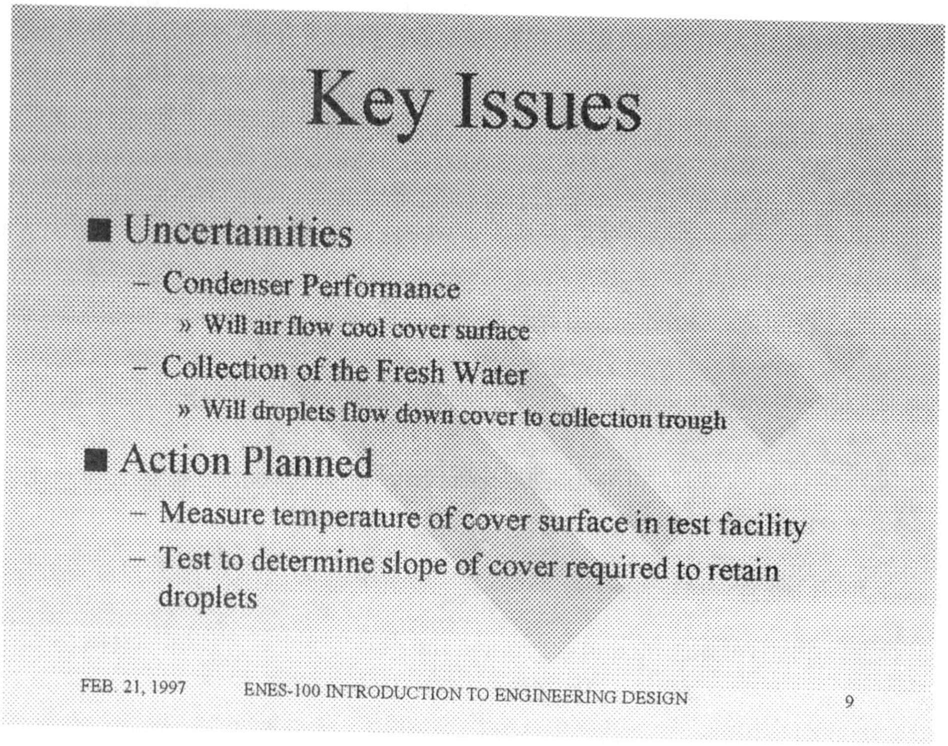

Key Issues

- **Uncertainities**
  - Condenser Performance
    - » Will air flow cool cover surface
  - Collection of the Fresh Water
    - » Will droplets flow down cover to collection trough
- **Action Planned**
  - Measure temperature of cover surface in test facility
  - Test to determine slope of cover required to retain droplets

FEB. 21, 1997   ENES-100 INTRODUCTION TO ENGINEERING DESIGN   9

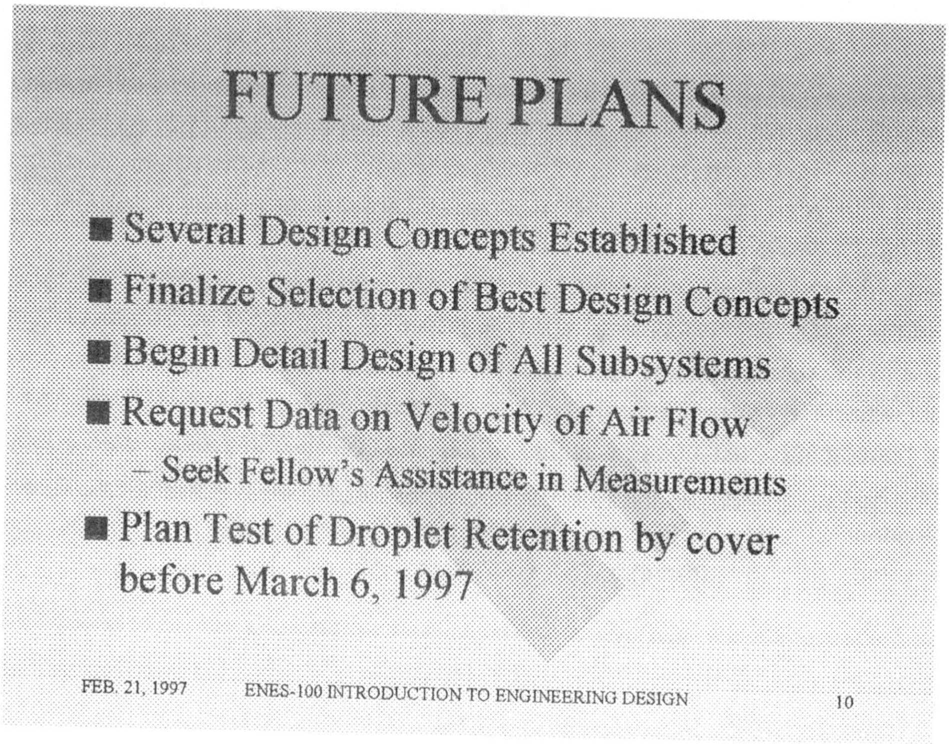

FUTURE PLANS

- Several Design Concepts Established
- Finalize Selection of Best Design Concepts
- Begin Detail Design of All Subsystems
- Request Data on Velocity of Air Flow
  - Seek Fellow's Assistance in Measurements
- Plan Test of Droplet Retention by cover before March 6, 1997

FEB. 21, 1997   ENES-100 INTRODUCTION TO ENGINEERING DESIGN   10

Fig. 5 The final two slides describe the key issues and the future plans.

TYPE OF VISUAL AIDS

Visual aids are essential for a technical presentation, because they control the content and the flow of the information that is conveyed to the audience. They provide visual information that reinforces the verbal information. You communicate using two of the individual's five senses. Take time to select carefully the best type of visual aid to convey your message.

In selecting visual aids, we are usually limited in two ways. The first limitation is in our ability to produce the visual aids, within the time available and for the amount we are willing to pay for them. The second limitation pertains to the equipment and the room in which the presentation is to be made. Is the room equipped with a 35 mm slide projector, an overhead projector, or a computer controlled projector? Another important consideration is the control of the light intensity in the room. Most rooms have light switch, and you can turn the overhead lights off. However, some rooms do not have blinds, and a bright sunshine will cause real problems in the visibility of the slides when they are projected.

The computer projected slides are an excellent choice if the room can be darkened, and if the projection equipment is available. (It is very expensive.) This selection has several advantages. The presentation is easy to prepare using PowerPoint. The slides are in color, and you can use slide transition and slide building features that enhance the visual impact of the presentation. It is also easy for you to copy your presentation on a floppy disk, use the computer attached to the projection system to load your program, and use the mouse to click through your slides line by line. Finally, you can prepare low cost hand-outs for the audience with six slides per page.

Projecting overhead transparencies is probably the most common method of presenting visual material. Overhead projectors are relatively inexpensive (a few hundred dollars compared to a few thousand dollars for the computer controlled projectors), and for this reason they are available in most rooms. Overhead projectors are the best choice if the room cannot be darkened. The projectors are bright enough to give good quality images without extinguishing the lights. Bright rooms help you keep the audience awake. Overhead transparencies are also easy to make on a copy machine. If you are willing to sacrifice the benefits of color, use inexpensive black and white transparencies. If you want to use color in the presentation because it is more effective, the costs increase significantly if you use a color laser printer or a color copier. However, ink jet printers can be used to produce good quality color transparencies at a reasonable cost.

The 35 mm slide is the third option. It is the preferred option if you have many photographs to project, because the quality of colored 35 mm slides is excellent. The slides are easy to prepare if you have a camera, and the time to have the film processed. Their cost is reasonable, if you make many slides and use the entire roll of film (24 exposures). It is possible to prepare colored slides from your PowerPoint files on a floppy disk; however, the equipment required is not always available. 35 mm slide projectors are common, but in an engineering college they usually are much more difficult to find than the overhead projector. The room must be darkened to view the image from a 35 mm projector. Another disadvantage, the relatively long distance required from the projector to the screen, precludes the use of very small conference rooms for presentations.

Sometimes speakers will employ two or three different types of projectors. The switch from one to the other is disruptive. If possible, use only one type of projector. However, if you must use more than one type of projector to convey your message, try to minimize the number of times you switch from one to another.

There are several other visual aids that are sometimes used in professional presentations. Video tapes are common, but the size of the TV monitors often make viewing difficult for a large audience. However, if you want to show motion, or group dynamics, video clips are clearly the best approach. Video cameras are readily available, and after a bit of practice, we all can become reasonably good video producers.

Motion picture films, particularly of older material with historical interest, is very effective. Finding an 8 mm or 16 mm motion picture projector may be difficult, so allow time in your schedule for making the necessary arrangements.

Hardware or materials to be used in the product is sometimes passed around the audience during a presentation. The hands on opportunity for the audience is a nice touch, but you pay for it with the loss of the attention by some members of the audience during the inspection period. We recommend that you defer passing materials to the audience during the presentation. Instead, invite the audience to inspect your exhibits that are placed on a strategically located table sometime after the presentation. This approach maintains the attention of the audience throughout the presentation, while giving those interested in the hardware time later for a much more thorough examination.

DELIVERY OF THE PRESENTATION

Excellent presentations require very well prepared slides, and a very smooth, well paced delivery. There are many aspects to the delivery part of the presentation process including, dress, body language, eye contact, voice control and timing. Let's start with dress. Broadly speaking there are four levels of dress. The highest level, black tie for men and formal gowns for women, fortunately is a rare event and never appropriate for design briefings. The next level, business attire with a suit for men, and a conservative dress for women, is sometimes appropriate for design briefings. A conservative Eastern company may have a dress code requiring business attire, whereas a less formal California company would encourage more casual attire. Casual attire should not be confused with sloppy attire. Casual attire is neat and tasteful, but without suits, ties and white shirts for men, and suits for women. Sloppy attire like old jeans, and a sweatshirt is taboo. We suggest that you select either business or casual attire as your dress for the presentation. We recognize that most students these days prefer the sloppy dress style. Resist the impulse to dress that way. If you look like a bum, or a street lady who will believe the message?

Posture is another important element in the presentation. In the words of former President Regan, stand tall. Your body language signals your attitude to the audience. You are the presenter, and you are in control. Make sure you are calm, cool and collected. Nervous gestures with your hands, rocking on the balls of your feet, scratching your head, pulling on your ear, etc. should be avoided.

Before you begin your presentation, take control of the audience. One approach is to pause before projecting the title slide, and immediately make eye contact with the entire audience. How do you look at everyone in the house? You scan the audience from left to right and then back, looking slightly over their heads. Occasionally drop your eyes and make eye contact for a second or so with one individual and then another. Pause long enough for the audience to become silent (10 to 20 seconds). If some one is rude, and keeps on talking, walk toward them, and politely ask for their attention. When you have everyone's attention, project the title slide and begin your delivery.

If you have rehearsed, you will not need notes. The slides carry enough information to trigger your memory. If they don't, you have not rehearsed long enough to remember the issues. Scripting the presentation is not recommended. People who script will eventually start to read their comments, and that is deadly. Rehearse until you are confident. Make notes to help you rehearse, but throw them away before the presentation.

When you begin to speak make sure that everyone can hear you. If you are not sure of this, ask those in the back of the room if they can hear. If you have a microphone with an amplifier and speakers, be careful. The tendency is to speak too loudly. Try to control the loudness of your voice within the first minute of the presentation, as you introduce the topic with the title slide. The audience will read that slide, and will bear with you as you adjust the volume of your voice.

Don't mumble. Speak slowly, clearly and carefully enunciate each word. You don't need to speak as slowly as Vice President Gore, but it is better to go too slowly that too rapidly. If you can improve your enunciation, you will be able to increase the rate of your delivery without loosing the audience.

Don't run out of breath while speaking. Learn to complete a sentence, pause for breath (without a gasp), and then continue with the next sentence. There is nothing wrong about an occasional pause in the presentation provided it is short.

If you forget some detail, don't worry. Skip it, and move to the next point that you are trying to make. If the detail is critical, count on one of your team members to raise the issue in the question period. We all forget some of the material that we intended to present, and introduce some additional items on an ad hoc basis. Frequently the audience will never recognize our omissions or additions.

Studies have clearly shown that people can listen faster that the presenter can speak. The trouble with following someone who speaks very rapidly is not the rate of speech, but the enunciation. Most folks who speak rapidly tend to slur their words, and we have trouble understanding poorly pronounced words. The trouble in listening to Al Gore, is to stay with his message. While your waiting for his next word, your mind goes off on a mental tangent. You anticipate that your mind will return to the speaker, in time for the next word, but unfortunately our minds are sometimes tardy and we miss key words or even sentences.

Listening is a skill, and many of us have not developed it. As speakers, we have the responsibility to keep the listener, even the poor ones on the topic. We use several techniques to keep the attention of the audience. Use of the screen is probably the most effective tool for this purpose. As you project the slide, walk to the screen and point to the line on the slide that corresponds to the topic that you are addressing. If a few members in the audience are coming back from their mental tangents, you reset their attention on the current topic.

When you use the image is projected on the screen, and good speakers use this technique, position yourself correctly. We show the proper position in Fig. 6. Stand to the left side of the screen, being careful not to block anyone's view. Face the audience and maintain eye contact. When you have to look at the slide, turn to the side and read over your shoulder. The 90° turn of your head and the glance at the slide should be quick, because you want to maintain eye contact. Under no circumstance, should you stand with your back to the audience and begin reading from the slide as if it was a script.

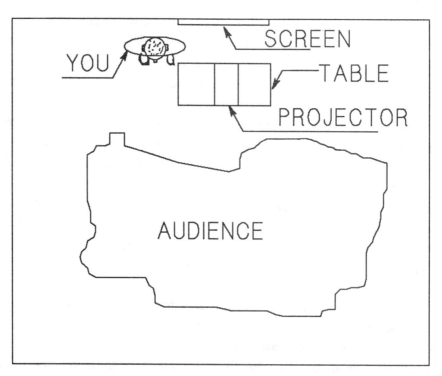

Fig. 6 Typical room arrangement for a presentation. Position yourself to the left of the screen and face the audience.

As you develop the discussion, point to key phrases to keep the audience focused on the topic. Assault both of their senses. Convey your message through their eyes and ears simultaneously. When you point to a line on the slide, point to the left side of the line. People read from left to right, so start them reading from the initial point on the left side.

As you speak modulate your tone and volume. Avoid both a monotone and a sing song delivery. A continuous tone of voice tends to put the audience asleep. A sing song delivery is annoying to many listeners. If you have a very high pitched voice, try to lower the pitch. A high pitch tone is also bothersome to many, and should be avoided if possible.

If a question is asked, answer it promptly, unless you intend to cover material later in the presentation that addresses the question. The answer should be brief, and you should try to avoid an extended dialog with some member of the audience. If a member of the audience is persistent, simply indicate that you will speak with them off-line after the presentation is concluded. The timing of you presentation can be destroyed by too many questions. Some questions are helpful because it permits limited audience participation, but excessive questions causes the speaker to loose control of the topic, the flow and the timing. The format of the communication changes from a presentation to a group discussion. Group discussions have there place, but they have a different purpose than a design briefing.

SUMMARY

The design briefing is extremely important to both the product development, and to your career. Information must be effectively transmitted to your peers, the management, and to external parties involved in the project. Clear messages, that accurately define the problems that the development team can effectively address, are imperative. The design briefing provides the opportunity to inform management and our peers of our progress and our problems.

There are three types of formal communication --- the speech, the professional presentation, and the group discussion. The characteristics of these three types of communication are described. For the engineer the professional presentation is the most important, and the speech is the least important. The main emphasis of the chapter is on the professional presentation, with particular focus on the design briefing.

Preparation for a presentation is essential. Accomplished speakers often spend the better part of a day preparing for a 20 minute briefing. There are three important elements in the preparation. First, know the characteristics of your audience, and make certain that the content that you include corresponds to their interests. Second, organize the presentation in a manner that is acceptable to the audience, and efficient so that you use the allotted time effectively. Finally, prepare high quality visual aids (slides) that will help you convey your message.

A structure for the presentation is recommended, that is commonly employed in design briefings. This outline includes four front end slides including the title, overview, status and introduction. The body of the presentation is devoted to technical details with from eight to twelve slides. The closure involves two slides, one for a summary and the other for the action items.

The type of visual aid that you select is important, and to some degree will affect the outcome of the presentation. The computer projected slides have some significant advantages, but the availability of the equipment and a suitable room often precludes their use. The overhead transparencies are the most common medium. 35 mm slides are the most suitable medium, if you have a presentation that includes many photographs, and a large room in which to deliver the presentation.

The delivery is the make or break part of the presentation. We have provided you with two pages of details about do this, and don't do that, but the best way to learn to deliver is by practicing your presentation. On your first two or three attempts, have a friend video tape the event. Then review your behavior during your presentation. You will identify many problems of which you were not aware. Another suggestion is to use one of your free electives to take a speech class. This course will not help much in crafting the content to include in a design briefing, but it will help develop very important delivery skills.

REFERENCES

1. Eisenberg, A., Effective Technical Communications, 2nd ed., McGraw Hill, New York, NY, 1992.
2. Goldberg, D. E., Life Skills and Leadership for Engineers, McGraw Hill, New York, NY, 1995.
3. Wilder, L. Talk Your Way to Success, Simon and Schuster, New York, NY, 1986.

EXERCISES

1. Write a brief description of the characteristic of your classmates in ENES 100. Focus on the characteristics that will influence the language and content in your design presentations.
2. Prepare an outline for a preliminary design review. Include in the outline the titles of all of the slides that you intend to use.

3. Prepare the title slide for your preliminary design review.
4. Prepare an overview slide for your preliminary design review.
5. Prepare a status slide for your preliminary design review.
6. Prepare the "Key Issues" slide for your preliminary design review.
7. Beg, borrow but don't steal a video camera, and video tape a practice presentation by a teammate. Critique the presentation with good taste.
8. Locate in the College of Engineering the projectors that you can borrow for the ENES 100 presentations in your classroom.
9. Practice the delivery of your presentation using the most suitable projector that you can arrange to borrow.